STUDY GUIDE
AND
COMPUTER WORKBOOK

Rachel Foster-Lifson
Central Michigan University

STATISTICS
FOR
PSYCHOLOGY

THIRD EDITION

Arthur Aron, Ph.D.

Elaine N. Aron, Ph.D.

Prentice Hall, Upper Saddle River, New Jersey 07458

© 2003 by PEARSON EDUCATION, INC.
Upper Saddle River, New Jersey 07458

10 9 8 7 6 5 4 3 2

ISBN 0-13-044723-4

Printed in the United States of America

Table of Contents

vi

Introduction
(How to Use this Study Guide and Computer Workbook)

This study guide is designed to help you master the material in your text. *First*, you should read the chapter in the text and work through the practice problems. *Then*, you should work through the material in the corresponding chapter here.

The first part of each chapter in this *Guide* helps you solidify your knowledge. It includes a list of learning objectives, a thorough outline of the chapter, formulas (including their expression in words and numbers, as well as what all the symbols stand for), and step-by-step instructions for doing the various procedures covered in the chapter.

In most chapters, the next part of each chapter in this *Guide* is a detailed outline of one or more of those essays on explaining the material in the chapter "to a person who has never had a course in statistics." These sections will help you carry out these essay exercises in each chapter (and to prepare you for possible exam questions of this kind). Plus, being able to write a strong essay of this kind is the surest way to be confident you have really mastered the material.

Next in each chapter is a set of Self-Tests--multiple-choice, fill-in, and problems/essays--to help you evaluate how well you have learned the material and to give you practice for course exams. The answers are in the back of this *Guide*.

The last part of each chapter helps you use one of the standardly available statistical computer programs—SPSS--to carry out the procedures and deepen your knowledge of the material covered in the text chapter. In addition to these sections in each chapter for the two programs, there is an appendix at the end of the book on how to get started using each of these programs.

Finally, at the very end of this *Guide* there is a set of glossary flash-cards to be cut out. Many students find that in statistics conquering the terminology is half the battle. These flash cards are designed to help you in that process.

Acknowledgements from first and second editions: Arthur Aron and Christina C. Norman. Many people helped me in the preparation of this manual. Elijah Aron, Ken Galaka, Kip Obenauf, Paul Sanders, and Rosemary Torrano all prepared draft items for the Self-Tests; and Ken, Rosemary, and Miles Holland reviewed the finished items for accuracy. Sami Corn and Elijah helped with the typing, and Menko Johnson formatted the typing for the final typeset printing. Above all, I am grateful to Elaine Aron who read, checked for accuracy, and offered helpful advice on the entire manuscript.

Acknowledgements for the second edition: Rachel Foster-Lifson. The revision of this study guide was aided enormously by the quality of the second edition, helpful comments from Arthur Aron, and editorial support from Jayme Heffler and Kevin Doughten. Special thanks to Steven A. Lifson, Ph.D.

Chapter 1
Displaying the Order in a Group of Numbers

Learning Objectives

To understand, including being able to carry out any necessary procedures:

- Descriptive versus inferential statistics.
- Terminology of variable, value, score, and levels of measurement.
- Frequency tables
- Grouped frequency tables.
- Histograms.
- Frequency polygons.
- Unimodal and bimodal frequency distributions.
- Symmetrical and skewed frequency distributions.
- Normal and kurtotic frequency distributions.
- Ways in which frequency tables and their graphic equivalents can be misused.

Chapter Outline

I.   The Two Branches of Statistical Methods

A. *Descriptive statistics* are used to summarize and make understandable a group of numbers collected in a research study. (This is the focus of Chapters 1-4.)

B. *Inferential statistics* are used to draw conclusions based on but going beyond numbers actually collected in the research. (This is the focus of Chapters 5-17.)

II.   Some Basic Concepts

A. Some basic terminology is needed
   1. *Variable* – a characteristic that can take on different values.
   2. *Value* – a number or category that a score can have.
   3. *Score* – a particular person's value on a variable.

B. Levels of Measurement
   1. Numeric variables are *quantitative* variables.   There are three types of numeric variable.
      a. *Equal interval variables*: numeric variables in which differences between values correspond to differences in the underlying thing being measured. These variables have equal intervals between each number; the distance from 1 to 2 is the same as the distance from 2 to 3, etc.
      b. *Rank-order variables*: numeric variable in which values correspond to the relative position of things being measured.

1

I. These variables show only the ranking between variables. In other words, rank-order indicates which score is first, second, and so on. The distance between the rankings, however, are not necessarily equal.

II. Rank-order variables are also called *ordinal* variables.

2. Categorical or *nominal* variables are *qualitative* variables. They are variables in which the values are categories. Examples are a person's gender or political affiliation.

III. Frequency Tables

A. They show how frequently each of the different values occurs.

B. They make the pattern of numbers clear at a glance.

C. There are four steps to creating a frequency table.

1. Make a list down the page of each possible value, starting from the highest and ending with the lowest.
2. Go one by one through the group of scores you wish to describe, making a mark for each next to the corresponding value on your list.
3. Make a neat table of how many times each value on your listing occurs.
4. Figure the percentage for how often each score appears.

IV. Grouped Frequency Tables

A. They are used when there are so many different possible values that the frequency table is too cumbersome to give a simple account of the information.

B. They group values of all cases within a certain interval.

V. Histograms

A. They are one type of graphic display of the information in a frequency table.

B. They are a kind of bar chart (in which the bars are put right next to each other without divisions); the height of each bar corresponds to the frequency of each value or interval in the frequency table.

C. They look like a city skyline.

D. There are four steps to creating a histogram.

1. Make a frequency table (or a grouped frequency table).
2. Place the scale of values (or intervals) along the bottom of a page.
   a. The values (or intervals) should go from left to right, from lowest to highest.
   b. For a grouped frequency table it is conventional to mark only the midpoint of each interval, in the center of each bar. (The midpoint is figured as the point between the start of the interval and the start of the next interval.)
3. Make a scale of frequencies along the left edge of the page.
4. Make a bar for each value (or interval), the height corresponding to the frequency of the value (or interval) it represents.

E. Making a histogram will be easiest if you use graph paper.

VI. Frequency Polygons

A. They are another type of graphic display of the information in a frequency table.

B. They are a kind of line graph in which the bottom of the graph shows the values or intervals (as in a histogram), and the line moves from point to point, with the height of each point showing the number of cases in that interval.

C. They look like a mountain–peak skyline.

D. There are five steps to creating a frequency polygon.

    1. Make a frequency table (or a grouped frequency table).

    2. Place the scale of values (or intervals) along the bottom.

       a. The values (or intervals) should go from left to right, from lowest to highest.

       b. Be sure to include one extra value (or interval) above and one extra value (or interval) below the values (or intervals) that actually have any scores in them.

       c. For a grouped frequency table, use the midpoint of each interval. (The midpoint is figured as the point between the start of the interval and the start of the next interval.)

    3. Along the left of the page make a scale of frequencies that runs from 0 at the bottom to the highest frequency in any value (or interval).

    4. Mark a point above the center of each value (or interval) corresponding to the frequency of that value (or interval).

E. Connect the points with lines.

VII. Shapes of Frequency Distributions

A. A frequency table, histogram, or frequency polygon describes a *frequency distribution*—how the number of cases or "frequencies" are spread out or "distributed."

B. It is useful to describe in words the key aspects of the way numbers are distributed—which can be thought of as the shape of the histogram or frequency polygon that represents the frequency distribution.

C. Unimodal and bimodal.

    1. A distribution with a single high peak is *unimodal*. (This is the most common in psychology.)

    2. A distribution with two major peaks is *bimodal*.

    3. Any distribution with two or more peaks is called *multimodal*.

    4. A distribution in which all the values have about the same frequency is called *rectangular*.

D. Symmetrical and skewed.

    1. A distribution with approximately equal numbers of cases (and a similar shape) on both sides of the middle is *symmetrical*. (Approximations to this are the most common in psychology.)

2. A distribution which is clearly not symmetrical is *skewed*.
   a. The direction of skew refers to the side with the long tail.
   b. A distribution that is skewed to the right–the positive side of the middle–is also called *positively skewed*.
   c. A distribution skewed to the left–the negative side of the middle–is also called *negatively skewed*.
3. In practice, highly skewed distributions come up in psychology mainly when what is being measured has some upper or lower limit.
   a. The situation in which many scores pile up at the low end because it is not possible to have any lower score is called a *floor effect*.
   b. The situation in which many scores pile up at the high end because it is not possible to have any higher score is called a *ceiling effect*.

E. Kurtosis.
1. If a distribution is particularly flat or particularly peaked it has something called *kurtosis*.
2. The standard of comparison is the *normal curve*, a bell–shaped curve that is widely approximated in frequency distributions in psychological research–and in nature generally. (See Chapter 5.) How peaked and pinched together versus flat and spread out a distribution is, compared to the normal curve, is called its degree of kurtosis.

VIII. **Controversies: How Frequency Tables and their Graphic Equivalents Can Be Misused**

A. Failure to use equal interval sizes.

B. Exaggeration of proportions.
1. Ordinarily the height of a histogram or frequency polygon should begin at 0 or the lowest value of the scale and continue to the highest value of the scale.
2. The overall proportion of the graph should be about 1.5 times as wide as it is tall.

IX. **Frequency Tables, Histograms, and Frequency Polygons in Research Articles**

A. They are mainly used by researchers as an intermediary step in the process of more elaborate statistical analyses.

B. Frequency tables are used in two situations.
1. Sometimes they are presented to compare frequencies on two or more variables or for two or more groups.
2. Most often they are used when the values of the variable are categories rather than numbers.

C. Histograms and frequency polygons almost never appear in research articles (except articles *about* statistics); but their shape is sometimes commented on in the text of the article, particularly if the distribution seems to be far from normal.

How to Make a Frequency Table

1. Make a list down the page of each possible value, starting from the highest and ending with the lowest.
2. Go one by one through the group of scores you wish to describe, making a mark for each next to the corresponding value on your list.
3. Make a neat table showing how many times each value on your list occurs.
4. Figure the percentage for how often each score appears.

How to Make a Histogram

1. Make a frequency table (or a grouped frequency table).
2. Place the scale of values (or intervals) along the bottom of a page.
   A. The values (or intervals) should go left to right, from lowest to highest.
   B. For a grouped frequency table, it is conventional to mark only the midpoint of each interval, placed in the center of each bar. (The midpoint is figured as the point between the start of the interval and the start of the next interval.)
3. Make a scale of frequencies along the left of the page that goes from 0 at the bottom to the highest frequency in any value (or interval).
4. Make a bar for each value (or interval), the height for the frequency of the value (or interval).

How to Make a Frequency Polygon

1. Make a frequency table (or a grouped frequency table).
2. Place the scale of values (or intervals) along the bottom of a page from left to right.
   A. Be sure to include one extra value (or interval) above and one extra value (or interval) below the values (or intervals) that actually have any scores in them.
   B. For a grouped frequency table, use the midpoint of each interval. (The midpoint is figured as the point between the start of the interval and the start of the next interval.)
3. Make a scale of frequencies along the left of the page that goes from 0 at the bottom to the highest frequency in any value (or interval).
4. Mark a point above each value (or interval) with a height for the frequency of that value (or interval).
5. Connect the points with a line.

Chapter Self–Tests

Multiple–Choice Questions

1. Psychologists use _____ statistics like frequency tables to help make sense of the numbers they collect.

   a. inferential.
   b. descriptive.
   c. intuitive.
   d. abstract.

2. A researcher studies the amount of self–confidence people have after doing well on a test. Self–confidence in this study is a

   a. score.
   b. descriptive statistic.
   c. value.
   d. variable.

3. A psychologist administers a personality scale on which people can get a score of any number between 24 to 86. The results would be described using a grouped frequency table rather than an ordinary frequency table because an ordinary frequency table would

   a. have too many values.
   b. not be able to include all cases.
   c. create a skewed distribution.
   d. have to start at 0 (or 0%).

4. What is generally the largest number of intervals you would want in a grouped frequency table?

   a. 5.
   b. 15.
   c. 45.
   d. 60.

5. A histogram

   a. is similar to a line graph.
   b. always approximates a normal curve.
   c. is a graphic description of frequency table.
   d. describes the relation between two variables.

6. In a frequency polygon, the vertical (up and down) dimension represents
    a. frequency.
    b. possible values the variable can take.
    c. intensity of the variable.
    d. mean score.

7. Suppose 50 people take a math exam – 25 math experts, and 25 people very poor at math. This distribution will probably be _____.
    a. unimodal.
    b. bimodal.
    c. normal.
    d. skewed

8. The standard of comparison when describing the shape of a distribution is
    a. rectangular distribution.
    b. a flat distribution.
    c. a bell-shaped curve.
    d. a square curve.

9. Describe the distribution of the following scores (you will probably need to make a frequency table, histogram, or frequency polygon to do this).
    1 10 6 8 7 5 5 4 9 2 9 8 6 7 8 3 4 3 5 5 7 6 4 6 6 7
    a unimodal and approximately normal.
    b. bimodal and negatively skewed.
    c. normal and positively skewed.
    d. normal and negatively skewed.

10. A graphic display of a frequency distribution is misleading when
    a. the proportions are close to 1–1/2 across to 1 up.
    b. the frequencies are grouped or percentages are used.
    c. some of the intervals are larger than others.
    d. the intervals (or values) are put across the bottom.

Fill–In Questions

11. When making a frequency table, the _____ are listed in the first column and the frequencies corresponding to each of these are listed in the next column.

12. A quantitative variable is a _____ variable.

13. Numeric variables that show the relative position of things being measured are _____.

14. A graph describing a frequency table and looking like a city skyline is called a(n) _____.

15. A(n) _____ distribution shows up in a frequency polygon as two peaks that are much higher than all the others.

16. If the number of scores at each value is approximately the same, this creates a(n) _____ distribution, which is also symmetrical.

17. The distribution of incomes in a small community tends to be _____ skewed, because most people earn small to modest incomes, and a decreasing number earn large incomes (though a very small number earn a very great deal).

18. In a pilot test of a planned memory study, the majority received a perfect score. Seeking to avoid such a(n) _____ in the real study, the researcher made the task more difficult.

19. The _____ represents a particular unimodal, symmetrical distribution commonly found in psychology research and nature generally.

20. _____ refers to a distribution being much more peaked or flat than is typical of distributions in psychology.

Problems and Essays

21. Under what conditions would you prefer to make a grouped frequency table over an ordinary frequency table? Why?

22. The grade point averages of students applying to a particular graduate program in psychology were as follows:

3.7	3.5	3.7	3.5	3.4	3.8	4.0
4.0	3.5	3.8	3.5	4.0	3.7	4.0
3.5	3.6	3.4	3.2	3.9	3.6	3.9
3.6	4.0	3.5	4.0	3.8	3.3	3.3

a. Make a frequency table.

a. Make a histogram based on the frequency table.

b. Describe in words the shape of the histogram.

23. The first introductory to statistics quiz produced the following scores:

    10 10 7 7 7 15 11 11 6 12 11 16 13 5 10 13 11 9 13
    14 11 10 14 8 8 8 14 8 14 10 17 6 6 12 15 3 8 9 9

    a. Make a frequency table.
    13. Make a frequency polygon.
    14. Describe in words the shape of the frequency polygon.

24. Twenty–four adolescent girls whose parents had just divorced completed a questionnaire about their attitudes toward their parents. Their scores were as follows (the scale goes from 0, very negative attitude, to 80, very positive attitude):

    16 11 9 14 22 18 19 21 22 16 22 18 16 21 16 12 20 20 18 10

    a. Make a frequency table.
    b. Make a histogram based on the frequency table.
    c. Describe in words the shape of the histogram.

25. The average life spans in captivity for 43 different mammals (as reported in the *1989 World Almanac*, p. 258) are as follows:

    12 20 18 25 20 5 15 12 12 20 6 15 8 12 35 40 15 7 10 8 15
    20 4 25 20 7 12 15 15 12 3 3 1 10 12 5 15 20 12 12 10 16 5

    a. Make a grouped frequency table with intervals of 5.
    b. Make a frequency polygon based on the frequency table.
    c. Describe in words the shape of the frequency polygon.

26. Explain what it means to have a floor effect in a distribution of scores. Give an example.

Using SPSS (11.0 for Windows) in this Chapter

If you are using SPSS for the first time, before proceeding with the material in this section, read the Appendix on Getting Started with SPSS.

You can use SPSS to create frequency tables and histograms, including grouped frequency tables and histograms based on those grouped frequency tables. You should work through the example, following the procedures step by step. Then look over the description of the general principles involved and try to create frequency tables and histograms on your own for some of the problems listed in the Suggestions for Additional Practice. Finally, you may want to try the suggestions for using the computer to deepen your understanding.

I.   An Example

A.   Data: Fourteen students rated the quality of social life in their dormitory on a 1 to 10 scale. The ratings were 6, 9, 9, 4, 9, 7, 1, 7, 4, 10, 7, 1, 9, and 4.

B.   Follow the instructions in the SPSS Appendix for starting up SPSS.

C.   Enter the data as follows.
   1.   Type **6**, the score for the first subject, and press Enter.
   2.   Type **9**, the score for the second subject, and press Enter.
   3.   Type the remaining scores, one per line. You can always move back to an earlier line by clicking the arrow in the space you wish to edit.

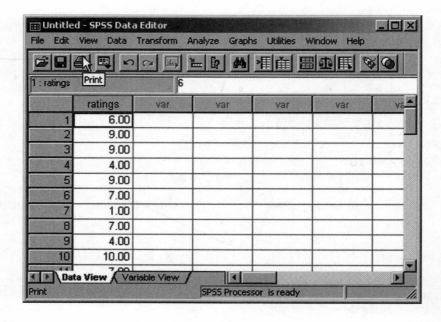

Figure SG1–1

D. Name your variable.

1. To replace the default variable name with a more descriptive variable name, click on the Variable View tab at the bottom of the dialogue box. Double click on VAR00001 at the top of the first column. This opens the Define Variable dialogue box. Delete the default variable name and type RATINGS in the Variable Name text box. Click on Data View at the bottom of the dialogue box. This will close the Variable View dialogue box and return you to the data window. At this point, the screen should look like Figure SG1-1.

Figure SG1-2

E. Make a frequency table and histogram, as follows.
   1. Analyze
      Descriptive statistics
      Frequencies
         At this point the screen should look like Figure SG1-2.
         [Select RATINGS by highlighting it with the mouse and then clicking on
         the arrow.]
            Charts
               [Select Histograms]
               Continue
               OK

   2. A frequency table will appear in the output window, followed by the histogram. The
   histogram should look like Figure SG1-3.
   3. Inspect the results.
      a. At the top of the screen (on the left), SPSS reminds you of the name of the variable
         you are examining (in this case, Ratings).
      b. The five columns of numbers are the frequency table itself. The left column, labeled
         VALUE, gives the various values, from lowest to highest. The column to its right,
         labeled **FREQUENCY,** gives the frequency. (This is different from an ordinary
         frequency table, such as those shown in the text, and the values would be listed going
         down from highest to lowest.) The next three columns show the percentage, valid
         percentage, and cumulative percentage.
      c. The histogram is shown next. It is like the histograms in the text.
   4. Print out the results from the output window by going into File and selecting Print or
   by clicking on the Print icon.
F.   Save your lines of data as follows:
   File
   Save As
      [Indicate what drive you would like it saved in and type in file name]
         [Press OK]

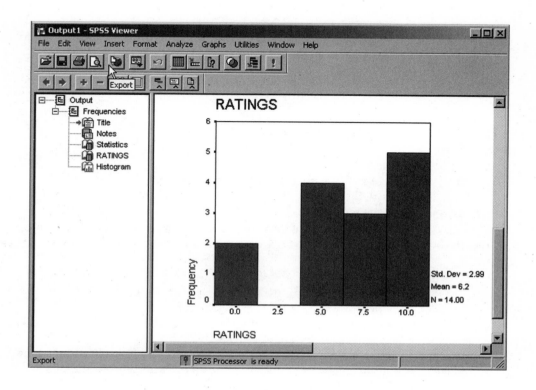

SG1-3

II. Systematic Instructions for Making a Frequency Table and Histogram and Grouped Frequency Table and Histogram

  A. Start up SPSS.

  B. Enter the data as follows.

      1. Type in a data point and press Enter. Continue until all data has been entered.

      2. Name your variable by selecting the Variable View tab. Return to Data View.

C. Make a frequency table and histogram as follows.
    Analyze
        Descriptive statistics
           Frequencies
                [Select variable by highlighting it with the mouse and then clicking on the arrow.]
                Charts
                    [Select Histogram]
                      Continue
                          OK

D. Save your lines of data as follows.
    File
        Save Data
            [Type in file name and indicate drive you would like it saved in]
            OK

III. Additional Practice

(For each data set, enter the data, create a frequency table and histogram and compare your results to those in the text. Also, be sure to save your data sets so that you can use them again in Chapter 2.)

A. Text examples.
1. Use the data shown in the text for the stress levels of students in the first week of their statistics class (from Aron, Paris, & Aron, 1993).
2. Use the data shown in the text for student's social interactions over the course of a week (from McLaughlin-Volpe and colleagues).
3. Note that these examples have a lot of data to enter, but they have the advantage of providing sufficient numbers of cases to give you a real sense of the value of a frequency table and histogram and of having a computer set it up for you.

B. Practice problems in the text: Questions 3, 4, and 5.

IV. Using the Computer to Deepen Your Knowledge

A. Getting a sense of a normal distribution.
1. Make up a data set of any 15 numbers and then make a histogram of it.
2. Print out the histogram and then go back to your data set and try to modify it to come out closer to a normal curve.
3. Repeat this process until your results are very close to a normal curve.
4. Try the process again starting with a whole new group of numbers.
5. Try to write down what you have learned about what goes into making a distribution come out normal.

B. Getting a sense of skew.
   1. Take one of the data sets from your normal curve approximations from the previous exercise and modify it to make the curve come out slightly skewed to one side.
   2. Now try to make it more skewed.
   3. Repeat this process, creating several different degrees of skew.
   4. Try to write down what you have learned about what goes into creating different degrees of skew.

Chapter 2
The Mean, Variance, Standard Deviation, and Z Scores

Learning Objectives

To understand, including being able to conduct any necessary computations:

- The mean.
- Statistical symbols and formulas.
- The mode and the median.
- Variance.
- Standard deviation.
- Z scores and converting to and from raw scores.
- Objections to using statistical methods.
- How mean, variance, and standard deviation are reported in research articles.

Chapter Outline

I. The Mean
   A. It is usually the best single number for describing a group of scores.
   B. It is the ordinary average, the sum of all the scores divided by the number of scores.
   C. It gives the *central tendency*, or the general, typical, or representative value of the group of scores.
   D. You can visualize the mean as a kind of balancing point for the distribution of scores: Imagine a board balanced over a log; on the board are piles of blocks distributed along the board, one for each score in the distribution; and the mean would be the point on the board where the weight of the blocks on each side would exactly balance.
   E. The formula for the mean is $M = \Sigma X / N$.
   1. M is a symbol for the mean.
   2. Σ is the symbol for "sum of."
   3. X refers to scores in the distribution of the variable X.
   4. N stands for number of scores in the distribution.
   F. The mode is an alternative measure of central tendency.
   1. It is the most common single number in a distribution.
   2. It is the value with the largest frequency in a frequency table, the high point or peak of a distribution's frequency polygon or histogram.
   3. In a perfectly symmetrical unimodal distribution, and in a few other cases, the mode is the same as the mean.

4. When the mode is not the same as the mean, it generally corresponds less well to what we intuitively understand as central tendency.
5. The mode, unlike the mean, can be unaffected by changes in some scores.
6. Psychologists rarely use the mode.

G. The median is another alternative measure of central tendency.
1. It is the middle score if you line up all the scores from highest to lowest.
2. If there are two middle scores, it is their average (when, as can happen with an even number of cases, the two "middle" scores would fall between two different values).
3. It is less distorted by a few extreme cases (outliers) than the mean.

II. The Variance and the Standard Deviation
A. These measure how spread out a distribution is.
B. Variance.
1. It is the average of each score's squared difference from the mean.
   a. First subtract the mean of the distribution from each score in the distribution.
   b. Square each of these deviation scores (to remove the effect of positive and negative deviations which would cancel each other out when summed).
   c. Add up all the squared deviation scores.
2. Divide this sum of squared deviations by the number of cases.
3. The variance plays an important role in many other statistical procedures, but is used only occasionally by itself as a descriptive statistic since it is scaled in squared units, a metric that is not very intuitively direct for giving a sense of just how spread out the distribution is.

C. The standard deviation.
1. It is the most widely used for describing the spread of a distribution.
2. It is the square root of the variance.
3. Roughly speaking, the standard deviation is the average amount that scores differ from the mean. (It is not exactly this because the squaring, summing, and taking the square root does not quite give the same result.)

D. The variance formula is $SD^2 = \Sigma(X\text{-}M)^2 / N$.
1. SD^2 is the symbol for the variance.
2. $\Sigma(X\text{-}M)^2$ describes the sum of squared deviations from the mean.
3. Sum of squared deviations from the mean is also symbolized as SS–thus, $SD^2 = SS/N$.

E. The standard deviation formula is $SD = \sqrt{SD^2}$

F. The above formulas are "definitional"; in other books you may see them in a different "computational" form.
1. Computational formulas are mathematically equivalent and easier to use when computing by hand or with a hand calculator.
2. The computational formula for the variance is $SD^2 = \dfrac{\Sigma X^2 - (\Sigma X)^2/N}{N}$
3. Computational formulas are rarely used today in research practice because most statistical computations are done by computer.

4. This textbook emphasizes the definitional formulas (the version of the formula that corresponds to and reminds you of the definition of the statistic).
   a. Thus, doing exercises reinforces understanding.
   b. But the exercises involve fewer and simpler numbers than that of most real research situations so that the total time to complete the exercises is no more than if you were using computational formulas.
5. The traditional computational formulas are provided in a Chapter Appendix.

G. Variance and standard deviation are sometimes figured using the sum of squared deviations divided by N-1.
   1. These situations are described beginning in Chapter 9.
   2. Hand calculators and computer outputs sometimes give this figure instead of the formula emphasized in this chapter.

III. *Z* Scores

A. It is an ordinary score transformed so that it better describes that score's location in a distribution.

B. It is the number of standard deviations the score is above the mean (if it is a positive Z score) or the number of standard deviations the score is below the mean (if it is a negative Z score). (Thus, the standard deviation serves as a kind of standard yardstick through changing raw scores to Z scores.)

C. Z scores have many practical uses and are crucial ingredients in many of the statistical procedures in the rest of this book.

D. Scores on different scales can be easily compared once they are converted to Z scores.

E. The formula for converting *from* a raw score is $Z = (X\text{-}M) / SD$.

F. The formula for converting *to* a raw score is $X = (Z)(SD) + M$.

G. There are three characteristics of a distribution of Z scores.
   1. The mean is always exactly 0 (because converting to a Z score involves subtracting the mean from each raw score).
   2. The standard deviation is always exactly 1.0 (because converting to a Z score involves dividing each raw score by the standard deviation).
   3. The variance is always 1.0 (because it is the square of the standard deviation, which is always 1.0).

H. Z scores are also called *standard scores*.

IV. Controversies: The Tyranny of the Mean

A. Although the use of statistics is a central part of psychology, there are several opposing schools of thought.

B. Behaviorism was the first to criticize statistical procedures.
   1. Behaviorism dominated much of the history of psychology research and rejected the study of inner states because they are impossible to observe objectively—hence it focused instead on externally observable behavior.

2. Its leading modern exponent, B. F. Skinner, was opposed to using statistics in behavioral research because the averaging of observations over many cases can lose or distort the information revealed from each case.

C. Humanistic psychology was the next to criticize statistics.
   1. In the 1950's it became the "third force," in reaction to behaviorism and psychoanalysis (the only significant applied psychology at the time).
   2. It holds that human experience should be studied intact, as a whole, as it is experienced by individuals.
   3. It does not object to all uses of statistics, but notes that human experience can never be fully reduced to numbers and each individual's experience is unique.
   4. This emphasis on an idiographic or in-depth study of the single person, over the nomothetic or the searching for general laws that apply over many persons, has been a long tradition in clinical and personality psychology as well.

D. Qualitative research is sometimes seen as an alternative or complement to quantitative research methods.
   1. Qualitative methods are based in part on phenomenology, a philosophical position opposed to logical positivism (a basis of modern scientific thinking that holds there is an objective reality to be known); phenomenology seeks instead to gain a deep understanding of the unique reality of each individual.
   2. Qualitative methods also come from the ethnographic research tradition in cultural anthropology.
   3. Many proponents hold that one should first use qualitative methods to discover which variables are most important, then determine their incidence in the larger population through quantitative methods.

E. The "statistical mood." Some depth psychologists raise the concern that emphasizing averages dilutes our feelings about the importance of the single individual and thus, among other consequences, makes immoral actions more likely.

V. The Mean, Variance, Standard Deviation, and Z Scores as Described in Research Articles
A. The mean, variance and standard deviation are commonly reported, and in a variety of ways—either in the text, in tables, or in graphs.
B. Z scores rarely appear in research articles.

19

Formulas

I. Mean (M)

    Formula in words: Sum of all the scores divided by the number of scores.

    Formula in symbols: $M = \Sigma X / N$

        Σ is an instruction to sum all the scores.

        X is each score in the distribution of the variable X.

        ΣX is the sum of all the scores in the distribution of the variable X.

        N is the number of scores in the distribution.

II. Variance (SD^2)

    Formula in words: Average of each score's squared difference from the mean.

    Formula in symbols: $SD^2 = \Sigma(X\text{-}M)^2 / N$ or SS / N

        $\Sigma(X\text{-}M)^2$ is the sum of squared deviations from the mean.

        SS is the sum of squared deviations from the mean.

III. Standard Deviation (SD)

    Formula in words: Square root of the variance (square root of the average of each score's squared difference from the mean).

    Formula in symbols: $SD = \sqrt{SD^2}$

IV. Z Scores from Raw Scores

    Formula in words: The number of standard deviations above or below the mean–the deviation score (the score minus the mean) divided by the standard deviation.

    Formula in symbols: $Z = (X - M) / SD$

V. Raw Scores from Z Scores

    Formula in words: Multiply the Z score times the standard deviation (to get the raw deviation above or below the mean) and add the mean.

    Formula in symbols: $X = (Z)(SD) + M$

How to Figure the Mean

1. Add up all the scores.
2. Divide by the number of scores.

How to Figure the Median

1. Line up all the scores from lowest to highest.
2. Figure how many scores there are to the middle score. If you have an odd number of scores, divide the number of scores in half and add ½. If an even number of scores, divide the number in half – this and the score above it are the middle scores.
3. Count up to the middle score. If you have an odd number of scores, this is the median. If an even number of scores, the median is the average of the two middle scores.

How to Figure the Variance

1. Figure the mean (*M*): Add up all the scores and divide by the number of scores.
2. Subtract the mean from each score. This gives each score's deviation score.
3. Square each of these deviation scores: Multiply each deviation score times itself.
4. Add up the squared deviation scores. This total is called the sum of squared deviations.
5. Divide the sum of squared deviations by the number of scores.

How to Figure the Standard Deviation

1. Figure the variance.
2. Take the square root.

How to Convert a Raw Score to a *Z* Score

1. Figure the deviation score: Subtract the mean from the raw score.
2. Figure the *Z* score: Divide the deviation score by the standard deviation.

How to Convert a *Z* Score to a Raw Score

1. Figure the deviation score: Multiply the *Z* score by the standard deviation.
2. Figure the raw score: Add the mean to the deviation score.

Outline for Writing Essays on the Logic and Computations for the Mean, Variance, Standard Deviation, and Z Scores

The reason for your writing essay questions in the practice problems and tests is that this task develops and then demonstrates what matters so very much–your comprehension of the logic behind the computations. (It is also a place where those better at words than numbers can shine, and for those better at numbers to develop their skills at explaining in words.)

Thus, to do well, be sure to do the following in each essay: (a) give the reasoning behind each step; (b) relate each step to the specifics of the content of the particular study you are analyzing; (c) state the various formulas in nontechnical language, because as you define each term you show you understand it (although once you have defined it in nontechnical language, you can use it from then on in the essay); (d) look back and be absolutely certain that you made it clear just *why* that formula or procedure was applied and *why* it is the way it is.

The outlines below are *examples* of ways to structure your essays. There are other completely correct ways to go about it. And this is an *outline* for an answer–you are to write the answer out in paragraph form. Examples of full essays are in the answers to Set I Practice Problems in the back of the text.

These essays are sometimes long for you to write (and for others to grade). But this is the very best way to be sure you understand everything thoroughly. You engrain it in your mind. The time is never wasted. It is an excellent way to study.

Essays on Finding the Mean, Variance, and Standard Deviation

I. **Find mean.**

    A. Procedure: $M = \Sigma X / N$.

    B. Explanation: This is the ordinary average, the sum of the scores divided by the number of scores.

II. **Find the variance.**

    A. Procedure: $SD^2 = \Sigma(X\text{-}M)^2 / N$.

    B. Explanation.

        1. Describes the spread of the scores.

        2.   Finds the average of the squared amount each score differs from the mean.

III. Find the standard deviation.

A. Procedure: $SD = \sqrt{SD^2}$.

B. Explanation.
1. The variance is an average of squared scores; by taking its square root, the measure of spread of the scores is returned to ordinary nonsquared scores.
2. The result is approximately the average amount each score varies from the mean.
3. To be exact it is the square root of the average squared deviation from the mean.
4. Due to the squaring, averaging, and square root process, it is not quite the same as the average amount each score varies from the mean, but the use of squaring in the process avoids mathematical problems (for example, it eliminates the sign of the deviations–the fact that some are negative and some positive).

Essays Involving Z Scores

I. Find a Z score based on a raw score.

A. Procedure: $Z = (X - M) / SD$.

B. Explanation.
1. Explain mean and standard deviation (as described in outline above).
2. Finding a Z score converts an ordinary score to its number of standard deviations above or below the mean.
3. This is done by subtracting the mean from the score and dividing the result by the standard deviation.
4. This puts the score on a scale that is highly standard–for example, high scores (those above the mean) are always positive Z scores, low scores (those below the mean) are always negative Z scores, and the amount a Z score is above or below the mean is in direct proportion to the standard deviation.
5. This procedure puts scores on different variables onto the same scale, permitting comparisons between them.

II. Find a raw score based on a Z score.

A. Procedure: $X = (Z)(SD) + M$.

B. Explanation.
1. Explain mean and standard deviation (as described in outline above).
2. This converts a Z score, a special score that indicates a score's number of standard deviations above or below the mean, back to an ordinary score.
3. This is done by multiplying the Z score times the standard deviation to get the number of ordinary score units above or below the mean, and then adding this to the mean to get the actual raw score.

Chapter Self-Tests

Multiple-Choice Questions

1. Six students record the amount of time studied on a particular evening (rounded off to the nearest hour). They report 0 0 1 1 4 and 6 hours. What is the mean time studied?

   a. 1.
   b. 2.
   c. 2.5.
   d. 3.5.

2. What does "ΣX" refer to?

   a. standard deviation of X.
   b. expected value of X.
   c. estimated value of X.
   d. sum of X.

3. What is the mode of the following scores? 0 1 1 1 2 3 7 8 8 9 15

   a. 1.
   b. 3
   c. 5.
   d. 8.

4. What is the median of the following scores? 0 1 1 1 2 3 7 8 8 9 15

   a. 1.
   b. 3.
   c. 5.
   d. 8.

5. In the following set of scores, which would be the preferred measure of central tendency?
   5 41 42 42 44 46 47 47 47

   a. mean.
   b. median.
   c. mode.
   d. standard error.

6. The variance is

   a. the sum of the squared deviations from the mean.
   b. the average of the deviations from the mean.
   c. the sum of the square roots of the deviations from the mean.
   d. the average of the squared deviations from the mean.

7. If the variance is 7, what is the standard deviation?
   a. $\sqrt{7}$.
   b. 7^2.
   c. $7 - M$.
   d. $(7-M)^2$.

8. What is the variance of the four scores, 1 5 5 and 9?
   a. 4.
   b. 5.
   c. 8.
   d. 16.

9. The standard deviation of a distribution of Z scores is always
   a. 0.
   b. 1.
   c. smaller than the mean of the raw scores.
   d. greater than the standard deviation of the raw scores.

10. A person has a Z score of .5. If the mean of the distribution is 71 and the standard deviation is 20, what is this person's raw score?
   a. 70.5.
   b. 71.5.
   c. 76.
   d. 81.

Fill-In Questions

11. The sum of the scores divided by the number of scores is the _____.

12. The mean, median, and mode are examples of indicators of the _____ of a distribution.

13. A study produces the scores 14, 15, 17, 18 and 18. What is N? _____.

14. The _____ of the scores 6, 6, 6, 7, and 9 is 6.

15. If you line up all the scores from highest to lowest, the middle score is the _____.

16. If a group of scores are 14, 17, 17, 18, 18, and 91, the score of 91 is called a(n) _____.

17. In symbols, the formula for the variance is _____.

18. A deviation score is the score minus _____.

19. The _____ is the most commonly used descriptive statistic for indicating spread of a group of scores.

20. The formula for converting a raw score to a Z score is _____.

Problems and Essays

21. A psychologist administers a test of hand-eye coordination to eight severely depressed adult men and finds scores of 3.1 3.8 4.0 4.5 4.5 5.4 6.0 and 8.7.
    a. Figure the mean, variance, and standard deviation.
    b. Explain what you have done and what the results mean to a person who has never had a course in statistics.

22. On an assertiveness scale, a randomly selected sample of police academy trainees scored as follows: 18 17, 17 10 21 12 24 13 16 18 13 17 28 22 16 21 21 20 14 19 10 16 16 15 21
    a. Figure the mean, variance, and standard deviation.
    b. Explain what you have done and what the results mean to a person who has never had a course in statistics.

23. A group of introductory psychology students took a test measuring attitudes toward recycling. Their scores were as follows: 7, 10, 9, 7, 13, 12, 9, 7, 8 10.
    a. Figure the mean, variance, and standard deviation.
    b. A person who scored 12 has a Z score of what?
    c. Explain what you have done and what the results mean to a person who has never had a course in statistics.

24. A person took an exam in a statistics course and received a Z score of 0. How did this person score in relation to the rest of the group?

25. A person visits a vocational counselor and is administered various tests. The person scores 50 on a test that measures aptitude for a career in sales (for people in general on this test, $M = 40$, $SD = 4$) and 95 on a test of aptitude for a career in education (for people in general on this test, $M = 80$, $SD = 20$). (On both tests high scores mean greater aptitude.)
    a. In relation to other people, what is this person's greater aptitude? (Be sure to show the calculations that are the basis of your answer.)
    b. Explain what you have done and the basis of your conclusion to a person who has never had a course in statistics.

26. Two children complete a standard test of vocabulary which was sent off to a special service for scoring. The school counselor received the results in terms of Z scores. One child, Mary, received a Z score of 1.23 and the other child, Susan, received a Z score of -.62. The school counselor is interested also in the raw number correct each student received. Looking up the information in the test's manual, the school counselor found out that the mean raw score for this test is 42 questions correct, with a standard deviation of 6.5.

    a. What are the raw numbers for each child?

    b. Explain what you have done and the basis of your conclusion to a person who has never had a course in statistics.

27. A researcher administered a questionnaire to a group of healthy adults all over 80 years old. The questionnaire included one item that asked about happiness with life, using a 10-point scale from 1 = very unhappy to 10 = very happy. The researcher reported the result on this scale as follows: "For the 65 subjects who completed this item, $M = 6.83$, $SD = 2.41$." Explain what this result means to a person who has never had a course in statistics.

Using SPSS (11.0 for Windows) with this Chapter

If you are using SPSS for the first time, before proceeding with the material in this section, read the Appendix on Getting Started and the Basics of Using SPSS.

You can use SPSS to *figure* the mean and variance and to convert a series of raw scores to Z scores. However, as you will see, the variance that SPSS gives you is *figured* using a slightly different formula than what you have been using in Chapter 2–instead of dividing the sum of squared deviations by N, it divides by N-1. (This other way of computing the variance is also correct, but is used for a different purpose.) Thus, when computing the variance using SPSS, you have to make an adjustment to what SPSS gives you, using your hand calculator. Once you have made the adjustment, you can take the square root of your result (again with your hand calculator) to get the standard deviation.

You should work through the example, following the procedures step by step. Then look over the description of the general principles involved and try the procedures on your own for some of the problems listed in the Suggestions for Additional Practice. Finally, you may want to try the suggestions for using the computer to deepen your understanding, and you can explore the additional, advanced SPSS procedure at the end, involving skew and kurtosis.

I. Example

A. Data: The number of therapy sessions for each of 10 clients of a psychotherapist (fictional data), from the example in the text. The numbers of sessions are 7, 8, 8, 7, 3, 1, 6, 9, 3, and 8.

B. Follow the instructions in the SPSS Appendix for starting up SPSS.

C. Enter the data as follows.

    1. Type **7**, the number of sessions for the first subject, and press Enter.

    2. Type **8**, the number of sessions for the second subject, and press Enter.

    3. Type the remaining numbers of sessions, one per line.

    4. To replace the default variable name with a more descriptive variable name, click on the Variable View tab at the bottom of the dialogue box. Double click on VAR00001 at the top of the first column. This opens the Define Variable dialogue box. Delete the default variable name and type SESSIONS in the Variable Name text box. Click on Data View at the bottom of the dialogue box. This will close the Variable View dialogue box and return you to the data window. Your screen should look like Figure SG2-1.

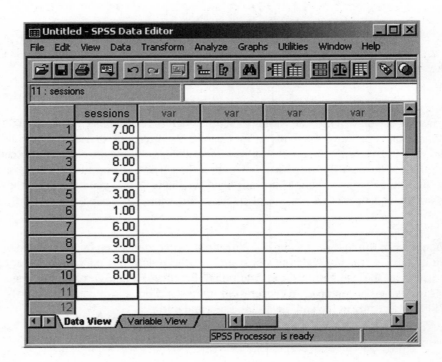

Figure SG2-1

28

D. Compute the mean and variance for the number of sessions as follows.
    1. Analyze
        Descriptive statistics
          Descriptives
          [At this point your screen should look like Figure SG2-2]
             [Highlight Sessions and then click on the arrow to move the
                Sessions over to the Variable(s) box.]
             Options
                [Check Mean and Variance, and Uncheck Std. Deviation]
                Continue
                OK

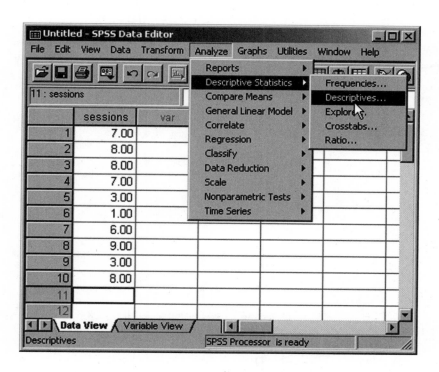

Figure SG2-2

29

2. The results should appear on the screen in the Output window and should look like Figure SG2-3.

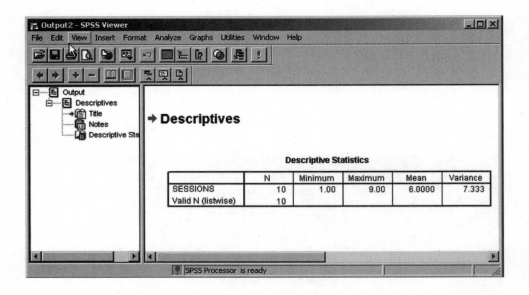

Figure SG2-3

E. Inspect and adjust the result.
    1. At the right is **SESSIONS**, the name of the variable being analyzed.
    2. In the second column appears the number of **Cases (N)**.
    3. The third and fourth columns gives the maximum and minimum values.
    4. The fifth column gives the **Mean**, which SPSS figured to be **6.00**, the same as was figured in the text for this example.

5. The sixth column continues with the **Variance**. However, this "variance" is based on the formula of $SS/(N-1)$ instead of the formula we are using in this chapter of SS/N. To adjust the result SPSS gives, you must multiply it by $N-1$ and then divide by N. In this example, SPSS displays **7.33**. There are 10 cases, so the adjustment is 9 times 7.333, divided by 10—which comes out to 6.6, the same as what was figured in the text. The square root of 6.6, the standard deviation, 2.57, is also the same as was figured in the text.

F. Print out a copy of the result by going to File and clicking on Print, or click on the Print icon.

G. Find the Z scores corresponding to the raw scores, using the following steps:

1. Transform
    Compute
        [Under target variable tell SPSS to create a new variable that consists of Z scores, labeled ZSESS]
            [Highlight SESSIONS and click on the arrow to move it over into the Numeric Expression box]
                [Type (SESSIONS-6)/2.57 in the Numeric Expressions box--your screen should now appear as Figure SG2-4]
                    OK

Figure SG2-4

31

The results should appear as shown in Figure SG2-5.

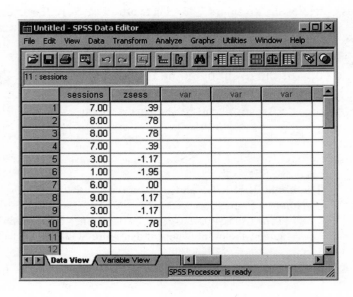

Figure SG2-5

2. Print out a copy of the result by going into File and clicking on Print or clicking the print icon.
3. Save your lines of data as follows:

 File
  Save Data
   Name your data and designate the drive you would like your data saved on]
   OK

II. Systematic Instructions for Computing the Mean and Variance and for Converting a Series of Raw Scores to *Z* Scores

A. Start up SPSS.
B. Enter the data as follows.
 1. Type **7**, the number of sessions for the first subject, and press Enter.
 2. Type **8**, the number of sessions for the second subject, and press Enter.
 3. Type the remaining number of sessions, one per line.

32

4. To replace the default variable name with a more descriptive variable name, click on the Variable View tab at the bottom of the dialogue box. Double click on VAR00001 at the top of the first column. This opens the Define Variable dialogue box. Delete the default variable name and type SESSIONS in the Variable Name text box. Click on Data View at the bottom of the dialogue box. This will close the Variable View dialogue box and return you to the data window.

C. Figure the mean and variance for the number of sessions as follows.
    1. Analyze
          Descriptive statistics
          Descriptives
               [Highlight Sessions and then click on the arrow to move the
               Sessions over to the Variable(s) box.]
                    Options
                        [Check Mean and Variance, and Uncheck Std. Deviation]
                        Continue
                          OK

    2. Print out a copy of the result
    3. Adjust the variance SPSS gives you to the kind of variance described in Chapter 2 of the text: Multiply SPSS's variance times the number of participants minus 1, then divide the result by the total number of participants. Take the square root of this number to get the standard deviation.

D. Find the Z scores corresponding to the raw scores, using the following steps:
    1. Transform
          Compute
               [Under target variable tell SPSS to create a new variable that consists of Z scores, labeled ZSESS]
                    [Highlight SESSIONS and click on the arrow to move it over into the Numeric Expression box]
                        [Type (SESSIONS-6)/2.57 in the Numeric Expressions box]
                        OK

    2. Print out a copy of the result by going into File and clicking on Print or clicking on the Print icon.
    3. Save your lines of data as follows:
        File
          Save Data
               [Name your data designate the drive you would like your data saved on]
                  OK

III. Additional Practice
(For each data set, enter the data and compute the mean and variance–adjusting the latter and determining the standard deviation. Then make *Z* scores. Finally, compare your results to those in the text.)

A. Text examples–use same data sets as for Chapter 1 computer problems.

B. Practice problems in the text: All problems listed for use with the computer in the last chapter.

IV. Using the Computer to Deepen Your Knowledge

A. The effect of outliers (extreme scores) on the mean.

   1. Use SPSS to compute the mean and variance for the example several times, each time changing one of the numbers of sessions to a more extreme number–such as changing the 9 to a 10, then to a 15, then a 20, then a 100 (someone getting long-term depth therapy perhaps).

   2. For each run record the mean and variance.

   3. Make a chart of the results and notice how sensitive both statistics are to the changes in a single score. (For purposes of this exercise, the unadjusted variance will be adequate to make the point clear.)

B. Mean and variance of *Z* scores.

   1. Use SPSS to compute the mean and variance of the *Z* scores created in the example and also in one of the other additional problems.

   2. Note that whatever the original mean and variance, the mean and variance of *Z* scores are always 0 and 1 respectively (within rounding error). (The variance is 1 only after you have made the adjustment to have a variance that was computed with *N*, not *N*-1.)

C. The effects of adding or subtracting a constant.

   1. Using the example, create a new variable that is the same as the number of sessions, but in which 8 is added to each score. (You can do this by going into Transform and clicking on Compute. Then enter a new Target Variable name and type in SESSIONS + 8 in the Numeric Expression box). Then run the mean and variance and compare to the original.

   2. Do the same thing, but this time subtracting 3 from each score. (This will create some negative numbers of sessions!)

   3. Notice that the mean is affected; it is the original mean but with the number you added or subtracted to each score added to or subtracted from it.

   4. But also notice that the variance (whether you adjust it or not) is not affected by adding or subtracting a constant.

   5. If you think in terms of a histogram of the distribution of scores, adding or subtracting a number to each score moves the whole distribution over to one side or the other, thus changing the mean. But the variation among the scores stays the same.

D. The effects of multiplying or dividing by a constant.
1. Using the example, create a new variable that is the same as the number of sessions, but in which each is multiplied by 8. Then have SPSS compute the mean and variance; make the adjustment of the variance and take its square root to get the standard deviation.
2. Do the same thing, but this time, dividing each score by 3.
3. Compare your results to the original.
a. Notice that the mean is affected; it is the original mean, but multiplied or divided by the number by which you multiplied or divided each score.
b. Also notice that in this case the variance and standard deviation are also affected.

V. **Advanced Procedures: Skewness and Kurtosis**
A. In this chapter you have learned that you can describe a distribution by computing numbers for its central tendency (the mean) and its variation (the variance and standard deviation). It is also possible to use numbers to describe the extent to which a distribution approximates a normal curve.
1. One such number describes the skew, the extent to which a distribution is not symmetrical. The closer this number is to 0, the more symmetrical. Positive numbers mean the distribution is skewed to the right (has a long tail to the right); negative numbers mean the distribution is skewed to the left.
2. Another such number describes the kurtosis, the extent to which a distribution is more or less peaked than a normal curve. The closer this number is to 0, the closer the distribution is to a normal curve. Positive numbers mean the distribution is too peaked; negative, too flat.
B. To get skew and kurtosis:
1. Analyze
Descriptive statistics
Descriptives
[Highlight the variable and click on the arrow to move the variable over to the Variable(s) box.]
Options
[Check Skewness and Kurtosis]
Continue
OK

Chapter 3
Correlation

Learning Objectives

To understand, including being able to conduct any necessary computations or carry out any necessary procedures:

- Scatter diagrams.
- Patterns of correlation: linear, positive, negative, curvilinear, and no correlation.
- The correlation coefficient (r).
- Causality and correlation.
- Use of proportionate reduction in error (r_) to compare correlations.
- Effect of restriction in range and unreliability of measurement on the correlation coefficient.
- How correlation results are presented in research articles.

Chapter Outline

I. **Key Terms and Concepts:** The pattern of high scores on one variable going with high scores on the other variable, low scores going with low scores, and moderate with moderate, is an example of a *correlation*.

II. **Graphing Correlations: The Scatter Diagram**

A. A *scatter diagram* displays the degree and pattern of relation of the two variables.

B. Making a scatter diagram involves three steps.

    1. Draw the axes and determine which variable should go on which axis.

       a. The independent or predictor variable goes on the horizontal axis.

       b. The predicted or criterion variable goes on the vertical axis.

    2. Determine the range of values to use for each variable and mark them on the axes.

       a. Your numbers should go upward on each axis, starting from where the axes meet.

       b. Ordinarily, begin with the lowest value your measure can possibly have, or zero, and continue to the highest value your measure can possibly have.

       c. When there is no obvious or reasonable lowest or highest possible value, begin or end at a value that is as high or low as people ordinarily score in the group of people of interest for your study.

    3. Mark a dot for the pair of scores for each case.

       a. Locate the place on the horizontal axis for that person's score on the predictor variable.

       b. Move up to the height on the vertical axis which represents that person's score on that variable and mark a clear dot.

c. If there are two cases in one place, you can either put the number "2" in that place or locate a second dot as near as possible to the first–if possible touching–but being sure it is clear that there are in fact two dots in the one place.

III. Patterns of Correlation

A. These can be identified by the general pattern of dots on the scatter diagram.

B. Linear correlation is where the pattern of dots follows a straight line.

C. Curvilinear correlation is one pattern.
   1. It refers to when the relationship between two variables does not follow any kind of straight line, positive or negative, but instead follows a curving or more complex pattern.
   2. Not all curvilinear relationships are even simple curves.

D. No correlation means no pattern–the two variables are completely unrelated to each other.
   1. On the scatter diagram the dots are spread everywhere, and there is no line, straight or otherwise, that is any reasonable representation of a simple trend.
   2. Note that in actual research situations sometimes the relationship between two variables does exist (that is, it is not really a no–correlation situation), but it is not very strong and thus hard to see visually in a scatter diagram.

E. Positive correlation (or positive linear correlation) is the term for one pattern.
   1. It refers to low scores on one variable going with low scores on the other variable, mediums with mediums, and highs with highs.
   2. On the scatter diagram, the dots follow a line which slopes up and to the right. (That is, the line has a positive slope.)

F. Negative correlation (or negative linear correlation) is the term for another pattern.
   1. It refers to low scores on one variable going with high scores on the other variable, mediums with mediums, and highs with lows.
   2. On the scatter diagram, the dots follow a line which slopes down and to the right. (That is, the line has a negative slope.)

IV. Computing an Index of Degree of Linear Correlation: The Pearson Correlation Coefficient (r)

A. The degree of correlation can be considered numerically or graphically.
   1. It is the extent to which there is a clear pattern, some particular relationship, between the distributions of scores on two variables.
      a. For a positive linear correlation, it is the extent to which high numbers go with highs, mediums with mediums, lows with lows.
      b. For a negative linear correlation, it is the extent to which lows go with highs, etc.
   2. In terms of a scatter diagram, a high degree of linear correlation means that the dots all fall very close to a straight line (the line sloping up or down depending on whether the linear correlation is positive or negative).

B. The computation of the degree of linear correlation has a clever logic behind it.
   1. The first requirement of any such measure is that it be a consistent way of deciding for both variables what is a high and what is a low score–and how high is a high and how low is a low–and this is accomplished by converting all scores to Z scores.
      a. This puts both variables on the same scale.
      b. A high score will always be positive.
      c. A low score will always be negative.
      d. The extent to which a score is high or low will be in proportion to its standard deviation.
   2. A second requirement is a way to combine this information to get a number that reflects the *degree* to which highs go with highs, etc.–this is accomplished by computing the sum of cross–products of Z scores.
      a. A cross–product of Z scores is the Z score of the subject on one variable times the Z score of that subject on the other variable.
      b. If highs go with highs (positive Z times positive Z) or lows with lows (negative Z times negative Z), the result is positive in either case–thus a high positive sum (of these cross–products, over all participants) results when there is a strong positive linear correlation.
      c. If highs go with lows (positive Z times negative Z) or lows with highs (positive Z times negative Z), the result is negative in either case–thus a high negative sum results when there is a strong negative linear correlation.
      d. If highs sometimes go with highs (positive Z times positive Z) but sometimes highs go with lows (positive Z times negative Z), and so forth, the result is that positives and negatives cancel out–thus the sum is near zero when there is no correlation.
   3. A third requirement is that the measure of the degree of correlation have some standard scale–this is accomplished by finding the average of the cross–products of Z scores (dividing the sum by the number of cases).
      a. This is called r, the Pearson correlation coefficient.
      b. When there is a perfect positive linear correlation, $r = 1$.
      c. When there is a perfect negative linear correlation, $r = -1$.
      d. When there is no linear correlation, $r = 0$.
      e. In-between degrees of correlation have values between 0 and 1 (for positive correlations) and between 0 and –1 (for negative correlations).
   4. In terms of a formula: $r = \Sigma(Z_X Z_Y) / N$.

V. Causality and correlation.
   A. For any particular correlation between variables X and Y, there are three possible directions of causality.
      1. X causes Y.
      2. Y causes X.
      3. Some third factor could be causing both X and Y.

   B. Sometimes a possible direction of causality can be logically eliminated. For example, if a researcher finds a correlation between gender and expressiveness, the researcher can logically conclude that level of expressiveness does not determine gender.

   C. Another way to determine causality is to conduct a true experiment, holding all variables constant except the variable of interest.

   D. The issue is confused by two uses of the word "correlation":
      1. A statistical procedure.
      2. A type of research design (that does not use random assignment and is often, but not always, analyzed using the correlation coefficient).

VI. Issues in Interpreting the Correlation Coefficient

   A. Testing statistical significance of the correlation coefficient
      1. The correlation coefficient, by itself, is a descriptive statistic–it describes the degree and direction of linear correlation in the particular group measured.
      2. However, when conducting research in psychology we are often more interested in a particular set of scores as representative of the larger population which we have not directly studied.
      3. A correlation is said to be "significant" if it is very unlikely (less than 5% or 1% probability) that we could have obtained a correlation this big if in fact the overall group had no correlation.
      4. The logic and procedures of statistical significance are the major focus of the text starting with Chapter 5, but are not considered in any more detail in this chapter on correlation (except in Chapter Appendix II).

   B. Comparing magnitude of correlations.
      1. Larger values of r (values further from zero) indicate a higher degree of correlation, but are not proportionally related: for example, an r of .4 is *not* twice as strong as an r of .2.
      2. To compare correlations with each other, the measure you use is r^2, called the *proportionate reduction in error*. (The meaning of this statistic is discussed in detail in Chapter 4.)

   C. Restriction in range: When only a limited range of the possible values on one or both variables are included in the group studied, the resulting correlation can not be properly extended to apply to the entire range of values the variable might have among people in general.

   D. Unreliability of measurement.
      1. A measure that is not perfectly accurate is unreliable.
      2. If one or both variables in a correlation are unreliable, the correlation is reduced (attenuated).
      3. More advanced texts describe formulas for estimating what the correlation between two variables would be if the two variables were perfectly reliable (called disattenuating or correcting for attenuation).

VII. Controversies: What is a Large Correlation?

A. Traditionally a large correlation is considered to be .5 or above, a moderate correlation to be about .3, and a small correlation to be about .1.

B. In fact, in psychology it is rare to obtain correlations greater than .4.

C. It is traditional to caution that a low correlation is not very important even if it is statistically significant.

D. Even experienced research psychologists tend to *over*estimate the degree of association that a correlation coefficient represents.

E. However, some researchers have argued that in many cases even very low correlations can have important practical implications.

F. They illustrate their point with a binomial-effect-size display. This is a table in which the cases are divided in half on each variable, and the number of cases in each of the four combinations is considered.

VIII. How Correlation Coefficients Are Described in Research Articles

A. Correlation coefficients are often described in the text of a research article.

   1. They are usually reported with the letter r, an equal sign, and the correlation coefficient (e.g., $r = .31$).

   2. Sometimes the significance level, such as "$p < .05$," will also be reported.

B. A table of correlations, called a *correlation matrix*, is common when correlations have been figured among many variables.

Formula

Correlation coefficient (r)

Formula in words: Average of the cross–product of Z scores.

Formulas in symbols: $r = \Sigma(Z_X Z_Y) / N$ (3–1)

Z_X is the Z score for each case on the X variable.

Z_Y is the Z score for each case on the Y variable.

$Z_X Z_Y$ is the cross–product of Z scores (for each case, Z_X times Z_Y).

N is the number of cases.

How to Graph and Figure a Correlation

1. **Construct a scatter diagram.**
   A. Draw the axes and determine which variable should go on which axis.
   B. Determine the range of values to use for each variable and mark them on the axes.
   C. Mark a dot for the pair of scores for each case.
2. **Estimate the direction and degree of linear correlation.**
3. **Figure the correlation coefficient.**
   A. Change all scores to Z scores.
   B. Figure the cross–product of the Z scores for each person.
   C. Add up all the cross–products of the Z scores.
   D. Divide by the number of people in the study.

Outline for Writing Essays on the Logic and Computations for a Correlation Problem

The reason for your writing essay questions in the practice problems and tests is that this task develops and then demonstrates what matters so very much–your comprehension of the logic behind the computations. (It is also a place where those better at words than numbers can shine, and for those better at numbers to develop their skills at explaining in words.)

Thus, to do well, be sure to do the following in each essay: a. give the reasoning behind each step; b. relate each step to the specifics of the content of the particular study you are analyzing; c. state the various formulas in nontechnical language, because as you define each term you show you understand it (although once you have defined it in nontechnical language, you can use it from then on in the essay); (d) look back and be absolutely certain that you made it clear just *why* that formula or procedure was applied and *why* it is the way it is.

The outlines below are *examples* of ways to structure your essays. There are other completely correct ways to go about it. And this is an *outline* for an answer–you are to write the answer out in paragraph form. Examples of full essays are in the answers to Set I Practice Problems in the back of the text.

These essays are necessarily very long for you to write (and for others to grade). But this is the very best way to be sure you understand everything thoroughly. One shortcut you may see on a test is that you'll be asked to write your answer for someone who understands statistics up to the point of the new material you are studying. You can choose to take the same shortcut in these practice problems (maybe writing for someone who understands right up to whatever point you yourself start being just a little unclear). But every time you write for a person who has never had statistics at all, you review the logic behind the entire course. You engrain it in your mind. Over and over. The time is never wasted. It is an excellent way to study.

I. Construct a scatter diagram.
A. Procedure: A two–dimensional graph with each variable on one axis and a dot for each score representing its score on the two variables.
B. Explanation: This graph shows the pattern of relationship among the two variables.

II. Estimate the direction and degree of linear correlation.
A. Procedure: Inspect the pattern of dots.
B. Explanation: The general pattern of dots shows whether highs go with highs, lows with lows (or the reverse), indicating the degree of association. (Note the pattern for your particular data.)

III. Figure the correlation coefficient.
A. Procedure: $r = \Sigma(Z_X Z_Y) / N$.
B. Explanation.
    1. The correlation represents the degree high scores go with high scores and low scores with low scores (or if describing a negative correlation, the reverse).
    2. One can identify the extent to which a score is high or low by converting to Z scores (explain meaning of a Z score, and mean and standard deviation in lay terms, as per the explanation in the outline for writing essays in Chapter 2 of this *Study Guide*).
        a. With Z scores, a high score is always positive.
        b. A low score is always negative.
        c. The degree to which a score is high or low is in proportion to the standard deviation.
    3. After converting all scores to Z scores, one multiplies each individual's Z score on one variable times that individual's Z score on the other variable.
        a. If describing a positive correlation, note that if highs go with highs then positives will always be multiplied by positives (giving a positive product) and if lows go with lows then negatives will always be multiplied by negatives (also giving a positive product)–the sum over all cases will thus be high and positive.
        b. If describing a negative correlation, note that if highs go with lows then positives will always be multiplied by negatives (giving a negative product)–the sum over all cases will thus be a large negative number.

4. One then sums the cross–products and divides by the number of cases to get an average cross–product (called r).

   a. If describing a positive correlation, note that the more highs go with highs and lows with lows (or the dots fall near a straight line that slopes up), the closer r is to 1, with no association being an r of 0. (Discuss the degree of correlation of your particular result.)

   b. If describing a negative correlation, note that the more highs go with lows and lows with highs (or the dots fall near a straight line that slopes down), the closer r is to –1, with no association being an r of 0. (Discuss the degree of correlation of your particular result.)

IV. Check the sign and size of your figured correlation coefficient against your estimate from the scatter diagram (Step II above).

Chapter Self–Tests

Multiple-Choice Questions

1. Which of these statements about scatter diagrams is true?

   a. their usual purpose is to describe the relationship between three or more variables.
   b. when the dots on the graph seem to form a straight line, this is called a curvilinear correlation.
   c. the lowest to highest values of the predictor variable are marked on the vertical axis and the lowest to highest values of the criterion variable are marked on the horizontal axis.
   d. each individual's pair of scores is represented as a dot on this two–dimensional graph.

2. A study finds that the more exercise people do, the less money they spend on medical treatment, but only up to a point. Beyond that point, the more exercise they do, the more money they spend on medical treatment. The relation between amount of exercise and money spent on medical treatment represents

   a. a positive linear correlation.
   b. a negative linear correlation.
   c. a curvilinear correlation.
   d. no correlation (that is, neither linear nor curvilinear).

3. Which choice best describes the data on this scatter diagram?

a. no correlation.
b. curvilinear correlation.
c. positive linear correlation.
d. negative linear correlation.

4. Which of the following statements is true about the correlation coefficient?

a. it is an index of the degree of curvilinear correlation.
b. it is the average of the cross–products of Z scores.
c. it is symbolized as c.
d. it is highly positive when there is a strong negative linear correlation.

5. An employer conducts a survey of how much coffee workers drink each day and how much work they get done. The result is a positive correlation that is statistically significant at the .05 level. What should she conclude?

a. Coffee increases the rate at which people work.
b. Working quickly causes people to drink more coffee.
c. Having a faster metabolism causes people to work faster and to crave coffee.
d. She cannot make any definite conclusions about the direction of causality just from knowing that the correlation is positive and significant.

6. Given that the correlation coefficient is .3, what is the proportionate reduction in error?

a. $(c)(.3)$
b. $(2)(.3) = .6$
c. $(10)(.3) = 3$
d. $.3^2 = .09$

7. Suppose you were conducting a study of the relation between appearance (good looks) and income. Which of the following is likely to DECREASE the size of the correlation you would find?

a. studying a group of people who vary a great deal on appearance.
b. using a measure of income that is highly exact.
c. using a measure of good looks that is fairly ambiguous.
d. none of the above.

8. In psychology a large correlation coefficient is traditionally considered to be a correlation that is at least

    a. .3
    b. .5
    c. .7
    d. .9

9. In a research article, the correlations among several variables are often presented in a table called a

    a. contingency table.
    b. scatter diagram.
    c. correlation matrix.
    d. C table.

Fill–In Questions

10. In a scatter diagram of the relation between amount of tiredness and confusion in thinking (in which tiredness is considered to be the cause of confusion in thinking), a dot located at 6 across and 4 up means the person had a score of 6 on _____.

11. A scatter diagram shows a pattern of dots that follow a line that starts going up and to the right and then about halfway along stops going up and just stays flat as it continues to the right. This pattern is an example of _____ correlation.

12. A study finds that the more self–confidence people have, the less fear they have of meeting new people. The relation between self–confidence and fear of meeting new people is an example of a(n) _____ correlation.

13. If two variables have a positive linear correlation, then in general the cross–products of Z scores should be _____.

14. When there is a perfect negative correlation, the average of the cross–product of Z scores equals _____.

15. If pairs of scores for a group of people are highly correlated, a researcher will often conclude that it is likely that for people in general these scores are highly correlated. The researcher would say that this result is statistically _____.

16. A correlation of .6 is considered to be _____ times as strong a relationship as a correlation of .2.

17. When a correlation is figured between two variables that are measured with questionnaires having a lot of ambiguous questions (and are thus not very reliable), the resulting correlation is likely to be _____ ("lower than," "higher than," or "the same as") if the two variables were measured with a completely unambiguous questionnaire.

18. Researchers have shown that even small correlations can have important implications. One way of illustrating this is by making a table in which each variable is divided into high and low and the numbers of cases falling into each high–low combination of the two variables is shown. This kind of a table is called a(n) _____.

Problems and Essays

19. Four individuals kept records for a month on how many eggs they ate per day and then were measured on their cholesterol level. Here are the (fictional) results:

Average Eggs Eaten Per Day	Cholesterol Level
2	210
0	100
1	180
5	270

a. Make a scatter diagram of the raw data.
b. Describe the general pattern of the data in words.
c. Figure the correlation coefficient.
d. Figure the proportionate reduction in error.
e. Indicate plausible directions of causality in terms of the variables involved.
f. Explain your result to a person who has never had a course in statistics.

20. A professor teaching a course in introductory statistics measured attendance and final grade (100 points possible). Here are the (fictional) results for 10 students:

Attendance	Grade
30	97
20	82
22	99
15	67
18	72
24	80
21	94
25	86
26	77
19	75

a. Make a scatter diagram of the raw data.
b. Describe the general pattern of the data in words.
c. Figure the correlation coefficient.
d. Figure the proportionate reduction in error.
e. Indicate plausible directions of causality in terms of the variables involved.
f. Explain your result to a person who has never had a course in statistics.

21. The following (fictional) data are from six LA gang leaders. Here are raw scores and Z scores of the size of each leader's gang and of each leader's willingness to help in a campaign to stop gang violence:

Gang Leader	Size of Gang Raw	Z	Rated Willingness to Help Campaign Raw	Z
Gang A	24	−1.2	10	1.6
Gang B	106	.4	4	−.5
Gang C	42	−.9	7	.5
Gang D	70	−.3	6	.2
Gang E	90	.1	5	−.2
Gang F	178	1.9	1	−1.6

a. Make a scatter diagram of the raw data.
b. Describe the general pattern of the data in words.
c. Figure the correlation coefficient.
d. Figure the proportionate reduction in error.
e. Indicate plausible directions of causality in terms of the variables involved.
f. Explain your answer to a person who has never had a course in statistics.

22. A Canadian social psychologist conducted a (fictional) survey of attitudes towards a particular immigrant nationality among members of that nationality. The survey also included questions about how much the respondents identified with their group of national origin and about how many generations the person's parents had been in Canada (which ranged from 1–first–generation immigrants–through 6). The researcher reported the following results: "There appears to be a strong association between positive attitudes and degree of identification, with a correlation between the two measures of $r = .51$, $p < .01$. However, there was little association between positive attitudes and number of generations, $r = .16$, not significant." Explain this result to a person who has never had a course in statistics. (Discuss the statistical–significance aspect only in a very general way.)

23. An educational psychologist analyzed the relation between high school students' performance in various classes as measured by their grades and reported the (fictional) results in the following table.

	English	Math	Science	History
English		.12	.19	.53**
Math			.68**	.09
Science				.28*
History				

$*p < .05$; $**p < .01$

Explain these results to a person who has never had a course in statistics. (Discuss the statistical–significance aspect only in a very general way.)

Using SPSS (11.0 for Windows) with this Chapter

If you are using SPSS for the first time, before proceeding with the material in this section, read the Appendix on Getting Started and the Basics of Using SPSS.

You can use SPSS to create a scatter diagram and to figure a correlation coefficient. You should work through the example, following the procedures step by step. Then look over the description of the general principles involved and try the procedures on your own for some of the problems listed in the Suggestions for Additional Practice. Finally, you may want to try the suggestions for using the figurer to deepen your understanding, and you can explore the advanced SPSS procedure, a correlation matrix, at the end.

I. Example

A. Data: The number of hours slept the night before and mood. The data are hours slept (7, 9, 8, 9, 8, 6, 8, 7, 10, 8) and mood (4, 5, 3, 7, 4, 1, 3, 2, 6, 5).

B. Follow the instructions in the SPSS Appendix for starting up SPSS.

C. Enter the data as follows.

    1. Type 7 and press enter. Then click on the next box on the same line and type 4 and enter. This will put the participants two scores on the same line next to each other.

    2. Click on the first box on the next line and type 9 and then enter. Then click on the second box on the second line and type 5 and enter.

    3. Type the scores for the remaining subjects, on each line one subject's hours slept and mood, in that order.

    4. To replace the default variable name with a more descriptive variable name, click on the Variable View tab at the bottom of the dialogue box. Double click on VAR00001 at the top of the first column. This opens the Define Variable dialogue box. Delete the default variable name (VAR00001) and type in HRSSLEPT in the Variable Name text box. Repeat for the second variable, replacing VAR00002 with MOOD. Your screen should look like Figure SG3-1. Click on Data View at the bottom of the dialogue box. This will close the Variable View dialogue box and return you to the data window. Your screen should now look like Figure SG3-2.

Figure SG3–1

49

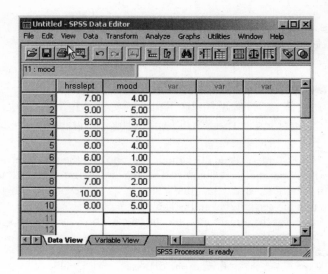

Figure SG3-2

D. Create a scatter diagram for the two variables as follows:

Graphs

Scatter

Simple

Define

[Highlight Mood and move it into the Y-axis box.
Then highlight HRSSLEPT and move it into the X-axis box.
Your screen should now look like Figure SG3-3.]

OK

The scatter diagram should look like Figure SG3–4.

50

Figure SG3-3

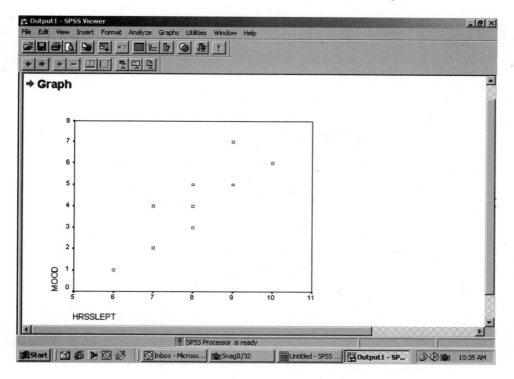

Figure SG3-4

51

E. Inspect the result.
    1. The label for the vertical axis, **MOOD**, is shown along the left side, and the label for the horizontal axis, **HRSSLEPT**, is shown along the bottom of the screen.
    2. The **dots** represent the data points.
    3. Notice that this scatter diagram corresponds closely to the one in the text for these data.
F. Print out a copy of the result by going to File and clicking on Print or clicking on the print icon.
G. Compute the correlation coefficient as follows:
    Analyze
        Correlate >
            Bivariate
                [Move MOOD and HRSSLEPT under Variables by highlighting them and clicking on the arrow. Your screen should appear as Figure SG3-5.]
                    OK

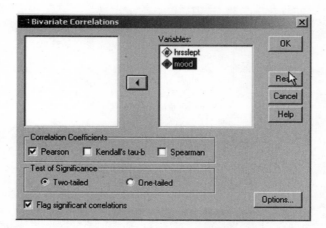

Figure SG3-5

1. Inspect the result: The screen shows the combination of variables with **1.000** for each variable's correlation with itself, and **.843** for the correlation between the two variables (the correlation in the chapter, in which everything was rounded off to two decimal places, was .84). The screen should look like Figure SG3-6.
2. Print out a copy of the result by going to File and then Print or clicking the print icon.
3. Save your lines of data as follows:
   File
      Save As
         [Name your data and designate the drive you would like your data saved in]
            OK

Figure SG3-6

II. Systematic Instructions for Creating a Scatter Diagram and Computing a Correlation Coefficient

A. Start up SPSS.

B. Enter the data as follows:

1. Type 7 and press enter. Then click on the next box on the same line and type 4 and enter. This will put the subjects' two scores on the same line next to each other.

2. Click on the first box on the next line and type 9 and then enter. Then click on the second box on the second line and type 5 and enter.

3. Type the scores for the remaining subjects, on each line one subject's number supervised and stress level, in that order.

4. To replace the default variable name with a more descriptive variable name, click on the Variable View tab at the bottom of the dialogue box. Double click on VAR00001 at the top of the first column. This opens the Define Variable dialogue box. Delete the default variable name (VAR00001) and type in HRSSLEPT in the Variable Name text box. Repeat for the second variable, replacing VAR00002 with MOOD. Click on Data View at the bottom of the dialogue box. This will close the Variable View dialogue box and return you to the data window.

C. Create a scatter diagram for the two variables as follows:

Graphs
   Scatter
      Simple
         Define
            [Highlight MOOD and move it into the Y-axis box. Then highlight HRSSLEPT and move it into the X-axis box.]
               OK

D. Compute the correlation coefficient as follows:

Analyze
   Correlate >
      Bivariate
         [Move MOOD and HRSSLEPT under Variables by highlighting them and clicking on the arrow.]
            OK

1. Print out a copy of the result by going to File and then Print or by clicking on the print icon.

2. Save your lines of data as follows:

   File
   Save As
      [Name your data and designate the drive you would like your data saved in]
         OK

III. Additional Practice (For each data set, create a scatter diagram, compute the correlation coefficient, and compare your results to those in the text.)

    A. Text examples: Fictional study of the effect of number of exposures on recall (from Table 3–2).

    B. Practice problems in the text: Questions 2 and 3.

IV. Using the Computer to Deepen Your Knowledge

    A. The effect of outliers (extreme scores) on the correlation coefficient.

        1. Use SPSS to compute correlations for the example several times, each time changing one of the numbers supervised to a more extreme number–such as changing the 7 to a 3, then to a 1, then a 14, then a 18. For each run record the correlation.

        2. Do the same with the original numbers, but changing one of the stress ratings, perhaps one of the 5s. For each run record the correlation.

        3. Do the same thing with the original numbers, but this time creating a joint outlier–perhaps making the 7,4 pair into a 13,8 pair, then a 15, 10 pair, etc. For each run record the correlation.

        4. Do the same thing, but this time creating a joint outlier that is not an outlier on either variable by itself. Try 6,2 and 9,6.

        5. Make a chart of the results and notice how sensitive the correlation coefficient is to outliers involving one variable and outliers involving two variables.

    B. The effect of adding, subtracting, multiplying, or dividing by a constant on the correlation coefficient.

        1. Use SPSS to compute the correlation coefficient using the example data–except this time add three to every mood score. Then add six. Then try adding 5 to every number-supervised score. Note that the correlations in each case are the same.

        2. Do the same, this time multiplying one of the scores by 2. Then try dividing one of the scores by 4. Again, there is no effect.

        3. Do the same, this time using Z scores. Again there is no effect.

    C. Estimating correlations.

        1. Begin with the example and modify the scores for two of the subjects until you have reduced the correlation to as close to .50 as you can.

        2. Modify as many scores as necessary to create a correlation near to zero.

        3. Modify as many scores as necessary to create a correlation near to –.50.

        4. Create a scatter diagram on paper that you think represents a correlation of about .25. Then enter the numbers and try it on the computer to see how close you get. Modify the scatter diagram until you have achieved a correlation of about .25.

        5. Do the same for correlations of –.50, –.25, 0, .50, and .75.

V. Advanced Procedure: Correlation Matrix

    A. Add a third variable to supervise/stress data representing cups of coffee. The scores for the cups of coffee (in the same order) are 3, 1, 2, 3, 4, 3, 1, 5, 3, 2. (To do this, you must add a variable name for this variable, such as **COFFEE**, and add each subject's scores to his or her line of scores.)

    B. Have SPSS compute the correlations among all three variables.

Chapter 4
Prediction

Learning Objectives

To understand, including being able to conduct any necessary computations:

- Bivariate prediction model with Z scores and associated formulas, terminology and symbols.
- Why prediction is sometimes called regression.
- Two methods of bivariate prediction with raw scores and associated terminology, formulas and symbols.
- Regression line.
- Proportionate reduction in error in bivariate prediction and associated formulas, terminology and symbols.
- Multiple regression with Z scores and associated formulas, terminology, and symbols. (You are not expected to be able to figure ßs, but should be able to interpret them and make predictions using them if they are given.)
- The multiple correlation coefficient.
- Limitations of regression.
- Basic issues in interpreting the relative importance of predictor variables in multiple regression.
- How results of studies using multiple regression are reported in research articles.

Chapter Outline

I.   Terminology of Bivariate Prediction

A. In bivariate prediction (same as bivariate regression), we use a person's score on a predictor to make predictions about a person's score on a criterion variable.

B. The predictor variable is usually labeled X, the criterion variable is labeled Y.

II.   The Bivariate Prediction Model with Z Scores

A. A person's predicted Z score on the criterion variable is found by multiplying a particular number, called a *regression coefficient*, times that person's Z score on the predictor variable.   .

B. Because we are working with Z scores (which are also called standard scores), the regression coefficient in this case is called a *standardized regression coefficient*.

   1. It is symbolized by the Greek letter beta (ß).
   2. Because it is a kind of measure of how much weight or importance to give the predictor variable, it is called a "beta weight."

C. Formula and symbols: Predicted $Z_Y = (\beta)(Z_X)$.

D. ß $= r$ (in bivariate prediction). Below is some insight as to why.

   1. If there is no correlation ($r = 0$), ß $= 0$: The predictor variable is irrelevant, and the best predictor is the mean of the criterion variable (a Z_Y of 0). ($Z_Y = [\beta][Z_X] = [0][Z_X] = 0$.)
   2. If there is a perfect correlation ($r = 1$), ß $= 1$: The criterion variable's Z score exactly equals the predictor variable's Z score. ($Z_Y = [\beta][Z_X] = [1][Z_X] = Z_X$.)
   3. Thus, in the intermediate cases, when r is between 0 and 1, the best number for beta is also between 0 and 1.

E. Why prediction is sometimes called regression.
   1. When there is less than a perfect correlation between two variables, the criterion variable Z score is some fraction (the value of r) of the predictor variable Z score.
   2. As a result, the criterion variable Z score is closer to its mean (that is, it regresses or returns to a Z of zero).

III. Bivariate Prediction Using Raw Scores
A. Convert the raw score on the predictor variable to a Z score.
B. Multiply beta times this Z score to get the predicted Z score on the criterion variable.
C. Convert the predicted Z score on the criterion variable to a raw score.

IV. Direct Raw-Score-to-Raw-Score Prediction
A. Reduces the three-step process (III above) to a single formula which automatically takes into account the conversion into and from Z scores.
   1. Start with the regression constant
   2. Add it to the result of multiplying a person's raw score by the raw-score regression coefficient (b).
B. Note that you should not predict from scores much higher or lower than those in the study used to figure the original correlation
C. Figuring the regression constant
   1. The regression constant is the predicted raw score on the criterion variable when the raw score is 0.
   2. To do this, figure the predicted raw score on the criterion variable when the predictor variable is 0 with raw-score prediction using the Z-score prediction model
      a. $Z_X = (X - M_X)/SD_X$ or $Z_X = (0 - M_X)/SD_X$
      b. Predicted $Z_Y = (r)(Z_X)$
      c. $\hat{Y} = (SD_Y)(\text{Predicted } Z_Y) + M_Y$
D. Figuring the raw-score regression coefficient
   1. The raw-score regression coefficient is how much the predicted criterion variable increases for every increase of 1 on the predictor variable.
   2. To do this, figure the predicted raw-score on the criterion variable when the predictor variable is 1 with raw-score prediction using the Z-score prediction model
      a. $Z_X = (X - M_X)/SD_X$
      b. Predicted $Z_Y = (r)(Z_X)$
      c. $\hat{Y} = (SD_Y)(\text{Predicted } Z_Y) + M_Y$
   3. Then take this number minus the regression constant.
E. Raw-score prediction formula: $\hat{Y} = a + (b)(X)$
   1. $\hat{Y}$ is the predicted raw score
   2. X is the person's raw score on the predictor variable
   3. b (the raw-score regression coefficient)
   4. a (the regression constant)

V. The Regression Line
A. Graphic representation of the prediction model.
B. A line in which the horizontal axis represents the predictor variable scores and the vertical axis represents the predicted scores on the criterion variable.

C. The slope of the regression line.
    1. It equals b, the raw-score regression coefficient.
    2. This equivalence (of the slope of the regression line and b) emphasizes that a regression coefficient serves as a kind of rate of exchange between the predictor and criterion variable (that is, for each unit increase in the predictor variable, there is a predicted fractional increase in the criterion variable equal to b).

D. The intercept of the regression line. The point where the regression line crosses the vertical axis, the "Y intercept," is the point at which $X = 0$, and thus $\hat{Y} = a$.

E. How to draw the regression line.
    1. Draw and label the axes of the graph, as for a scatter diagram.
    2. Pick any value of the predictor variable, figure (using the prediction rule) the corresponding predicted value on the criterion variable, and mark the point on the graph.
    3. Do the same thing again, starting with any other value of the predictor variable (it is easiest to draw an accurate line if the predictor-variable values used in this step and 2 are far apart).
    4. Draw a line that passes through the two marks.

F. You can check the accuracy of a drawn regression line by finding any third point.

VI. Error and Proportionate Reduction of Error

A. The accuracy of predictions using a prediction model can be estimated by considering how much error would result using the prediction model to predict the scores used to figure the correlation coefficient in the first place.

B. Error is the actual score minus the predicted score.

C. We used squared error (in part because positive and negative errors will offset each other): $\text{Error}^2 = (Y - \hat{Y})^2$.

D. Graphic interpretation of error: The vertical distance between the dot for a subject's actual score and the regression line.

E. Proportionate reduction in error.
    1. It is the most common way to think about the accuracy of a prediction model.
    2. It is a comparison of squared errors indicating how much better predictions are likely to be using a particular model than making predictions without the model.

F. Strategy for computing proportionate reduction in error
    1. Figure total of squared errors not using a prediction model (that is, predicting the mean for each criterion variable score): $SS_{\text{Total}} = \Sigma(Y-M)^2$.
    2. Figure total of squared errors using the prediction model: $SS_{\text{Error}} = \Sigma(Y - \hat{Y})^2$.
    3. Figure the reduction using the prediction rule: Reduction $= SS_{\text{Total}} - SS_{\text{Error}}$.
    4. Figure the proportionate reduction: Reduction/SS_{Total} or $(SS_{\text{Total}} - SS_{\text{Error}})/SS_{\text{Total}}$.

G Some insight into meaning of proportionate reduction in error.
    1. If the prediction model is no improvement, $SS_{\text{Error}} = SS_{\text{Total}}$; thus, reduction = 0 and proportionate reduction = 0 or 0%.
    2. If the prediction model predicts perfectly, $SS_{\text{Error}} = 0$; thus reduction $= SS_{\text{Total}} - 0 = SS_{\text{Total}}$, and proportionate reduction = 1 or 100%.
    3. For in between cases, where the prediction rule is some improvement but does not predict perfectly, proportionate reduction in error is between 0% and 100%.

H. Proportionate reduction in error $= r^2$.

I. Proportionate reduction in error is also called the proportion of variance accounted for (because SS_{Total} is also the sum of squared deviations from the mean, the essential ingredient in the variance).

J. Graphic interpretation of proportionate reduction in error.
    1. If each score is predicted to be the mean, the line representing these predictions would be a horizontal line.
    2. The proportionate reduction in error can be thought of as the extent to which the regression line's accuracy is greater than the horizontal line's accuracy.

VII. Extension to Multiple Regression and Correlation
A. The association between a criterion variable and two or more predictor variables is called *multiple correlation*; making predictions in this situation is called *multiple regression.*
B. These procedures have become increasingly important in psychology and are today very widely used.
C. Because this is an advanced topic, it is only introduced in a general way in this text.
D. Z score prediction model in multiple regression: Predicted $Z_Y = (\beta_1)(Z_{X1}) + (\beta_2)(Z_{X2}) + (\beta_3)(Z_{X3})$ ......
E. In multiple regression, ß for a predictor variable is *not* the same as *r* for that predictor variable with the criterion variable.
    1. ß is usually lower (closer to 0) than *r* because part of what any one predictor variable measures will overlap with what the other predictor variables measure.
    2. In multiple regression, ß is based on the unique, distinctive contribution of the variable, excluding any overlap with other predictor variables.
G. The multiple correlation coefficient (*R*) describes the overall correlation between the predictor variables, taken together, and the criterion variable.
    1. Due to overlap in predicting the criterion variable, *R* is usually less than (and can not be more than) the sum of each predictor variable's *r* with the criterion variable.
    2. *R* ranges from 0 to 1.0 (unlike *r*, it can not be negative).

VIII. Controversies
A. The limitations of correlation (see Chapter 3) apply with equal or greater force to bivariate and multiple prediction.
    1. It only assesses the linear aspect of a relationship.
    2. It is distorted by restriction in range.
    3. It is distorted by unreliability of measures.
    4. It does not indicate direction of underlying causal relationships.
B. There is controversy over how to assess the relative importance of the several predictor variables in predicting the criterion variable.
    1. For purely predictive purposes, the regression coefficients (either standardized or raw score) serve well.
    2. But for a theoretical understanding of the relative importance of the different predictors, the regression coefficients are not necessarily the best indicators.
        a. They reflect only the unique contribution of the predictor variable to the prediction after considering all the other predictors.
        b. Thus, when predicting by itself, without considering the other predictors (that is, using *r*), a variable may appear to have a quite different importance relative to the other predictors.
    3. Whenever the predictor variables are correlated with each other (called multicollinearity, the usual situation in multiple regression) there is no agreed-upon approach to the question of the relative importance of these sorts of predictor variables.

IX. Prediction Models as Described in Research Articles
A. Bivariate prediction models are rarely cited in psychology research articles–in most cases, simple correlations are reported.
B. Multiple regression models are commonly reported (either in the text or a table), including the following.
   1. The regression coefficients (ßs or *a* and *b*s or all of these).
   2. R^2.
   3. R.
   4. Statistical significance of R^2, regression coefficients, or both.

Formulas

I. Predicted Z score for a particular subject on the criterion variable (predicted Z_Y) in bivariate prediction.

Formula in words: Standardized regression coefficient times the subject's Z score on the predictor variable.

Formula in symbols: Predicted $Z_Y = (\beta)(Z_X)$

ß   is the standardized regression coefficient.

Z_X is the known subject's known Z score on the predictor variable.

II. Standardized regression coefficient (ß) in bivariate prediction.

Formula in words: It is the same as the correlation coefficient.

Formula in symbols: $\beta = r$

r   is the ordinary correlation coefficient between the predictor variable and the criterion variable.

III. Predicted raw score for a particular subject on the criterion variable ($\hat{Y}$) in bivariate prediction

Formula in words: The raw-score regression constant plus the product of the raw score regression coefficient times the subject's score on the predictor variable.

Formula in symbols: $\hat{Y} = a + (b)(X)$

a   is the raw score regression constant.

b   is the raw score regression coefficient.

X   is the subject's known raw score on the predictor variable.

IV. Sum of squared error using the prediction rule (SS_{Error})

Formula in words: Sum over all the scores of the square of each criterion variable score minus its predicted score using the prediction rule.

Formula in symbols: $SS_{Error} = \Sigma(Y - \hat{Y})^2$

V. Sum of squared error predicting each score from the mean (SS_{Total})

Formula in words: Sum over all the scores of the square of each criterion variable score minus the mean of the criterion variable scores.

Formula in symbols: $SS_{Total} = \Sigma(Y-M)^2$

VI. Proportionate reduction in error (r²)

Formula in words: Amount of squared error reduced (sum of squared error using the mean to predict minus sum of squared error using the prediction rule) divided by the total squared error available to be reduced (sum of squared error using the mean to predict).

Formula in symbols: $r^2 = (SS_{Total} - SS_{Error}) / SS_{Total}$ (4-6)

VII. Predicted Z score for a particular subject on the criterion variable (predicted Z_Y) in multiple prediction.

Formula in words: Sum, over all predictor variables, of the product of each predictor variable's standardized regression coefficient times the subject's Z score on that predictor variable.

Formula in symbols: Predicted $Z_Y = (ß_1)(Z_{X1}) + (ß_2)(Z_{X2}) + (ß_3)(Z_{X3})$ ......   (4-8)

VIII. Predicted raw score for a particular subject on the criterion variable ($\hat{Y}$) in multiple prediction.

Formula in words: Raw-score regression constant, plus the sum over all predictor variables of the product of each predictor variable's regression coefficient times the subject's score on that predictor variable.

Formula in symbols: $\hat{Y} = a + (b_1)(X_1) + (b_2)(X_2) + (b_3)(X_3)$ ......   (4-9)

How to Construct a Z-Score Prediction Model in Bivariate Regression

1. Determine the standardized regression coefficient.
2. Multiply the standardized regression coefficient by the person's Z score on the predictor variable.

How to Make a Z-Score Prediction for a Particular Subject in Bivariate Regression

1. Determine the standardized regression coefficient.
2. Multiply the standardized regression coefficient by the person's Z score on the predictor variable.

How to Make a Raw Score Prediction for a Particular Subject in Bivariate Regression Based on a Z-Score Prediction Rule

1. Change the person's raw score on the predictor variable to a Z score.
2. Multiply the standardized regression coefficient by the person's predictor variable Z score.
3. Change the person's predicted Z score on the criterion variable to a raw score.

How to Construct a Raw-Score Prediction Model in Bivariate Regression

1. **Figure the regression constant.** To do this, figure the predicted raw score on the criterion variable when the predictor variable is 0 with raw-score prediction using the Z score prediction model.
2. **Figure the raw-score regression coefficient.**
   A. To do this, figure the predicted raw score on the criterion variable when the predictor variable is 1 with raw-score prediction using the Z score prediction model.
   B. Then, take this number minus the regression constant.
3. **Find the person's predicted raw score on the criterion variable.** To do this, multiply the person's raw score regression coefficient by the person's score on the predictor variable, then add this result to the regression constant.

How to Make a Raw-Score Prediction for a Particular Subject in Bivariate Regression Based on a Raw-Score Prediction Rule

1. **Determine the raw-score prediction model.**
2. **Substitute the subject's raw score on the predictor variable into the prediction model and solve.**

How to Draw a Regression Line

1. **Draw and label the axes for a scatter plot.**
2. **Figure the predicted value on the criterion variable for a low value on the predictor variable, and mark the point on the graph.**
3. **Do the same thing again, but for a high value on the predictor variable.**
4. **Draw a line that passes through the two marks.**

How to Figure the Proportionate Reduction in Error in Bivariate Regression
(Using the Method Involving Computation of Errors)

1. **Figure the sum of squared errors using the mean to predict: Take each score minus the mean, square it, and add these up.** This gives SS_{Total}.
2. **Figure the sum of squared errors using the prediction rule: Take each score minus the predicted score for this person, square it, and add these up.** This gives SS_{Error}.

3, Figure the reduction in error: This is the sum of squared errors using the mean to predict (from Step 1) minus the sum of squared error using the prediction model (from Step 2).

4. Figure the proportionate reduction in squared error. This is the reduction in squared error (from Step 3) divided by the total squared error when using the mean to predict (from Step 1).

Outline for Writing Essays on the Logic and Computations for a Bivariate Prediction Problem

The reason for your writing essay questions in the practice problems and tests is that this task develops and then demonstrates what matters so very much–your comprehension of the logic behind the computations. (It is also a place where those better at words than numbers can shine, and for those better at numbers to develop their skills at explaining in words.)

Thus, to do well, be sure to do the following in each essay: (a) give the reasoning behind each step; (b) relate each step to the specifics of the content of the particular study you are analyzing; (c) state the various formulas in nontechnical language, because as you define each term you show you understand it (although once you have defined it in nontechnical language, you can use it from then on in the essay); (d) look back and be absolutely certain that you made it clear just *why* that formula or procedure was applied and *why* it is the way it is.

The outlines below are *examples* of ways to structure your essays. There are other completely correct ways to go about it. And this is an *outline* for an answer–you are to write the answer out in paragraph form. Examples of full essays are in the answers to Set I Practice Problems in the back of the text.

These essays are necessarily very long for you to write (and for others to grade). But this is the very best way to be sure you understand everything thoroughly. One shortcut you may see on a test is that you may be asked to write your answer for someone who understands statistics up to the point of the new material you are studying. You can choose to take the same shortcut in these practice problems (maybe writing for someone who understands right up to whatever point you yourself start being just a little unclear). But every time you write for a person who has never had statistics at all, you review the logic behind the entire course. You engrain it in your mind. Over and over. The time is never wasted. It is an excellent way to study.

I. Construct a scatter diagram and figure the correlation: Carry out and explain procedures as described in the Outline for Writing Essays in Chapter 3. (This also includes explaining mean, standard deviation and Z scores.)
II. Identify the predictor and criterion variable in your particular problem.

III. Determine the bivariate prediction model with Z scores.

A. Procedure: Set up formula, Predicted $Z_Y = (\text{ß})(Z_X)$, setting ß equal to r.

B. Explanation.

    1. The formula describes the optimal principle that allows prediction.

    2. Some insight into why the correlation coefficient represents that key relationship.

        a. If there is no correlation ($r = 0$), the predictor variable is irrelevant and the best predictor is the mean of the criterion variable (which for any Z score is 0). ($Z_Y = [\beta][Z_X] = [0][Z_X] = 0$.)

        b. If there is a perfect correlation ($r = 1$), ß = 1: The criterion variable's Z score exactly equals the predictor variable's Z score. ($Z_Y = [\beta][Z_X] = [1][Z_X] = Z_X$.)

        c. Thus, in the intermediate cases, when r is between 0 and 1, the best number for beta is also between 0 and 1.

IV. Determine bivariate prediction model using raw scores.

A. Procedure: Figure a and b and set up the formula of $\hat{Y} = a + (b)(X)$.

    1. Figure the regression constant. To do this, figure the predicted raw score on the criterion variable when the predictor variable is 0 with raw-score prediction using the Z-score prediction model.

    2. Figure the raw-score regression coefficient. To do this, figure the predicted raw score on the criteron variable when the predictor variable is 1 with raw-score prediction using the Z-score prediction model. Then, take this number minus the regression constant.

    3. Find the person's predicted raw score on the criterion variable.

B. Explanation.

    1. One could figure raw-score predictions by converting the predictor variable raw score to a Z score, making the prediction using the Z-score prediction rule, and then converting the predicted Z score to a raw score.

    2. However, by combining the formulas for converting raw scores to Z scores and vice versa into the Z-score prediction formula, you get a set of formulas that use the means and standard deviations and allow you to end up with a formula that makes direct predictions from raw scores to raw scores. (You do *not* need to explain the specific arithmetic of this, just the principle.)

    3. Give the specific raw-score prediction formula for your data.

V. Draw the regression line.

A. Procedure.

    1. Draw and label the axes of the graph, as for a scatter diagram.

    2. Pick a low value of the predictor variable, figure (using the prediction rule) the corresponding predicted value on the criterion variable, and mark the point on the graph.

    3. Do the same thing again using a high value of the predictor variable.

    4. Draw a line that passes through the two marks.

    5. Pick an intermediate value of the predictor variable, find the corresponding dot, and check that it falls on the regression line you have drawn.

B. Explanation.

    1. The regression line is a graphic representation of the prediction model.

    2. The line represents the predicted scores on the criterion variable.

VI. Find the proportionate reduction in error.

A. Procedure.

    1. Figure for each criterion variable score the corresponding raw-score predicted value for that score (using the prediction model).

2. Find the sum of squared errors using the prediction model to predict.
   a. Find the error for each score: Error $= Y - \hat{Y}$.
   b. Square each error.
   c. Sum the squared errors: $SS_{Error} = \Sigma(Y - \hat{Y}^2)$.
3. Find the sum of squared errors using the mean to predict.
   a. Find the error for each score: Error $= Y - M_y$.
   b. Square each error.
   c. Sum the squared errors: $SS_{Total} = \Sigma(Y - M_Y)^2$.
4. Find the proportionate reduction in error: Proportionate reduction in error $= (SS_{Total} - SS_{Error}) / SS_{Total}$.
5. Cross check: Proportionate reduction in error $= r^2$.

B. Explanation.
   1. The accuracy of predictions using a prediction model can be estimated by considering how much error would result using the prediction model to predict the scores used to figure the correlation coefficient in the first place.
   2. Error is the actual score minus the predicted score. Give an example of one of the scores in your data. (Also note that error can be seen graphically as the vertical distance between the dot for a subject's actual score and the regression line.)
   3. We used squared error (in part because positive and negative errors will offset each other).
   4. Proportionate reduction in error is the most common way to think about the accuracy of a prediction model.
   5. Proportionate reduction in error is a comparison of squared errors indicating how much better predictions are likely to be using a particular model than making predictions without the model.
   6. Predicting without the model is the same as using the mean to predict.
   7. Thus, we compare squared error using the prediction rule to squared error using the mean to predict.
   8. The proportionate reduction is the reduction from using the prediction model (squared error using the mean to predict minus squared error using the prediction rule) as a proportion of (that is, divided by) the squared error without the model (the squared error using the mean to predict). (Give all the figures from the data in your sample as you explain this.)
   9. This gives a proportion between 0% and 100%. (Below is some insight as to why.)
      a. If the prediction model is no improvement, error using the two methods (the prediction rule and predicting from the mean) are equal, thus there is a 0% reduction and a 0% proportionate reduction.
      b. If the prediction model predicts perfectly, there is no error using the prediction rule, thus the reduction in error (error using the mean minus error using the prediction model) is the same as the error using the mean to predict. When divided by the error using the mean to predict, this gives a 100% reduction in error.
      c. In your data (probably), the reduction is in between, since there is some improvement but not a perfect prediction.
   10. Also note that the extent to which the regression line is different from horizontal (the line for predicting from the mean) represents the proportionate reduction in error.
   11. It turns out that the proportionate reduction in error is the same as the square of the correlation coefficient. This serves as a check on the computations. (Give the equivalent numbers.)

Chapter Self-Tests

Multiple-Choice Questions

1. In the equation, predicted $Z_Y = (\beta)(Z_X)$, the symbol Z_X stands for the

   a. known Z score of the predictor variable.
   b. standardized regression coefficient.
   c. predicted value of the Z score for the criterion variable.
   d. regression constant.

2. Suppose that there is a .52 correlation between performance on the midterm exam and performance on the final exam. If a person's midterm exam score is 3 standard deviations above the mean (Z score = +3), then what is the person's predicted Z score on the final?

   a. $3/.52 = 5.8$.
   b. $.52 + 3 = 3.52$.
   c. $.52/3 = .17$.
   d. $(.52)(3) = 1.56$.

3. Suppose that every time a person's score goes down 2 points on a depression scale it is associated with a decrease of 3 points on predicted amount of insomnia. In this example the 3 is the

   a. proportionate reduction in error.
   b. regression constant.
   c. raw score regression coefficient.
   d. standardized regression constant.

4. On a scatter diagram, a horizontal line whose height is the mean of the criterion variable represents

   a. the regression line when $r = 1$.
   b. the squared error of estimate line.
   c. predictions using the mean as the predictor.
   d. the regression line when $r = -1$.

5-6 A study is done of three students during finals week, which involves predicting tension from the number of finals to be taken. The participants' scores on the tension questionnaire were 12, 8, and 4. Their respective predicted scores, using a bivariate prediction rule from the data, were 10, 8, and 6.

   5. Which of the following is the correct computation for SS_{Total}?

      a. $12^2 + 8^2 + 4^2$
      b. $(12-10)^2 + (8-8)^2 + (4-6)^2$
      c. $(12-8)^2 + (8-8)^2 + (4-8)^2$.
      d. $(10-8)^2 + (8-8)^2 + (6-8)^2$

   6. Which of the following is the correct computation for SS_{Error}?

      a. $10^2 + 8^2 + 6^2$
      b. $(12-10)^2 + (8-8)^2 + (4-6)^2$
      c. $(12-8)^2 + (8-8)^2 + (4-8)^2$.
      d. $(10-8)^2 + (8-8)^2 + (6-8)^2$

7. What does the proportionate reduction in error tell you?

   a. The reduction in error when predicting from the mean versus when predicting from the raw scores.
   b. The amount of error when predicting from the mean.
   c. The amount of error when predicting from the raw scores.
   d. How much of an advantage it is to use the prediction model to make a prediction over predicting from the mean.

8. The proportionate reduction in error equals

   a. the correlation coefficient squared.
   b. the regression coefficient.
   c. the regression constant.
   d. the raw-score regression coefficient squared.

9. By figuring the predicted raw score on the criterion when the predictor variable is 0 with raw-score prediction using the Z score prediction model, you are computing the
   a. regression constant.
   b. raw-score regression coefficient.
   c. predicted criterion standard.
   d. criterion variable.

10. How are prediction models described in research articles?

    a. Prediction models, both bivariate and multiple regression, are rarely cited in research articles, in most cases, only the simple correlations are reported.
    b. Both bivariate and multiple regression prediction models are often reported in research articles, usually in the form of a table.
    c. Bivariate prediction models are rarely cited; however, multiple regression models are commonly reported using a table that includes the betas, the regression constant, and R^2, as well as other statistics.
    d. Bivariate prediction models are often reported in research articles, using a table that includes the betas, regression constant, and R^2, as well as other statistics, whereas multiple regression models are rarely cited.

Fill-In Questions

11. Bivariate prediction is also called bivariate _____.

12. In the bivariate prediction model for your data, a=15 and b=3. For an individual whose score on X is 8, the predicted score for Y is _____.

13. When making a prediction using the raw-score regression equation, each subject's predicted score is the raw-score regression coefficient times his or her score on the predictor variable, plus the _____ (do not give a symbol).

14. The _____ of the regression line corresponds to the raw-score regression coefficient.

15. _____ is the person's actual score minus the person's predicted score.

16. If $SS_{Total} = 80$ and $SS_{Error} = 60$, $r^2 =$ _____.

17. The proportionate reduction in error is also called _____. (Do not give a symbol.)

18. _____ describes the situation when there are correlations among the predictor variables in multiple regression.

19-20 In a multiple prediction situation with two predictor variables, it has been found that $\beta_1 = .3$, $\beta_2 = -.4.$, $a = -16.2$, $b_1 = 2.5$, and $b_2 = -16$.

19. A particular subject's Z score on the first predictor variable is -1.5, and this subject's Z score on the second predictor variable is .8. This subject's predicted Z score on the criterion variable is _____.

20. A particular subject's raw score on the first predictor variable is 14, and this subject's raw score on the second predictor variable is 2. This subject's predicted raw score on the criterion variable is _____.

Problems and Essays

21. A researcher is interested in predicting how well people will do who participate in an outdoor training program (ratings by instructor at end of program on a 100-point scale from 0 to 10) on the number of hours they exercise each week. In a pilot study of five people, these results were obtained.

Person Tested	Hours Exercised Per Week		Performance in Training Program	
	X	Z_X	Y	Z_Y
1	3	-.59	45	-.54
2	11	1.76	90	1.47
3	6	.29	53	-.18
4	1	-1.17	25	-1.43
5	4	- .29	72	.67

$M=5$ $M=57$
$SD=3.41$ $SD=22.35$

The correlation was found to be .87. Based on the above information, (a) give the Z-score prediction formula for predicting performance in the training program based on the number of hours of exercise per week; (b) figure the proportionate reduction in squared error based on the scores in this sample (do this based on making actual predictions for each score–show your work for the entire process); (c) draw a diagram showing the regression line; (d) using the bivariate prediction rule, predict the performance in the training program for a person who has exercised 8 hours per week; and (e) explain what you have done to a person who has never taken a course in statistics.

22. A psychologist is interested in predicting number of days to recover from a particular illness, based on the number of stressful events the person experienced in the preceding month. The scores for four people studied are shown here (all data are fictional):

Person Tested	Number Stressful Events		Number Days to Recover	
	X	Z_X	Y	Z_Y
A	2	-.39	5	-.63
B	0	-1.17	4	-1.26
C	3	0	7	.63
D	7	1.57	8	1.26
	$M=3$		$M=6$	
	$SD=2.55$		$SD=1.58$	

The correlation was found to be .93. Based on the above information, (a) give the Z-score prediction formula for predicting the number of days to recover from number of stressful events; (b) figure the proportionate reduction in squared error based on the scores in this sample (do this based on making actual predictions for each score–show your work for the entire process); (c) draw a diagram showing the regression line; (d) using the bivariate prediction rule, predict the number of days to recover for a person who has experienced 5 stressful events in the previous month; and (e) explain what you have done to a person who has never taken a course in statistics.

23. A researcher was interested in the effect of stress level on the quality of marital interaction. She measured stress level and then observed the number of times a spouse spoke sharply during a two-hour test period, producing an irritability score. The (fictional) data from 4 target participants are as follows:

Subject	X (Stress lvl)	Y (Irritability)
1	4	10
2	10	15
3	2	7
4	6	7

$M_X = 5.5 \qquad M_Y = 9.75$
$SD_X = 2.96 \qquad SD_Y = 3.27$
$r = 0.81$

(a) give the raw score prediction formula for predicting the irritability from stress level; (b) figure the proportionate reduction in squared error based on the scores in this sample (do this based on making actual predictions for each score–show your work for the entire process); (c) draw a diagram showing the regression line; (d) using the bivariate prediction rule, predict the irritability level for someone with a stress level of 9; and (e) explain what you have done to a person who has never taken a course in statistics.

24. Based on insurance company statistics, a health psychologist figured the following multiple regression equation for predicting how long a person can expect to live based on a study of women in a particular industrial nation (fictional data):

Predicted Years = 75 - (.1) (pounds overweight)
- (4) (packs of cigarettes smoked per day)
+ (.9)(hours exercised per week)
+ (3) (number of grandparents who lived past 80)

(a) Figure the predicted life expectancy for a woman from this nation who is 15 pounds overweight, does not smoke, exercises 2 hours a week, and has one grandparent who lived past 80. (b) Figure the predicted life expectancy for another woman from this nation who is not at all overweight, smokes two packs of cigarettes a day, exercises 1 hour a week, and has no grandparents who lived past 80. (c) Explain what you have done (including why the predictions for the two women are different) to a person who has never had a course in statistics.

25. A sports psychologist is interested in what psychological and social factors predict winning in a particular team sport. She administered questionnaires to members of 100 college teams at the beginning of the season and then used these factors to predict how many games each team won during the season. The report of the results of this fictional study noted, "The overall R^2 was .49, which was statistically significant . . ., and the betas were .22 for a positive attitude towards the team, .11 for a positive attitude towards the coach, -.15 for personal depression, and .06 for love of the sport."

Explain what these results mean, both substantively and statistically (in a general way), to a person who has never had a course in statistics.

Using SPSS (11.0 for Windows) with this Chapter

If you are using SPSS for the first time, before proceeding with the material in this section, read the Appendix on Getting Started and the Basics of Using SPSS.

You can use SPSS to carry out a linear regression analysis, including constructing a Z-score and raw-score regression model. You should work through the example, following the procedures step by step. Then look over the description of the general principles involved and try the procedures on your own for some of the problems listed in the Suggestions for Additional Practice. Finally, you may want to try the suggestions for using the figurer to deepen your understanding, and you can explore the additional, advanced SPSS procedure, multiple regression, at the end.

I. Example
A. Data: The number of hours slept and mood (fictional data), from the example in the text. The scores for the two variables, are hours slept (7, 9, 8, 9, 8, 6, 8, 7, 10, 8) and mood (4, 5, 3, 7, 4, 1, 3, 2, 6, 5). These are the same data used for the SPSS example for Chapter 3 of this *Study Guide and Computer Workbook*. If you followed that example, you should now have the data (and instructions) saved in a file. If you did not carry out that example, you can turn back to it now to follow the steps and illustrations for creating a file with these data.

B. Follow the instructions in the SPSS Appendix for starting up SPSS and be sure the cursor is in the Scratch Pad window.

C. Call up the file from Chapter 3.

    1. Click on File, then select CH3XMPL. Click on OK.

D. Run the linear regression analysis.

    2. Analyze

        Regression >

            Linear

                [Highlight MOOD and move it to the Dependent Variable box.
Highlight HRSSLEPT and move to the Independent Variable box. The screen should appear like Figure SG4-1]

                    OK

E. The screen of results that now appears should look like Figure SG4-2.

Figure SG4-1

71

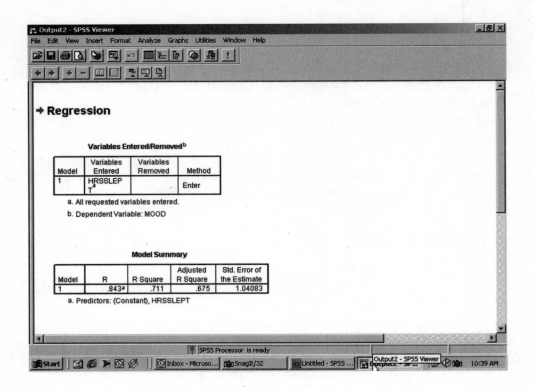

Figure SG4-2

F. Inspect the results on this screen.
  1. There is a great deal of information in this screen and you only need to attend to a small part of it. (The rest involves more advanced material.)
  2. The first important line is **Multiple R**. Because this same output screen layout is used for both multiple and bivariate prediction situations, SPSS describes a "multiple" R. But when using SPSS for bivariate prediction, this is actually the ordinary bivariate r. Notice that the figure given, **.843**, is, within rounding error, what was computed for r in the text (and when using SPSS to compute correlation in the previous chapter).
  3. The next line, **R Square** is the same as r^2, the proportionate reduction in error.
G. Scroll the output screen down. The next screen of results should look like Figure SG4-3.

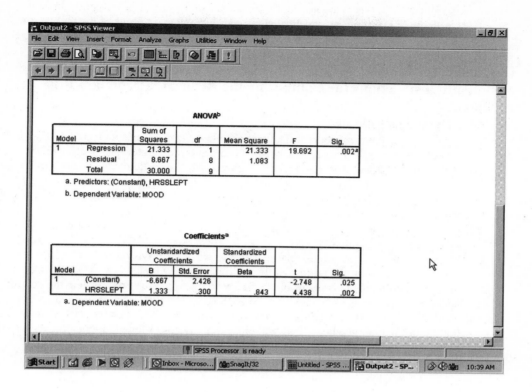

H. Inspect the results–the **Coefficients** section provides the information for the prediction rules.

1. The first column, **Model**, lists the predictor variables. In the case of bivariate prediction, there is one predictor variable (in this case, **HRSSLEPT**). If this were a result of a multiple regression problem, there would be additional predictor variables listed. In addition, in any prediction situation, when working with raw scores, part of the prediction is always the regression constant.

2. The second column, **B**, gives the figures for the raw-score prediction model. The first figure given, which is in the **(Constant)** row, is the raw-score regression constant, a. In the example, it is **–6.667**. The second figure given, which is in the **MOOD** row, is the raw-score regression coefficient, b. In the example it is **1.333**. Thus, the raw score prediction model is Predicted Stress Score = -6.667 + (1.333)(Hours of Sleep). Within rounding error, this is what was computed in the text.

3. Now skip to the fourth column, **Beta**, which gives the standardized regression coefficient, the information needed for making predictions with Z scores. When predicting with Z scores there is no regression constant to add in, so the figure in the **CONSTANT** row will always be blank. The key figure, the beta itself, is in the row for the predictor variable. In this case, beta is **.843**–as always in bivariate prediction, this is the same as the correlation coefficient.

4. The fifth and sixth columns give information regarding statistical significance. In general, if the figure under **Sig** in the row for the predictor variable is .05 or less, we say the result is "significant." In this example, the figure is **.002**, so this result is not quite statistically significant. (The topic of statistical significance is the main focus of the text beginning in Chapter 6, and in the context of correlation is considered briefly in the second appendix to Chapter 3.)

I. Print out the result.

II. Systematic Instructions for Computing the Bivariate Prediction Rule

A. Start up SPSS.

B. Enter the data as follows.

1. The scores for the managers for the two variables, are Hours Slept (7, 9, 8, 9, 8, 6, 8, 7, 10, 8) and mood (4, 5, 3, 7, 4, 1, 3, 2, 6, 5). Type 7 and press enter. Then click on the next box on the same line and type 4 and enter. This will put the participants' two scores on the same line next to each other.

2. Click on the first box on the next line and type 9 and then enter. Then click on the second box on the second line and type 5 and enter.

4. Type the scores for the remaining subjects, on each line one subject's number supervised and stress level, in that order.

5. To replace the default variable name with a more descriptive variable name, click on the Variable View tab at the bottom of the dialogue box. Double click on VAR00001 at the top of the first column. This opens the Define Variable dialogue box. Delete the default variable name (VAR00001) and type in HRSSLEPT in the Variable Name text box. Repeat for the second variable, replacing VAR00002 with MOOD. Click on Data View at the bottom of the dialogue box. This will close the Variable View dialogue box and return you to the data window.

C. Carry out the regression analysis.

a. Analyze
   Regression >
   Linear
      [Highlight MOOD and move it to the Dependent Variable box.
      Highlight HRSSLEPT and move to the Independent Variable box Y].
   OK

D. Locate the key information from among all of the output.

1. Note the correlation coefficient (listed as **Multiple R**) and proportionate reduction in error (listed as R Squared).

2. Formulate the raw-score prediction rule: a is the first number in the column labeled **B**; b is the first number in this column.

3. Formulate the Z-score prediction rule: ß is the same as the correlation coefficient. (It is also the number in the column labeled **Beta**.)

4. Note whether the result is statistically significant: It is significant if the first number in the column labeled **Sig** is .05 or less.

E. Print out a copy of the result.

III. Additional Practice

A. For each data set, determine the raw-score and Z-score prediction rules and compare your results to those in the text.

B. Use the same text examples and practice problems as listed in the Chapter 3 section on using the computer.

IV. Using the Computer to Deepen Your Knowledge

A. The effect of changing the scale on the raw-score and Z-score prediction rules.

1. Use SPSS to compute prediction rules for the example several times, each time changing the scale of the dependent variable by adding a constant to it, such as 5 or 10. Notice that *a* is affected, but neither *b* nor ß are. Think about why this might be the case. (Consider the effect of adding a constant to the mean and standard deviation–and how this effect impacts Z scores, which is what affects the correlation coefficient, and about what goes into the formula for computing *b*.)

2. Use the original values for the dependent variable, but this time add the same constant to the independent variable. Again, only *a* is affected–and it is affected a bit differently. Think about why. (Focus on the formula for computing *a*.)

3. Use the original values for both variables, but this time multiply the independent variable by 5 and then do it again using 10. Notice the effects and think about why they might occur in this way.

4. This time multiply the dependent variable by 5 and then by 10 and think about the effects, comparing the result to what was obtained when you multiplied these constants times the independent variable.

B. *Z* score and raw score prediction: Using the example data, convert both variables to Z scores and compute the prediction rules. What happens to the raw score prediction rule? Why?

V. Advanced Procedure: Multiple Regression

A. Add a third variable to your data for cups of coffee (3, 1, 2, 3, 4, 3, 1, 5, 3, 2), using the data described in the SPSS Advanced Procedure section of Chapter 3 of this *Study Guide and Computer Workbook*.

B. Have SPSS compute the multiple-regression prediction rule for predicting mood from the combination of hours slept and cups of coffee. The instruction line is:

Analyze
> Regression >
>> Linear
>>> [Highlight MOOD and move it to the Dependent Variable box. Highlight HRSSLEPT and COFFEE and move both to the Independent Variable box.]
>>> OK

Chapter 5
Some Ingredients for Inferential Statistics:
The Normal Curve, Probability, and Population versus Sample

Learning Objectives

To understand, including being able to conduct any necessary computations:

- The shape of the normal distribution.
- The 50%-34%-14% approximations for normal curve areas.
- The normal curve table.
- Converting Z and raw scores to percentages of cases in a normal distribution.
- Converting percentages of cases in a normal distribution to Z and raw scores.
- Long-run relative-frequency interpretation of probability.
- Subjective interpretation of probability.
- Calculating probabilities.
- The normal curve as a probability distribution.
- Sample and population.
- Random and nonrandom methods of sampling.
- Statistical terminology and symbols regarding samples and populations.

Chapter Outline

I. **The Normal Distribution**
   A. The distributions of many variables that psychologists measure follow a unimodal, roughly symmetrical, bell-shaped distribution.
   B. These bell-shaped histograms or frequency polygons approximate a precise and important mathematical distribution called the *normal distribution*, or more simply, the *normal curve*.
   C. Why the normal curve is so common in nature.
      1. The score on any particular variable can be thought of as influenced by a large number of essentially random factors, which on the average balance out to a middle value, with equal but decreasing numbers of cases balancing out above and below the middle value.
      2. This produces a unimodal, symmetrical distribution.
      3. It can be shown mathematically that in the long run, if the influences are truly random, a precise normal curve will result.
   D. Because this shape is standard, there is a known percentage of cases below or above any particular point.
   E. Approximate percentages of cases in a normal curve.
      1. Because the distribution is symmetrical, exactly 50% of the cases fall below the mean and exactly 50% above the mean.
      2. Approximately 34% of the cases fall between the mean and one standard deviation from the mean in each direction.
      3. Approximately 14% of the cases fall between one and two standard deviations from the mean in each direction.
      4. These 50%, 34%, and 14% approximations are useful practical rules.

5. Knowing these percentages, if you know a distribution on a variable is normal, you can determine what percentage of cases fall between, above, or below various whole number Z scores.
6. Knowing these percentages also permits you to approximate a person's number of standard deviations from the mean from their percentage in relation to other people in their distribution.

F. The normal curve table and Z scores.
1. Because the normal curve is exactly defined, it is also possible to figure the exact percentage of cases between any two Z scores.
2. Statisticians have created helpful tables of the normal curve that give the percentage of cases between the mean (a Z score of 0) and any other Z score. (Table B-1 in the text is a normal curve table.)
3. This table can be used to figure the percentage of cases from Z scores or from raw scores (by converting them to Z scores).

II. Probability

A. Scientific research does not permit determining the truth or falsity of theories or applied procedures.
B. Inferential statistics can be applied to results of research to permit probabilistic conclusions about theories or applied procedures.
C. Probability is a large and controversial topic, but there are only a few key ideas you need to know to understand basic inferential statistical procedures.
D. The long-run relative-frequency interpretation of probability. Probability is the long-run, expected relative frequency of a particular outcome.
1. An *outcome* is the result of an experiment (or virtually any event, such as a coin coming up heads or it raining tomorrow).
2. *Frequency* means how many times something occurs.
3. *Relative frequency* means the number of times something occurs relative to the number of times it could have occurred.
4. *Long run relative frequency* is what you would expect to get, in the long run, if you were to repeat the experiment many times.

E. Subjective interpretation of probability: How certain one is that a particular thing will happen.
F. Calculating a probability: The number of possible successful outcomes divided by the number of all possible outcomes.
G. The range of probabilities.
1. Something that has no chance of happening has a probability of 0.
2. Something that is certain to happen has a probability of 1.

H. Probability is usually symbolized by the letter p and expressed as equaling, greater than, or less than some fraction or percentage.
I. The normal distribution can also be thought of as a probability distribution: The proportion of cases between any two Z scores is the same as the probability of selecting a case between those two Z scores.

III. Sample and Population

A. A *population* is the entire set of things of interest.
B. A *sample* is the subset of the population about which you actually have information.

C. Why samples are studied (instead of populations).
    1. Usually it is not practical to study entire populations.
    2. The goal of science is to make generalizations or predictions about events beyond our reach, such as the behavior of entire populations.

D. The general strategy of psychology research is to study a sample of individuals who are believed to be representative of the general population (or of some particular population of interest).

E. At the minimum, researchers try to study people who at least do not differ from the general population in any systematic way which would be expected to matter for that topic of research.

F. There are several methods of sampling.
    1. The ideal method of sampling is *random selection*: The researcher obtains a complete list of all the members of a population and randomly selects some number of them to study.
    2. *Haphazard selection* is quite different from true random selection and is likely to produce a sample that is a biased subset of the population as a whole.
    3. In psychology research it is rarely possible to employ true random sampling, but researchers try to study a sample that is not systematically *un*representative of the population in any known way.

G. Statistical terminology for samples and populations.
    1. The mean, variance, and standard deviation of a population are called population parameters.
        a. A population parameter is usually an unknown which is, at best, estimated from sample information.
        b. Population parameters are symbolized by Greek letters.
            i. Population mean = μ.
            ii. Population standard deviation = σ.
    2. The mean, variance, and standard deviation you calculate to describe a sample are *sample statistics*.
        a. A sample statistic is figured from known information.
        b. Generally, the symbols for sample statistics (which is what we have used so far) are ordinary letters.
            i. Sample mean = M.
            ii. Sample standard deviation = SD.

IV. Controversies

A. Is the normal curve really so common?
    1. It is widely assumed that it is, and this assumption plays an important role in carrying out statistical analyses of research in psychology.
    2. One recent study indicates that the measures most commonly used in psychology often do not yield scores that are normally distributed.
    3. Still more recent research, however, suggests that the kinds of variations from normal that have been found may not create serious problems for the typical applications of statistical methods in psychology.

B. Bayesian methods.
    1. These are based on the subjective interpretation of probability.
    2. Bayesians hold that science is about conducting research in order to adjust our pre-existing beliefs in light of evidence we collect.
    3. Bayesian methods are based on this principle.
    4. Critics of Bayesian methods argue that conclusions drawn from each study would depend too heavily on the subjective belief of the particular scientist conducting the study.

C. The appropriateness of drawing conclusions from nonrandom samples.
   1. Samples used in psychology experiments are usually nonrandom (whoever is available) and small.
   2. Psychologists are fairly comfortable with this situation because they are mainly interested in the pattern of relationships among variables, which are thought to be fairly constant even if mean levels of variables vary greatly across populations.

V. **Normal Curves, Probabilities, Samples, and Populations as Described in Research Articles**
   A. These topics, which are important fundamentals, are rarely found discussed explicitly in research articles (except articles *about* methods or statistics).
   B. The normal curve is sometimes mentioned when describing the distribution of scores on a particular variable.
   C. Probability is rarely discussed directly, except in the context of statistical significance (see Chapter 6 and beyond).
   D. The method of selecting the sample from the population is sometimes described, particularly if the study is a survey.

How to Determine the Percentage of Cases above or below a Particular Score Using a Normal Curve Table

1. If it is a raw score, change it to a Z score: $Z = (X-M)/SD$.
2. Draw a picture of the normal curve, where the Z score falls, and shade in the area for which you are finding the percentage.
3. Make a rough estimate of the shaded area's percentage based on the 50%34%14% percentages.
4. Find the exact percentage using the normal curve table.
   A. For a percentage of cases above a particular Z score.
      1. If the Z score is positive, subtract this percentage from 50% (that is, 50% minus this percentage).
      2. If the Z score is negative, add 50% to it.
   B. For a percentage of cases below a particular Z score.
      1. If the Z score is positive, add 50% to this percentage.
      2. If the Z score is negative, subtract this percentage from 50% (that is, 50% minus this percentage).
5. Check that the exact percentage is similar to the rough estimate in Step 3.

How to Determine a Score from Knowing the Percentages of Cases above or below that Score Using a Normal Curve Table

1. Draw a picture of the normal curve, and shade in the approximate area for your percentage using the 50%34%14% percentages.
2. Make a rough estimate of the Z score where the shaded area starts.
3. Find the exact Z score using the normal curve table (including adding or subtracting 50% if necessary).
4. Check that the exact Z score is similar to the rough estimate from step 2.
5. Convert the Z score to a raw score: $X = (Z)(SD) + M$.

Outline for Writing Essays on the Logic and Computations for Determining a Percentage of Cases in a Normal Distribution from a Score or Vice Versa

The reason for your writing essay questions in the practice problems and tests is that this task develops and then demonstrates what matters so very much--your comprehension of the logic behind the computations. (It is also a place where those better at words than numbers can shine, and for those better at numbers to develop their skills at explaining in words.)

Thus, to do well, be sure to do the following in each essay: (a) give the reasoning behind each step; (b) relate each step to the specifics of the content of the particular study you are analyzing; (c) state the various formulas in nontechnical language, because as you define each term you show you understand it (although once you have defined it in nontechnical language, you can use it from then on in the essay); (d) look back and be absolutely certain that you made it clear just *why* that formula or procedure was applied and *why* it is the way it is.

The outlines below are *examples* of ways to structure your essays. There are other completely correct ways to go about it. And this is an *outline* for an answer--you are to write the answer out in paragraph form. Examples of full essays are in the answers to Set I Practice Problems in the back of the text.

These essays are necessarily very long for you to write (and for others to grade). But this is the very best way to be sure you understand everything thoroughly. One shortcut you may see on a test is that you may be asked to write your answer for someone who understands statistics up to the point of the new material you are studying. You can choose to take the same shortcut in these practice problems (maybe writing for someone who understands right up to whatever point you yourself start being just a little unclear). But every time you write for a person who has never had statistics at all, you review the logic behind the entire course. You engrain it in your mind. Over and over. The time is never wasted. It is an excellent way to study.

Determining a Percentage from a Score

I.   **If a raw score, change it to a Z score (see outlines for essays on Z scores, mean, and standard deviation from Chapter 2 of this *Study Guide*).**

II. **Find the percentage of cases between this Z score and the mean.**

    A. Procedure: Look up the Z score in the Z column and find the percentage in the adjacent *% Mean to Z* column.

    B. Explanation.

        1. The normal distribution.

          a. It is bell-shaped.

          b. It is a highly common distribution in psychology.

          c. This shape is so common because a score on anything is usually a kind of average of a number of influences which have random variation; the chance of getting many of these random influences all in the same extreme direction is low, making most cases (each case representing an average of random influences) fall near the middle.

          d. It can be shown mathematically that in the long run, if the influences are truly random, a precise normal curve will result.

2. The normal curve table.
   a. Because this shape is mathematically defined, there is a known percentage of cases below or above any particular point.
   b. Statisticians have created tables which give the percentage of cases between the mean and any particular number of standard deviations (including fractions of standard deviations) from the mean--that is, between the mean and any positive Z score.
3. Describe what the percentage is for your particular Z score.

III. To determine the percentage above your score.
A. If the Z score is positive.
   1. Procedure: Subtract this percentage from 50%.
   2. Explanation.
      a. Since the Z score is positive (that is, it is above the mean), the amount above this score is the 50% above the mean less what is between this score and the mean (the percentage from the table).
      b. Give your actual difference.
      c. Illustrate with a picture of a normal curve showing your situation.
B. If the Z score is negative.
   1. Procedure: Add 50% to this percentage.
   2. Explanation.
      a. Since the Z score is negative (that is, it is below the mean), the total above this score is what is between it and the mean (the percentage from the table) plus the 50% above the mean.
      b. Give your actual sum.
   3. Illustrate with a picture of a normal curve showing your situation.

IV. To determine the percentage below your score.
A. If the Z score is positive.
   1. Procedure: Add 50% to this percentage.
   2. Explanation.
      a. Since the Z score is positive (that is, it is above the mean), the total below this score is the amount between it and the mean (the percentage from the table) plus the 50% below the mean.
      b. Give your actual total.
      c. Illustrate with a picture of a normal curve showing your situation.
B. If the Z score is negative.
   1. Procedure: Subtract this percentage from 50%.
   2. Explanation.
      a. Since the Z score is negative (that is, it is below the mean), the amount below this score is the 50% below the mean less the percentage between the mean and this score (the amount figured earlier).
      b. Give your actual difference.
      c. Illustrate with a picture of a normal curve showing your situation.

Determining a Score from a Percentage

I. Explain the logic of the normal curve and a normal curve table.

    A. The normal distribution.

        1. It is bell-shaped.

        2. It is a highly common distribution in psychology.

        3. This shape is so common because a score on anything is usually a kind of average of a number of influences which have random variation; the chance of getting many of these random influences all in the same extreme direction is low, making most cases (each case representing an average of random influences) fall near the middle.

        4. It can be shown mathematically that in the long run, if the influences are truly random, a precise normal curve will result.

    B. Explain the logic of Z scores (see outlines for essays on Z scores, mean, and standard deviation from Chapter 2 of this *Study Guide*).

    C. The normal curve table.

        1. Because this shape is mathematically defined, there is a known percentage of cases below or above any particular point.

        2. Statisticians have created tables which give the percentage of cases between the mean and any particular number of standard deviations (including fractions of standard deviations) from the mean--that is, between the mean and any positive Z score.

II. For a situation in which there is a particular percentage of cases higher than the score.

    A. If the percentage is less than 50%.

        1. Procedure.

            a. Subtract the percentage from 50% (that is, 50% minus the percentage).

            b. Look up the closest percentage to this difference in the *% Mean to Z* column and find the Z score in the adjacent Z column.

        2. Explanation.

            a. The percentage between the mean and the score (the percentage that can be looked up on the table to find the corresponding Z score) is what remains between the percentage above the score and 50% (the total above the mean).

            b. Give your figures.

            c. Illustrate with a picture of a normal curve showing your situation.

    B. If the percentage is greater than 50%.

        1. Procedure.

            a. Subtract 50% from the percentage (that is, the percentage minus 50%).

            b. Look up the closest percentage to this difference in the *% Mean to Z* column and find the Z score in the adjacent Z column.

            c. Make this Z score negative (put a minus sign in front of it).

        2. Explanation.

            a. The percentage between the mean and the score (the percentage that can be looked up on the table to find the corresponding Z score) is what remains after subtracting out the 50% above the mean.

            b. Since there are more than 50% above this score, the score must be below the mean, and hence a negative Z score.

            c. Give your figures.

            d. Illustrate with a picture of a normal curve showing your situation.

III. For a situation in which there is a particular percentage of cases lower than the score.

A. If the percentage is less than 50%.
   1. Procedure.
      a. Subtract the percentage from 50%.
      b. Look up the closest percentage to this difference in the *% Mean to Z* column and find the *Z* score in the adjacent *Z* column.
      c. Make this *Z* score negative (put a minus sign in front of it).
   2. Explanation.
      a. The percentage between the mean and the score (the percentage that can be looked up on the table to find the corresponding *Z* score) is what remains after subtracting it from the total of 50% below the mean.
      b. Since there are less than 50% below this score, the score must be below the mean and hence a negative *Z* score.
      c. Give your figures.
      d. Illustrate with a picture of a normal curve showing your situation.

B. If the percentage is more than 50%.
   1. Procedure.
      a. Subtract 50% from the percentage (that is, the percentage minus 50%).
      b. Look up the closest percentage to this difference in the *% Mean to Z* column and find the *Z* score in the adjacent *Z* column.
   2. Explanation.
      a. The percentage between the mean and the score (the percentage that can be looked up on the table to find the corresponding *Z* score) is what remains above the mean after subtracting out the 50% below the mean.
      b. Give your figures.
      c. Illustrate with a picture of a normal curve showing your situation.

IV. Convert the *Z* score to a raw score.

A. Procedure: $X = (Z)(SD) + M$.

B. Explanation: See outline for essay on converting a *Z* score to a raw score in Chapter 2 of this *Study Guide*.

Chapter Self-Tests

Multiple-Choice Questions

1. A normal curve is

   a. bimodal and slightly skewed to the right.
   b. unimodal and symmetrical.
   c. unimodal and slightly skewed to the left.
   d. bimodal and roughly symmetrical.

2. The mean score on a depression scale is 10 and the standard deviation is 3. The distribution is normal. Using the approximation rules for normal curves, how many people would get a score between 10 and 16?

   a. 50%.
   b. 34%.
   c. 34% + 14% = 48%.
   d. 34% + 34% = 68%.

3. A person received a test score that was in the top 30% of all the cases. Using the normal curve table, what was this person's Z score?

   a. .52.
   b. .84.
   c. 5.03.
   d. 5.34.

4. A person has a creativity score of 6.8, which equals a Z score of +2.4. What is the percentage of cases above this score?

   a. 49.18% - 50% = -.82%.
   b. 100% - 49.18% = 50.82%.
   c. 50% + 49.18% = 99.18%.
   d. 50% - 49.18% = .82%.

5. What is the Z score a person would have to receive to be in the top 2% of their class?

   a. -2.05.
   b. 0.05.
   c. .48.
   d. 2.05.

6. *Approximately* what Z score would a person have to have to be in the bottom 16% of their group?

   a. -2.
   b. -1.
   c. 0.
   d. +1.

7. How do you calculate probability?

   a. The number of all possible outcomes divided by the number of possible successful outcomes.
   b. The number of all possible outcomes multiplied by the number of possible successful outcomes.
   c. The number of possible successful outcomes divided by the number of possible outcomes.
   d. The number of all possible outcomes minus the number of possible successful outcomes.

8. What is the difference between random selection and haphazard selection?

   a. There is no difference--they mean the same thing.
   b. In random selection you take whoever is available, whereas in haphazard selection you choose people in a way that systematically avoids a regular rotation.
   c. In random selection you obtain a complete list of all members of a population and randomly select some of them, whereas in a haphazard selection you select whoever is available.
   d. In random selection you just choose who happens to be at the top of the list of the members in the population, whereas in haphazard selection you take volunteers.

9. Which of the following statements is most accurate about population parameters?
   a. They are essential to making any statements about probability.
   b. They are rarely known.
   c. They are usually smaller than the sample parameters.
   d. They are essential and cannot be estimated from the sample information.

10. What is the "Bayesian" approach?
   a. It says that science is about conducting research in order to adjust our pre-existing beliefs in light of new evidence we collect.
   b. It says that it is better not to make any assumptions about prior beliefs; instead one should just look at the evidence as it is.
   c. It says that one should avoid using theory when conducting scientific research.
   d. It emphasizes that studies should not be conducted by people who have a biased opinion.

Fill-In Questions

11. In a normal curve approximately _____ percent of the cases fall between the mean and one standard deviation above the mean.

12. In a normal curve approximately 14% of the cases fall between a Z score of _____ and a Z score of -2.

13. The percentage of cases between any two Z scores on a normal curve can be exactly determined based on a formula for the normal curve or by using a(n) _____.

14. A person says that the chances he will get a new job are about 80%--meaning that on a scale of 0% to 100% this feels like how likely it is. This is an example of the _____ interpretation of probability.

15. The normal curve can be thought of as a frequency distribution or as a _____ distribution.

16. To pick 15 people for a study of faculty opinion at a particular college, a student gives a questionnaire to each faculty member who arrives at the faculty club on a particular evening. This is an example of _____ selection.

17. A characteristic of a population, such as its mean, is called a(n) _____.

18. A characteristic of a sample, such as its standard deviation, is called a(n) _____.

19. σ^2 is to SD^2 as M is to _____.

20. _____ is the branch of statistics which draws conclusions about populations based on information in samples.

Problems and Essays

21. Suppose a test of musical ability has a normal distribution with a mean of 50 and a standard deviation of 5. Approximately what percentage of people are (a) above 55, (b) below 40, and (c) above 45. (Use the normal curve approximation rules.) (d) Explain your answers to a person who has never had a course in statistics.

22. Suppose the number of clients seen in any given week by full time psychotherapists in a particular city is normally distributed with a mean of 15.3 and a standard deviation of 2.8. (a) A therapist who is in the top 5% of number of clients seen would be seeing at least how many? (b) What is the most a therapist could be seeing and still be in the bottom 10%? (c) Explain your answers to a person who has never had a course in statistics.

23. A student took a test with a mean of 500 and a standard deviation of 100. (a) If the student scored 740, what percentage of test takers scored higher? (b) What percentage scored lower? (c) If the student scored 380, what percentage scored higher? (d) What percentage scored lower?

24. Thirty students in a particular elementary school classroom include 8 girls who are of an ethnic minority, 4 boys of an ethnic minority, 7 girls who are not of an ethnic minority, and 11 boys not of an ethnic minority. A student is selected at random to represent the class. (a) What is the probability that student will be a girl? (b) What is the probability the student will be of an ethnic minority?

25. A health psychologist plans to conduct a mail survey of a sample of doctors in a particular U.S. state to ask about their attitudes toward drug advertisements. What would be the best way to go about selecting the sample of doctors to study? Explain what you would do and why to a person who is unfamiliar with research methods or statistics.

Note. There is no section on using SPSS with this chapter because none of the procedures covered are easily implemented using standard computerized statistical packages.

Chapter 6
Introduction to Hypothesis Testing

Learning Objectives

To understand, including being able to carry out any necessary procedures or computations:

- The core logic of hypothesis testing.
- The populations involved in hypothesis testing (Populations 1 and 2).
- The research hypothesis.
- The null hypothesis.
- The comparison distribution.
- Determining the cutoff score on the comparison distribution.
- Significance and conventional levels of significance.
- When to reject the null hypothesis and the implications of this decision.
- When not to reject the null hypothesis and the implications of this decision.
- The steps of hypothesis testing and their relation to the core logic.
- Directional and nondirectional hypotheses.
- One–tailed versus two–tailed tests.
- How results of studies using hypothesis–testing procedures are reported in research articles.

Chapter Outline

I. **The Core Logic of Hypothesis Testing**
  A. The key idea is that we test (and hopefully reject) the notion that the experimental manipulation made no difference. If the notion of no difference can be rejected, this supports the idea it does make a difference.
  B. Put another way, we draw conclusions by evaluating the probability of getting our research results if the opposite of what we are predicting were true.
  C. This double–negative, roundabout kind of logic is awkward, but necessary.

II. **The Steps of Hypothesis Testing (as applied to the situation in which a single individual is exposed to the experimental manipulation and compared to a known population distribution of people not so exposed)**
  A. Reframe the question into a research hypothesis and a null hypothesis about populations. (Step 1.)
    1. Research is conducted using samples to test hypotheses about populations.
    2. One population (Population 1) is the people who are exposed to the experimental manipulation.
      a. This population does not usually exist (except for the one person in the sample being studied), but is a logical construction of the group to whom the results of the experiment might be applied.
      b. The characteristics of the distribution of this population (μ, σ, shape) are unknown.
    3. The other population (Population 2) is the people who have not been exposed to the experimental manipulation.
      a. This is a real population (usually the population at large of people of the same category as those in the sample, but these people were not exposed to the experimental manipulation).

b. The characteristics of the distribution of this population are known (for example, from previous research).

4. The research hypothesis is a statement about a predicted difference between populations.

a. Typically the difference predicted is that the mean of one population is different (or more specifically, higher or lower) than the mean of the other.

b. The prediction is usually based on theory or practical experience.

5. The null hypothesis is a statement about a relation between populations which represents the crucial opposite of the research hypothesis.

a. It usually is a prediction of no difference (or that if there is a difference it is in the direction opposite to what is predicted).

b. It has this name because it predicts a "null" or nondifference.

6. The research hypothesis and the null hypothesis are opposites and mutually exclusive.

a. It is this oppositeness which is at the heart of the hypothesis–testing process.

b. Because the null hypothesis is so important to the logic of the process, the research hypothesis is often called the "alternative hypothesis."

B. Determine the characteristics of the comparison distribution. (Step 2.)

1. In terms of hypothesis–testing language, the crucial question is as follows: Given a particular sample value, what is the probability of obtaining it if the null hypothesis is true?

2. To determine this probability, we need to know the characteristics of the distribution the score would come from if the null hypothesis is true; this is necessary to permit us to determine the likelihood of getting a particular extreme score from this distribution.

3. This crucial distribution is called the *comparison distribution*.

4. If the null hypothesis is true, both populations are the same and the score in Population 1 comes from a distribution with the same characteristics as that of Population 2.

5. Thus, the comparison distribution (in the situation considered in this chapter) has the characteristics of Population 2 (the known population of individuals not exposed to the experimental manipulation).

C. Determine the cutoff sample score on the comparison distribution at which the null hypothesis should be rejected. (Step 3.)

1. Before making an observation, researchers consider what kind of observation would be sufficiently extreme to reject the null hypothesis.

2. Researchers do not usually use an actual number of units on the direct scale of measurement of the comparison distribution; instead they state how extreme a score should be in terms of a Z score on this distribution (and the associated probability of getting a Z score that extreme on this distribution).

3. Very small percentages (probabilities of getting this extreme a score) are taken as the cutoff.

4. Since the comparison distribution is ordinarily a normal curve, the cutoff is found in a normal curve table.

5. The cutoff percentage is called the "level of significance."

6. Conventional levels of significance used by psychology researchers are 5% (the .05 significance level) or 1% (the .01 significance level).

7. When a sample value is so extreme that the null hypothesis is rejected, the result is said to be *statistically significant*.

D. Determine the sample's score on the comparison distribution. (Step 4.)

1. This is the result of the actual experiment or observation.

2. The raw–score result is converted to a Z score on the scale of the comparison distribution to make it comparable to the cutoff Z score.

E. Compare the scores obtained in Steps 3 and 4 to determine whether or not to reject the null hypothesis. (Step 5.)
    1. This step is entirely mechanical.
    2. If the actual sample's Z score (from Step 4) is more extreme than the cutoff Z score (from Step 3), the null hypothesis is rejected.
       a. Thus, the research hypothesis is supported.
       b. However, the research hypothesis is not "proven" or shown to be "true"–no pattern of results can prove a hypothesis based on research data; it can only support or fail to support a particular hypothesis.

III. Implications of Rejecting or Failing to Reject the Null Hypothesis

A. You cannot *prove* the research hypothesis because the results of research studies are based on probabilities, you can only demonstrate that the likelihood of obtaining those results due to chance alone are very low *if the null hypothesis is true.*

B. Similarly, when the results are not extreme enough to reject the null hypothesis, you do not say your results support the null hypothesis.
    1. Showing the null hypothesis to be true would mean there is absolutely no difference between the two populations.
    2. It is possible that there is a difference, but not large enough for the study to detect.
    3. Therefore, when the results are not extreme enough to reject the null hypothesis, they are inconclusive.

IV. One–Tailed and Two–Tailed Hypothesis Tests

A. A *directional hypothesis* is used when there is a specific predicted direction of effect (such as predicting an increase or predicting a decrease).
    1. The research hypothesis is that Population 1's mean is higher (or lower, if that is the prediction) than Population 2's mean.
    2. The null hypothesis is that Population 1's mean is not higher (or lower, if that is the prediction) than Population 2's mean. That is, the null hypothesis is true if Population 1's mean is the same as or lower than Population 2's (presuming higher was predicted).
    3. Significance testing is carried out as follows (for simplicity, points a and b below assume a higher score was predicted and the 5% significance level used).
       a. To reject the null hypothesis, the obtained score has to be in a region of the comparison distribution that is in its upper 5%.
       b. That is, it has to be in the area on one tail only, and thus this is called a *one–tailed test.*

B. A *nondirectional hypothesis* is used when the researcher predicts one population will be different from the other, without specifying whether they will be different by Population 1's having higher or lower scores.
    1. The research hypothesis is that Population 1's mean is different from Population 2's mean.
    2. The null hypothesis is that Population 1's mean is not different.
    3. Significance testing is carried out as follows (for simplicity, points a through c below assume the 5% significance level is used).
       a. To reject the null hypothesis, the obtained score has to be in a region of the comparison distribution that is in either the upper 2.5% or the lower 2.5%, making a total of 5% of the area in which the null hypothesis could be rejected.
       b. That is, it can be in either tail of the distribution, and thus this is called a *two–tailed test.*
       c. Using a two–tailed test requires a more extreme cutoff than a one–tailed test for the same situation.

C. When to use one–tailed versus two–tailed tests.
1. It is "easier" to reject the null hypothesis with a one–tailed test--easier in the sense that a sample result need not be so extreme before an experimental result is significant.
2. But there is a price: If the result is extreme in the other direction, no matter how extreme, the null hypothesis can not be rejected.
3. In principle you plan to use a one–tailed test when you have a clearly directional hypothesis and a two–tailed test when you have a clearly nondirectional hypothesis.
4. In practice, the situation is not so simple.
   a. Even when a theory clearly predicts a particular result, we sometimes find that the result is just the opposite of what we expected and that this reverse of what we expected may actually be more interesting.
   b. For this reason, by using one–tailed tests we run the risk of having to ignore possibly important results.
5. Thus, there is debate as to whether one–tailed tests should be used, even when there is a clearly directional hypothesis.
6. To be safe, many researchers use two–tailed tests both when there are nondirectional hypotheses and also when there are directional hypotheses.
7. In most psychology articles, unless the researcher specifically notes that a one–tailed test was used, it is usually assumed that it was a two–tailed test.
8. In most cases the final conclusion is not really affected by whether a one– or two–tailed test is used (the result is either extreme enough to reject the null hypothesis either way, or not extreme enough to reject the null hypothesis either way).
9. If a result is so close that it matters which method is used, results should be interpreted cautiously pending further research.

V. **Controversies: Should we ban significance testing?** There are several issues that are points of debate.

A. One issue relates to whether it makes sense to worry about rejecting the null hypothesis when a hypothesis of no effect is extremely unlikely to be true.

B. A second issue is about the foundation of hypothesis testing in terms of populations and samples, since in most experiments the samples we use are not randomly selected from any definable population.

C. A third issue is the appropriateness of concluding that if the data are inconsistent with the null hypothesis, this should be counted as evidence for the research hypothesis.

D. A fourth issue is the misuse of significance tests. There is a tendency for researchers to decide that if a result is not significant, the null hypothesis is shown to be true. We have emphasized repeatedly that when the null hypothesis is not rejected, the results are inconclusive.

VI. **Hypothesis Tests As Reported in Research Articles**

A. Hypothesis tests are usually reported in the context of one of the specific statistical procedures covered in later chapters.

B. For each result of interest, the article usually gives the following information.
1. Whether the result was statistically significant.
2. The name of the specific technique used in determining the probabilities (these are what is covered in later chapters).
3. An indication of the significance level, such as "$p < .05$," or "$p < .01$."
   a. "$p < .05$" means that the probability of these results if the null hypothesis were true is less than .05 (5%).
   b. If a result is close but did not reach the significance level chosen, it may be reported anyway as a "near significant trend," with "$p < .10$," for example.

90

c. If the result is not significant, sometimes the actual p level will be given (for example, "$p = .27$"), or the abbreviation "ns," for "not significant," will be used.

4. If a one–tailed test was used, that will usually also be noted. (Otherwise assume a two–tailed test was used.)

C. Sometimes the results of hypothesis testing are shown simply as starred results in a table; a result with a star has attained significance (at a level given in a footnote) and one without has not.

D. The steps of hypothesis testing, or which is the null and which is the research hypothesis, are rarely made explicit.

How to Test an Hypothesis

(When the sample consists of one individual and the distribution of the population not exposed to the experimental manipulation is known.)

1. **Restate the question as a research hypothesis and a null hypothesis about populations. (Step 1.)**

A. Identify the two populations.

1. Population 1 is people like those who have been exposed to the experimental manipulation.
2. Population 2 is people like those studied but who have not been exposed to the experimental manipulation (this is usually the category studied from the general public).

B. State the research hypothesis.

1. Decide whether this will be directional or nondirectional.
2. State in terms of the two populations (that the mean of one will be higher, lower, or the same as the other).

C. State the null hypothesis: Populations 1 and 2 are the same; the manipulation lacks impact.

D. Check that the research and null hypothesis are consistent (in terms of both being in relation to a directional or nondirectional prediction).

2. **Determine the characteristics of the comparison distribution. (Step 2.)**

A. This will be the distribution of Population 2.

B. Note its μ, σ^2, and shape (which will usually be normal).

3. **Determine the cutoff sample score on the comparison distribution at which the null hypothesis should be rejected. (Step 3.)**

A. Decide on the significance level (1% or 5%).

B. Determine the percentage of cases between the mean and where the appropriate percentage begins on the normal curve.

1. If a one–tailed test, this is 50% minus the significance level.
2. If a two–tailed test, this is 50% minus 1/2 the significance level.

C. Look up the Z corresponding to this percentage in the *% Mean to Z* column in the normal table–this is the cutoff Z.

4. **Determine the sample's score on the comparison distribution. (Step 4.)**

A. Conduct the study and note the score of the individual (or note the result as given to you in the problem).

B. Convert the raw–score result to a Z score on the comparison distribution: $Z = (X-\mu)/\sigma$.

5. **Compare the scores obtained in Steps 3 and 4 to determine whether or not to reject the null hypothesis. (Step 5.)**
   A. If the actual sample's Z score (from Step 4) is more extreme than the cutoff Z score (from Step 3).
      1. The null hypothesis is rejected.
      2. Thus, the research hypothesis is supported.
   B. If the actual sample's Z score (from Step 4) is not more extreme than the cutoff Z score (from Step 3).
      1. The null hypothesis is not rejected.
      2. Thus, the experiment is inconclusive.

Outline for Writing Essays for Hypothesis–testing Problems
Involving a Single Sample of One Subject and a Known Population

The reason for your writing essay questions in the practice problems and tests is that this task develops and then demonstrates what matters so very much–your comprehension of the logic behind the computations. (It is also a place where those better at words than numbers can shine, and for those better at numbers to develop their skills at explaining in words.)

Thus, to do well, be sure to do the following in each essay: (a) give the reasoning behind each step; (b) relate each step to the specifics of the content of the particular study you are analyzing; (c) state the various formulas in nontechnical language, because as you define each term you show you understand it (although once you have defined it in nontechnical language, you can use it from then on in the essay); (d) look back and be absolutely certain that you made it clear just *why* that formula or procedure was applied and *why* it is the way it is.

The outlines below are *examples* of ways to structure your essays. There are other completely correct ways to go about it. And this is an *outline* for an answer–you are to write the answer out in paragraph form. Examples of full essays are in the answers to Set 1 Practice Problems in the back of the text.

These essays are necessarily very long for you to write (and for others to grade). But this is the very best way to be sure you understand everything thoroughly. One shortcut you may see on a test is that you may be asked to write your answer for someone who understands statistics up to the point of the new material you are studying. You can choose to take the same shortcut in these practice problems (maybe writing for someone who understands right up to whatever point you yourself start being just a little unclear). But every time you write for a person who has never had statistics at all, you review the logic behind the entire course. You engrain it in your mind. Over and over. The time is never wasted. It is an excellent way to study.

I. **Reframe the question into a research hypothesis and a null hypothesis about populations. (Step 1 of hypothesis testing.)**
   A. State in ordinary language the hypothesis–testing issue: Does the score of the person studied represent a higher (or lower or different) score than would be expected if this person had just been a randomly selected example of people in general–that is, does this person represent a different group of people from people in general?
   B. Explain language (to make the rest of the essay easier to write by not having to repeat long explanations), focusing on the meaning of each term in the concrete example of the study at hand.
      1. Populations.
      2. Research hypothesis.
      3. Null hypothesis.
      4. Rejecting the null hypothesis to provide support for the research hypothesis.
II. **Determine the characteristics of the comparison distribution. (Step 2 of hypothesis testing.)**
   A. Explain the principle that the comparison distribution is the distribution (pattern of spread of the scores) of the population which did not undergo the experimental manipulation–this is the distribution from which we would expect our case to be a random sample if the null hypothesis were true.
   B. Explicitly identify the characteristics of your comparison distribution, explaining what each characteristic means.
      1. Its mean (explain that this is the arithmetic average).
      2. Its standard deviation.
         a. This is a standard measure of how spread out it is.
         b. It is roughly the average amount that scores vary from the mean.
         c. Exactly speaking, the square root of the average of the squares of the amount that each score differs from the mean.
      3. Its shape.
         a. Usually it is a normal curve.
         b. Describe the shape (or draw it).
         c. Note that this is a highly common shape for distributions; the percentage of cases above any given point (as measured in standard deviations from the mean) is available in tables.
III. **Determine the cutoff score on the comparison distribution at which the null hypothesis should be rejected. (Step 3 of hypothesis testing.)**
   A. Before you figure out how extreme your particular score is on this distribution, you want to know how extreme it would have to be to decide it was too unlikely that it could be just a randomly drawn case from this comparison distribution.
   B. Since this is a normal curve, you can use a table to tell you how many standard deviations from the mean your score would have to be to be in the top so many percent.
   C. Note that the number of standard deviations from the mean is called a Z score. (By explaining this term, you make writing simpler later on.)
   D. To use these tables, you have to decide the kind of situation you have; there are two considerations.

1. Are you interested in the chances of getting this extreme a score that is extreme in only one direction (such as only higher than for people in general) or in both? (Explain which is appropriate for your study.)

2. Just how unlikely would the extremeness of a particular group's average have to be? The standard figure used in psychology is less likely than 5% (though 1% is sometimes used to be especially safe). (Say which you are using in your study–if no figure is stated in the problem and no special reason given for using one or the other, the general rule is to use 5%.)

E. With a little manipulation of numbers you can then look up the percentage in the table and find the Z score corresponding to that percentage.

IV. Determine the score of your sample on the comparison distribution. (Step 4 of hypothesis testing.)

A. At this point the study would be conducted and the score of the individual obtained.

B. The next step is to find where your actual score would fall on the comparison distribution, in terms of a Z score–that is, how many standard deviations it is above or below the mean on this distribution.

C. State this Z score.

V. Compare the scores obtained in Steps 3 and 4 to decide whether to reject the null hypothesis. (Step 5 of hypothesis testing.)

A. State whether your score (from Step 4) does or does not exceed the cutoff (from Step 3).

B. If your score exceeds the cutoff.
1. State that you can reject the null hypothesis.
2. State that by elimination, the research hypothesis is thus supported.
3. State in words what it means that the research hypothesis is supported (that is, the study shows that the particular experimental manipulation appears to make a difference in the particular thing being measured).

C. If your score does not exceed the cutoff.
1. State that you can not reject the null hypothesis.
2. State that the experiment is inconclusive.
3. State in words what it means that the study is inconclusive (that is, the study did not yield results which give a clear indication of whether or not the particular experimental manipulation appears to make a difference in the particular thing being measured).
4. Explicitly note that even though the research hypothesis was not supported in this study, this is not evidence that it is false–it is quite possible that it is true but it has only a small effect which was not sufficient to produce a score extreme enough to yield a significant result in this study.

Chapter Self–Tests

Multiple–Choice Questions

1. Which of the following statements is most accurate about hypothesis testing?

   a. It is a nonsystematic way of using your intuition to draw possible hypotheses about the result of a study.
   b. It is a systematic procedure for determining whether the results of an experiment provide support for a particular theory.
   c. It is a systematic procedure for disproving or, more importantly, proving your theory.
   d. It is an unimportant procedure that is rarely used anymore because of other mathematical procedures that have been found to be more efficient.

2. Suppose that a researcher wants to know if college students drink more coffee than people in general of college–student age. What would the research hypothesis be in this case?

   a. People over college–student age will drink less coffee than the students will.
   b. There will be no difference between the two populations.
   c. College students do not drink more coffee than people in general of college–student age.
   d. College students drink more coffee than people in general of college–student age.

3. Which of the following is true about the comparison distribution?

   a. It is another name for hypothesis testing.
   b. It is another name for Population 1.
   c. It represents the situation in which the null hypothesis is true.
   d. It represents the situation in which the research hypothesis is true.

4. What does it mean when a researcher chooses the cutoff on the comparison distribution to be .01?

   a. It means that to reject the null hypothesis the result must be higher than a Z score of .01.
   b. It means that to reject the null hypothesis there must be less than a 1% chance that the result would have happened by chance if the null hypothesis were true.
   c. It means that if the result is larger than .01 (such as .02 or .03), it is "statistically significant."
   d. It means that the research hypothesis is definitely true if the sample's score on the comparison distribution is less extreme than the cutoff that corresponds to the most extreme .1% of that comparison distribution.

5. What can be concluded if the null hypothesis is rejected?

   a. The research hypothesis is supported.
   b. The research hypothesis is true and the null hypothesis is false.
   c. The null hypothesis is true and the research hypothesis is false.
   d. The null hypothesis should have been based on a directional hypothesis.

6. Suppose a researcher wants to know if there is a gender difference in the number of dreams people remember. The results of such a study would be analyzed using

   a. a one–tailed test because only one issue is discussed–dreams.
   b. a one–tailed test because there is only one interaction, which is between gender and number of dreams.
   c. a two–tailed test because there is no predicted direction of the difference; the men could remember more or the women could.
   d. a two–tailed test because there are two variables involved–dreams and gender.

7. What should you do if you want to use a 5% significance level on a two–tailed test?

   a. Reject the null hypothesis if the sample is so extreme that it is in either the top 5% or the bottom 5% of the comparison distribution.
   b. Reject the null hypothesis if the sample is so extreme that it is in either the top 2.5% or the bottom 2.5% of the comparison distribution.
   c. Use a comparison distribution that is not a normal curve, such as a Poisson distribution.
   d. Use a comparison distribution that is a normal curve, but which has a standard deviation twice as large as you would use for a one–tailed test.

8. What does it mean if the research hypothesis is clearly directional?

   a. You use a one–tailed test.
   b. You use a two–tailed test.
   c. It is fairly clear that the null hypothesis will be supported so long as the comparison distribution follows a normal curve.
   d. It is fairly clear that the research hypothesis will be supported so long as the comparison distribution follows a normal curve.

9. Researchers are reluctant to use one–tailed tests because

   a. using a one–tailed test dramatically reduces the chance of getting a significant result, even if your research hypothesis is true (that is, even if the null hypothesis is false).
   b. research in psychology rarely involves studies which have a basis for predicting a particular direction of result.
   c. when using a one–tailed test, if a result comes out opposite to that which is predicted, it can not be considered significant no matter how extreme it is.
   d. all of the above.

10. If a research report describes a result and notes "$p < .05$," this means

   a. the result is not statistically significant at the .05 level.
   b. the sample score falls in either the upper 5% or the lower 5% of the comparison distribution (making in reality a 10% chance of getting this result by chance).
   c. there is a 95% chance that the research hypothesis is true.
   d. the chances of getting this result if the null hypothesis is true are less than 5%.

Fill–In Questions

11. _____ is a procedure of inferential statistics in which you draw conclusions about hypotheses based on information in samples.

12–15   A study is conducted to test whether people who have taken a growth hormone are taller (that is, whether their height is greater) than people in general.

   12.   Population 1 is people who have taken the growth hormone. Population 2 is _____.

   13.   What is the research hypothesis? _____
        (state in terms of Populations 1 and 2).

   14.   What is the null hypothesis?_____
        (state in terms of Population 1 and 2).

   15.   The comparison distribution is the distribution of _____.

16. In any study the comparison distribution represents the distribution of sample scores you would expect if the _____ is true.

17. In psychology conventional levels of significance are _____ and _____.

18. If the cutoff Z score is -1.96 and the Z score of your sample is -2.13, what should you conclude? _____.

19. It is not correct to plan on using a one–tailed test, but if the result comes out in the opposite direction, to then apply a two–tailed test. For example, if the researcher were using the 5% significance level, using this plan would make the total probability of rejecting the null hypothesis by chance actually equal not to 5% but to _____%.

20. A study is done with a sample of one case. The general population (Population 2) has a mean of 10 and a standard deviation of 2. The cutoff Z score for significance in this study is 1.64. The raw score of the sample is 13. What should you conclude? _____.

Problems and Essays

21. A researcher was interested in whether "mom's old cure," a glass of warm milk before bedtime, actually facilitates falling asleep. His previous research indicated that an unassisted subject falls asleep in a laboratory situation after an average of 27 minutes with a standard deviation of 7 minutes. He had a test subject drink a glass of warm milk and then measured the amount of time it took for the subject to fall asleep. It took the subject 14 minutes. (These are all fictional data.)
   a. Based on these data, did the subject fall asleep significantly faster? (Use the .05 significance level.) Solve this problem explicitly using all five steps of hypothesis testing and illustrate your answer with a sketch showing the comparison distribution, the cutoff (or cutoffs), and the score of the sample on this distribution.
   b. Explain your conclusion and procedure to a person who has never had a course in statistics.

22. The government reports that the average plane arrives 10 minutes late, with a standard deviation of 1.5 minutes. Your experience, however, is that a particular airline typically arrives later than other airlines. To test this, you go to the airport and check the arrival on a randomly selected flight from this company. The flight arrives 13.25 minutes late. (These are all fictional data.)
   a. Based on these data, what should you conclude about this company's timeliness compared to airlines in general? (Use the .05 significance level.) Solve this problem explicitly using all five steps of hypothesis testing and illustrate your answer with a sketch showing the comparison distribution, the cutoff (or cutoffs), and the score of the sample on this distribution.
   b. Explain your conclusion and procedure to a person who has never had a course in statistics.

23. Can drugs affect memory? A psychologist interested in this question administered a new drug to a group of students in order to see if their ability to immediately recall information was affected in any way. The psychologist had been using nonsense syllables in her studies and found that the average subject was able to immediately recall 7 items with a standard deviation of 2. The first data available from the drug study indicated that the subject had been able to recall only 4 items.
   a. Was this finding significant at the .05 level? Solve this problem explicitly using all five steps of hypothesis testing and illustrate your answer with a sketch showing the comparison distribution, the cutoff (or cutoffs), and the score of the sample on this distribution.
   b. Explain your conclusion and procedure to a person who has never had a course in statistics.

24. A researcher suspects that a particular fast-food restaurant takes longer to fill orders than other restaurants. The average restaurant fills orders in 6.3 minutes, with a standard deviation of 2 minutes. The restaurant took 7 minutes.
   a. Was this finding significant at the .05 level? Solve this problem explicitly using all five steps of hypothesis testing and illustrate your answer with a sketch showing the comparison distribution, the cutoff (or cutoffs), and the score of the sample on this distribution. Solve this problem explicitly using all five steps of hypothesis testing and illustrate your answer with a sketch showing the comparison distribution, the cutoff (or cutoffs), and the score of the sample on this distribution.
   b. Explain your conclusion and procedure to a person who has never had a course in statistics.

25. A social psychologist was interested in whether teenagers who had played a lot of video games as children were able to learn to drive more quickly than the average. He obtained previous data regarding the amount of time (in hours) that it took the average teenager to learn to drive. Then he selected one high school student who reported having spent many hours playing video games and measured the amount of time it took for her to learn how to drive. Her Z score ($Z = 1.23$) was not significant at the .05 level.

   Explain these results and the steps of hypothesis testing to someone unfamiliar with statistics.

Note. There is no section on using SPSS with this chapter because none of the procedures covered are easily implemented using standard computerized statistical packages. (The material in this chapter is mainly preparation for carrying out procedures that are widely used, however, and for which the computer can be very helpful.)

Chapter 7
Hypothesis Tests with Means of Samples

Learning Objectives

To understand, including being able to carry out any necessary procedures or computations:

- Why the distribution of means is the appropriate comparison distribution when using a sample of more than one case.
- How you would construct a distribution of means.
- The mean of the distribution of means, including why it equals the mean of the population of individual cases.
- The variance of the distribution of means.
- Why the variance of the distribution of means is less than the variance of the population of individual cases.
- Why the larger the sample size, the smaller the variance of the distribution of means.
- The standard deviation of the distribution of means.
- The shape of a distribution of means, including why it tends to be unimodal and symmetrical.
- The conditions under which the distribution of means is or closely approximates a normal curve.
- Conducting a hypothesis test with a sample of more than one case and a known population distribution.
- What confidence intervals are, and how to figure them.
- The use of the standard error in reporting research results.

Chapter Outline

I.   **The Distribution of Means as a Comparison Distribution**
   A. When testing hypotheses with a sample of more than one case, the comparison distribution is not simply the distribution of Population 2 (the general population, people not exposed to the experimental manipulation).
      1. The score of interest in your sample in this case is the mean of the group of scores.
      2. But the distribution of Population 2 is a distribution of individual cases.
      3. Thus using Population 2's distribution as the comparison distribution would be a mismatch.
   B. The appropriate comparison distribution in this case is a *distribution of means*, the distribution of all possible means of samples of the size of your sample.
   C. It helps to have an intuitive understanding of how one would construct such a distribution.
      1. Select a random sample of cases of the given size (that is, of the given number of cases) from the population and figure its mean.
      2. Select another random sample of this size from the population and figure its mean.
      3. Repeat this process a very large number of times.
      4. Make a distribution of these means.
      5. Note that this procedure is only to explain the idea, and would be too much work and unnecessary in practice.

II. Characteristics of a Distribution of Means

A. There is an exact mathematical relation of a distribution of means to the population of individual cases the samples are drawn from. This means that the characteristics of the distribution of means can be determined directly from knowledge of the characteristics of the population and the size of the samples involved.

B. The mean of a distribution of means (μ_M).
 1. Rule: The mean of the distribution of means is the same as the mean of the population of individual cases from which the samples are taken.
 2. Formula: $\mu_M = \mu$.
 3. Explanation.
   a. Each sample is based on randomly selected values from the population.
   b. Thus, sometimes the mean of a sample will be higher and sometimes lower than the mean of the whole population of individuals.
   c. There is no reason for these to average out higher or lower than the original population mean.
   d. Thus the average of these means (the mean of the distribution of means) should in the long run equal the population mean.

C. The variance of a distribution of means (σ_M^2).
 1. Principle: The distribution of means will be less spread out than the population of individual cases from which the samples are taken.
   a. Explanation.
     1. Any one score, even an extreme score, has some chance of being selected in a random sample.
     2. However, the chance is less of two extreme scores being selected in the same random sample, particularly since in order to create an extreme sample mean they would have to be two scores which were extreme in the same direction.
     3. Thus, there is a moderating effect of numbers: In any one sample, the deviants tend to be balanced out by middle cases or by deviants in the opposite direction, making each sample tend towards the middle and away from extreme values.
     4. With fewer extreme values for the means, the variance of the means is less.
   b. Principle: The more cases in each sample, the less spread out is the distribution of means of that sample size. With a larger number of cases in each sample, it is even harder for extreme cases in that sample not to be balanced out by middle cases or extremes in the other direction in the same sample.
   c. Rule: The variance of a distribution of means is the variance of the distribution of the population of individual cases divided by the number of cases in the samples being selected.
   d. Formula: $\sigma_M^2 = \sigma^2/N$. (N is the number of cases in each sample.)

D. The standard deviation of a distribution of means (σ_M).
   a. Rule: The standard deviation of the distribution of means is the square root of the variance of the distribution of means.
   b. Formula: $\sigma_M = \sqrt{\sigma_M^2} = \sqrt{(\sigma^2/N)}.$
   c. Special name: the standard error of the mean or the standard error, for short.

E. The shape of a distribution of means.
 1. It tends to be unimodal. This is due to the same basic process of extremes balancing each other out that we noted in the discussion of the variance–middle values are more likely and extreme values less likely.

2. Tends to be symmetrical for the same reason: since skew is caused primarily by extreme scores, if there are fewer extreme scores, there is less skew.
3. As the number of subjects in each sample gets larger, the distribution of means of all possible samples of that number of subjects is a better and better approximation to the normal curve.
4. With samples of 30 or more each, even with a quite nonnormal population of individual cases, the approximation of the distribution of means to a normal curve is so close that the percentages in the normal curve table will be extremely accurate.
5. Whenever the population distribution of individual cases is normal, a distribution of means, of whatever sample size, will always be normal.

III. Hypothesis Testing Involving a Distribution of Means

A. The distribution of means is the comparison distribution to which the sample mean can be compared in order to see how likely it is that such a sample mean could have been selected if the null hypothesis is true.

B. It is the characteristics of the distribution of means that must be determined in Step 2 of the hypothesis testing process.

C. It is the location of your sample on the comparison distribution that must be determined in Step 4 of hypothesis testing.
   1. You are now finding a Z score of a sample mean on a distribution of means (instead of the Z score of a single subject on a distribution of a population of single subjects).
   2. Thus, the formula is $Z = (M-\mu)/\sigma_M$.

D. Other than using the distribution of means as the comparison distribution and locating the mean of your sample on this distribution, the process of hypothesis testing is exactly the same as in Chapter 6 (which focused on hypothesis testing involving a sample of just one subject).

IV. Estimation and Confidence Limits

A. Sometimes it is necessary to estimate an unknown population mean based on the scores in a sample.
   1. The best estimate of the population mean is the sample mean.
   2. Whenever we estimate a specific value of a population parameter, it is called a point estimate.
   3. When we estimate a range of possible means that are likely to include the population mean, it is called an interval estimate.

B. The accuracy of a point estimate
   1. One approach to assessing the accuracy of a point estimate of the population mean is to figure how much the means vary in a distribution of means.
   2. The goal is to estimate the population mean; therefore, the amount of variance in the distribution of means is how much in error your estimate is likely to be.
   3. The standard error of the mean is a measure of how much error you can expect, on average, for an estimate of the population mean using the sample mean.

C. A confidence interval is an interval which is wide enough to be quite sure it includes the population mean. The wider the interval estimate, the more confident you can be that it includes the population mean. In general, you want an interval that is wide enough to ensure that it includes the population mean. This is called a confidence interval. If you want to be 95% sure, you want a 95% confidence interval.

D. Confidence limits are the upper and lower boundaries of a confidence interval.
   1. To find a 95% confidence, you need to find the cutoff points for the top and bottom 2.5% (this leaves a total of 95% in the middle).
   2. Here are three steps for computing confidence intervals:
      a. Determine the characteristics of the distribution of means.

      b. Use the normal curve table to find the Z scores that go with the upper and lower percentages that you want.

      c. Convert these Z scores to a raw score on your distribution of means. These are the upper and lower confidence limits.

E. The subtle logic of confidence intervals

    1. Confidence intervals tell us the range of means likely to come from a population with the true mean equal to the mean of the sample.

    2. However, what most researchers want to know is the range likely to include the population mean. Unfortunately, this is unknowable.

    3. What confidence intervals allow us to do is to say we are 95% confident the true mean is within the specified range.

    4. At a given confidence level (say, 95%) the lower confidence limit is the lowest possible population mean that would have a 95% likelihood of including the sample mean, and the upper confidence limits the highest possible population mean that would have a 95% likelihood of including the sample mean.

F. Confidence intervals and hypothesis testing

    1. You can use confidence intervals as a way to do hypothesis testing. If the confidence interval does not include the mean of the null hypothesis distribution, then the result is significant.

    2. The confidence limits are the points at which a more extreme true population would not include the sample mean 95% of the time.

V. Controversies: Confidence Intervals or Significance Tests?

A. Those who favor replacing significance tests with confidence intervals cite several major advantages.

    1. Confidence intervals give more information than significance tests, such as the estimation of the range of values that we can be quite confident include the true population mean.

    2. Confidence intervals focus attention on estimation instead of hypothesis testing.

    3. Confidence intervals are also valuable when the results are not significant because knowing the confidence interval gives you an idea of how far from no effect the true mean is likely to be found.

    4. Researchers are less likely to misuse confidence intervals.

VI. Topics of this Chapter as Reported in Research Articles

A. Research situations in which there is a known population mean and standard deviation are quite rare in psychology, so they seldom appear in research articles; the main reason we have asked you to learn about this situation is because it is a necessary building block to understanding hypothesis testing in the more common research situations.

B. When such hypothesis tests are reported, the procedure may be described as a "Z test."

C. Researchers will sometimes report one statistic discussed in this chapter, the standard deviation of the distribution of means.

    1. This is done as an indication of the amount of variation that might be expected among means of samples of a given size from this population.

    2. In this context it is usually identified as the "standard error" or abbreviated as *SE*.

    3. Often the lines that go above and below the tops of the bars in a bar graph refer to standard error (instead of standard deviation).

D. When researchers report the standard error of a result, they also give information regarding the confidence interval. Confidence intervals are becoming increasingly standard in research articles.

Formulas

I.   Variance of a distribution of means (σ^2_M)

   Formula in words: The variance of the distribution of the population of individual cases divided by the number of individual cases in each sample.

   Formula in symbols: $\sigma^2{}_M = \sigma^2 / N$

   σ^2 is the variance of the population of individual cases.

   N is the number of individual cases in each sample.

II.   Standard deviation of a distribution of means, standard error (σ_M)

   Formula in words: The square root of the variance of the distribution of means.

   Formula in symbols: $\sigma_M = \sqrt{\sigma_M{}^2}$

   or $\sqrt{(\sigma^2/N)}.$

III.   Location of the sample mean on the distribution of means (Z)

   Formula in words: Deviation of the mean of the sample from the mean of the known population (same as mean of the distribution of means), divided by the standard deviation of the distribution of means.

   Formula in symbols: $Z = M - \mu / \sigma_M$

   M is the mean of the sample.

   μ is the mean of the known population (same as the mean of the distribution of means).

How to Test a Hypothesis Involving a Single Sample of More than One Subject and a Known Population

1.   **Reframe the question into a research hypothesis and a null hypothesis about populations. (Step 1.)**
   A. Identify the two populations.
      1. Population 1 is people like those studied who have been exposed to the experimental manipulation.
      2. Population 2 is people like those studied but who have not been exposed to the experimental manipulation. (This is usually people from the general public, of the category studied.)
   B. State the research hypothesis.
      1. Decide whether this will be directional or nondirectional.
      2. State in terms of the two populations (that the mean of one will be higher, lower, or the same as the other).
   C. State the null hypothesis–Populations 1 and 2 are the same; the manipulation had no impact.
   D. Check that the research and null hypothesis are consistent (in terms of both being in relation to a directional or nondirectional prediction).

2. **Determine the characteristics of the comparison distribution. (Step 2.)**
   A. This will be a distribution of means of samples of the number of subjects in the sample being studied.
   B. Its mean is the same as the mean of the population of individual cases from which the samples are taken: $\mu_M = \mu$.
   C. Its standard deviation is the square root of the result of dividing the variance of the distribution of the population of individual cases by the number of cases in the samples being selected: $\sigma_M = \sqrt{(\sigma^2/N)}$.   ($N$ is the number of cases in each sample.)
   D. Its shape.
      1. Normal if the population is normal.
      2. Very close to normal if N is greater than 30, regardless of population shape.
      3. Otherwise, unimodal and symmetrical, but not normal.
3. **Determine the cutoff sample score on the comparison distribution at which the null hypothesis should be rejected. (Step 3.)**
   A. Decide on the significance level (1% or 5%).
   B. Determine the percentage of cases between the mean and where the appropriate percentage begins on the normal curve.
      1. If a one-tailed test, this is 50% minus the significance level.
      2. If a two-tailed test, this is 50% minus 1/2 the significance level.
   C. Look up the Z corresponding to this percentage in the *% Mean to Z* column in the normal table–this is the cutoff Z.
4. **Determine the sample's score on the comparison distribution. (Step 4.)**
   A. Conduct the study and figure the mean of the scores in the sample studied (or note the result as given to you in the problem).
   B. Convert the raw score result to a Z score on the comparison distribution (the distribution of means): $Z = (M - \mu)/\sigma_M$.
5. **Decide whether or not to reject the null hypothesis. (Step 5.)**
   A. If the actual sample's Z score (from Step 4) is more extreme than the cutoff Z score (from Step 3).
      1. The null hypothesis is rejected.
      2. Thus, the research hypothesis is supported.
   B. If the actual sample's Z score (from Step 4) is not more extreme than the cutoff Z score (from Step 3).
      1. The null hypothesis is not rejected.
      2. Thus, the experiment is inconclusive.

How to Figure Confidence Limits

1. **Figure the standard error.**
   A. Find the standard deviation of the distribution of means in the usual way: The standard deviation is the square root of the result of dividing the variance of the distribution of the population of individual cases by the number of cases in the samples being selected: $\sigma_M = \sqrt{(\sigma^2/N)}$.   ($N$ is the number of cases in each sample.)

2. **For the 95% confidence interval, figure the raw scores for 1.96 standard errors above and below the sample mean; for the 99% confidence interval, figure the raw scores for 2.57 standard errors above and below the sample mean.**

Outline for Writing Essays for Hypothesis Testing-Problems Involving a Single Sample of More than One Subject and a Known Population

The reason for your writing essay questions in the practice problems and tests is that this task develops and then demonstrates what matters so very much–your comprehension of the logic behind the computations. (It is also a place for those of you who are better at words than numbers to shine. And for those better at numbers to develop their skills at explaining in words.)

Thus, to do well you need to be sure to do the following in each essay: (a) give the reasoning behind each step; (b) relate each step to the specifics of the content of the particular study you are analyzing; (c) state the various formulas in nontechnical language, because as you define each term you show you understand it (although once you have defined it in nontechnical language, you can use it from then on in the essay); (d) look back and be absolutely certain that you made it clear just why that formula or procedure was applied and why it is the way it is.

The outlines below are *examples* of ways to structure your essays. There are other completely correct ways to go about it. And this is an *outline* for an answer–you must write the answer out in paragraph form. Examples of full essays are in the answers to Set 1 Practice Problems in the back of the text.

These essays are necessarily very long for you to write (and for others to grade). But this is the very best way to be sure you understand everything thoroughly. One shortcut you may see on a test is to write your answer for someone who understands statistics up to the point of the new material you are studying. You can choose to take the same shortcut in these practice problems (maybe writing for someone who understands right up to whatever point you yourself start being just a little unclear). But every time you write for a person who has never had statistics at all, you review the logic behind the entire course. You engrain it in your mind. Over and over. The time is never wasted. It is an excellent way to study.

I. **Reframe the question into a research hypothesis and a null hypothesis about populations. (Step 1 of hypothesis testing.)**
  A. State in ordinary language the hypothesis testing issue: Does the average of the scores of the group of persons studied represent a higher (or lower or different) mean than would be expected if this group of persons had just been a randomly selected example of people in general–that is, does this set of people studied represent a different group of people from people in general?

B. Explain language (to make the rest of the essay easier to write by not having to repeat long explanations each time), focusing on the meaning of each term in the concrete example of the study at hand.
   1. Populations.
   2. Sample.
   3. Mean.
   4. Research hypothesis.
   5. Null hypothesis.
   6. Rejecting the null hypothesis to provide support for the research hypothesis.

II. **Determine the characteristics of the comparison distribution. (Step 2 of hypothesis testing.)**
   A. Explain the principle that the comparison distribution is the distribution (pattern of spread of the means of scores) that represents what we would expect if the null hypothesis were true and our particular mean were just randomly sampled from this population of means.
   B. Note that because we are interested in the mean of a sample of more than one case, we have to compare our actual mean to a distribution not of individual cases but of means.
   C. Give an intuitive understanding of how one might construct a distribution of means for samples of a given size from a particular population.
      1. Select a random sample of the given size (number of subjects) from the population and figure its mean.
      2. Select another random sample of this size from the population and figure its mean.
      3. Repeat this process a very large number of times.
      4. Make a distribution of these means.
      5. Note that this procedure is only to explain the idea, and would be too much work and unnecessary in practice.
   D. There is an exact mathematical relation of a distribution of means to the population the means are drawn from, so that in practice the characteristics of the distribution of means can be determined directly from knowledge of the characteristics of the population and the size of the samples involved.
   E. The mean of a distribution of means.
      1. It is the same as the mean (average) of the scores in the known population of individual cases.
      2. State what it is in the particular problem you are working on.
      3. Explanation.
         a. Each sample is based on randomly selected values from the population.
         b. Thus, sometimes the mean of a sample will be higher and sometimes lower than the mean of the whole population of individuals.
         c. There is no reason for these to average out higher or lower than the original population mean.
         d. Thus the average of these means (the mean of the distribution of means) should in the long run equal the population mean.

F. The standard deviation of a distribution of means.
   1. The distribution of means will be less spread out than the population of individual cases from which the samples are taken.
      a. Any one score, even an extreme score, has some chance of being selected in a random sample.
      b. However, the chance is less of several extreme scores being selected in the same random sample, particularly since in order to create an extreme sample mean they would all have to be scores which were extreme in the same direction.
      c. Thus, there is a moderating effect of numbers. In any one sample, the deviants tend to be balanced out by many more middle cases or by deviants in the opposite direction, making each sample tend towards the middle and away from extreme values.
      d. With fewer extreme values for the means, the variation among the means is less.
   2. The more cases in each sample, the less spread out is the distribution of means of that sample size. With a larger number of cases in each sample, it is even harder for extreme cases in that sample not to be balanced out by middle cases or extremes in the other direction in the same sample.
   3. Explain the idea of standard deviation.
      a. It is a standard measure of how spread out it is.
      b. It is roughly the average amount scores vary from the mean.
      c. Exactly speaking, it is the square root of the average of the squares of the amount that each score differs from the mean.
   4. The standard deviation of the distribution of means is found by a formula that divides the average of squared deviations from the mean of the population by the number of subjects in the sample (thus making it smaller in proportion to the number of subjects in the sample), and taking the square root of this result.
   5. State what it is in the particular problem you are working on, describing the steps of computation.
G. The shape of a distribution of means.
   1. If your N is greater than 30.
      a. The distribution of means will be approximately normal.
      b. Explain that a normal curve is a bell-shaped distribution that is very common in psychology.
      c. The distribution tends to be normal due to the same basic process of extremes balancing each other out that we noted in the discussion of the standard deviation–middle values are more likely and extreme values less likely.
   2. If the population of individual cases in your situation is normal.
      a. The distribution of means will be approximately normal.
      b. This is because the distribution of means will have nothing to distort it from looking like the distribution of individual cases.

III. **Determine the cutoff score on the comparison distribution at which the null hypothesis should be rejected. (Step 3 of hypothesis testing.)**
   A. Before you figure out how extreme your particular sample's mean is on this distribution of means, you want to know how extreme it would have to be to decide it was too unlikely that it could have been a randomly drawn mean from this comparison distribution of means.
   B. Since in this problem the comparison distribution is a normal curve, you can use a table to tell you how many standard deviations from the mean your score would have to be to be in the top so many percent.
   C. Note that the number of standard deviations from the mean is called a Z score. (By explaining this term, you make the writing simpler later on.)

107

D. To use these tables you have to decide the kind of situation you have; there are two considerations.

1. Are you interested in the chances of getting this extreme of a mean that is extreme in only one direction (such as only higher than for people in general) or in both? (Explain which is appropriate for your study.)
2. Just how unlikely would the extremeness of a particular mean have to be? The standard figure used in psychology is less likely than 5% (though 1% is sometimes used to be especially safe). (Say which you are using in your study—if no figure is stated in the problem and no special reason given for using one or the other, the general rule is to use 5%.)

E. With a little manipulation of numbers you can then look up the percentage in the table and find the Z score corresponding to that percentage.

F. State the cutoff for your particular problem.

IV. Determine the score of your sample on the comparison distribution. (Step 4 of hypothesis testing.)

A. At this point the study would be conducted and the mean score of the sample studied obtained. (State what it is.)

B. The next step is to find where your actual sample's mean would fall on the comparison distribution, in terms of a Z score.

C. State this Z score.

V. Compare the scores obtained in Steps 3 and 4 to decide whether to reject the null hypothesis. (Step 5 of hypothesis testing.)

A. State whether your mean (from Step 4) does or does not exceed the cutoff (from Step 3).

B. If your mean exceeds the cutoff.

1. State that you can reject the null hypothesis.
2. State that by elimination, the research hypothesis is thus supported.
3. State in words what it means that the research hypothesis is supported (that is, the study shows that the particular experimental manipulation appears to make a difference in the particular thing being measured).

C. If your score does not exceed the cutoff.

1. State that you can not reject the null hypothesis.
2. State that the experiment is inconclusive.
3. State in words what it means that the study is inconclusive (that is, the study did not yield results which give a clear indication of whether or not the particular experimental manipulation appears to make a difference in the particular thing being measured).
4. Explicitly note that even though the research hypothesis was not supported in this study, this is not evidence that it is false—it is quite possible that it is true but it has only a small effect which was not sufficient to produce a mean extreme enough to yield a significant result in this study.

Chapter Self-Tests

Multiple-Choice Questions

1. When testing an hypothesis in which the group studied is a mean of a sample of scores, the proper comparison distribution is

   a. the original population from which the sample was taken.
   b. the population that would exist if the null hypothesis were true.
   c. the distribution of all possible means of the sample size (N) from the known population.
   d. the distribution of the individual scores from which the sample mean was calculated.

2. The mean for the general population on a particular standardized test is known to be 56 with a standard deviation of 8. What would be the mean of the distribution of means for a study involving this test?

   a. 7.
   b. 7.48.
   c. 56.
   d. 112.

3. The variance of a distribution of means is calculated by

   a. multiplying the variance of the population of individual cases by the number of subjects in each sample.
   b. dividing the variance of the population of individual cases by the number of subjects in each sample.
   c. subtracting the sample's variance from the population variance.
   d. taking the squareroot of the variance of the population of individual cases.

4. In comparison to the original population data, the shape of the distribution of means is

   a. a bimodal configuration.
   b. a rectangular shape.
   c. more spread out than the original population.
   d. less spread out than the original population.

5. When calculating the Z score of your sample's mean on a distribution of means, you should

   a. estimate the variance of the comparison distribution by taking the square root of the sample's variance.
   b. treat the sample mean like a single score and find its Z score on the distribution of means.
   c. divide the variance of the distribution of means by the mean of the sample.
   d. take the square root of the differences between the two means.

6-9 An experimenter was interested in the relation of social class to motivation, using a standard test of motivation (for the general population, the mean is 90 and the standard deviation is 10). Based on a theory she had constructed, she expected that those in the upper class would score lower. She administered the test to 20 members of an upper-class community. Her obtained sample mean on the test was 87.

6. In this example, the null hypothesis would be

    a. upper-class communities have higher motivation than the population in general.
    b. the mean of the population the sample represents is no lower than the mean of the general population.
    c. the sample variance will equal the population variance.
    d. there will be no difference between the population and the distribution of means.

7. The characteristics of the comparison distribution are

    a. mean=90, variance=5.
    b. mean=90, variance=.5.
    c. mean=90, variance=9.
    d. mean=90, variance=20.

8. The cutoff Z score (using the .05 level) is

    a. ±1.64.
    b. +1.96.
    c. -1.64.
    d. -2.33.

9. If the sample mean's score on the comparison distribution is more extreme than the cutoff, what should the researcher conclude?

    a. Upper class people are more motivated.
    b. Upper class people are less motivated.
    c. Upper class people are neither more nor less motivated, but have approximately the same level of motivation.
    d. The results are inconclusive.

10. If you have a 95% confidence interval from 208.24 to 231.76,

    a. all of the subject's scores fall within this range.
    b. you have a large effect size.
    c. you can be 95% sure that this interval includes the true population mean.
    d. all of the above

Fill-In Questions

11. When a study is being conducted in which a group of people are studied to see if they represent a group that is different from the general population, the comparison distribution is a(n) _____ .

12. The three characteristics of a comparison distribution are its mean, variance (or standard deviation), and _____ .

13-14. $\mu = 40.8$, $\sigma = 8$, and there are 16 people in the sample being studied, which has a mean of 44.9.

    13. $\mu_M = $ _____ .

    14. $\sigma_M = $ _____ .

15. In a different study, $\mu_M = 107$, $\sigma_M = 3$. If a group of 40 people studied has a mean of 101, what is their Z score on the comparison distribution? _____.

16. If a distribution of means comes from a nonnormal population, its distribution is nevertheless considered normal for all practical purposes as long as the sample size is at least _____.

17. The standard error of the mean is the same as _____.

18. An interval that is wide enough to ensure that it includes the population mean is called a _____.

19. Whenever we estimate a specific value of a population parameter, it is called a _____.

20. It is rare that psychologists actually carry out hypothesis testing procedures involving a single sample and a population whose mean and variance is known (the kind of hypothesis tests we are considering in this chapter). But when they do carry out such a procedure and report the result in a research article, it is called a(n) _____.

Problems and Essays

21. A psychologist interested in the effects of music administers a measure of logical reasoning ability to 5 subjects (randomly selected from the general population of adults) while they are listening to soothing music. Their scores on the test were 68, 39, 55, 73, and 80. Previous research using this test indicates that in the general population the distribution is normal, with $\mu = 48$ and $\sigma = 12$.

    a. Do people do better when listening to soothing music (use the .01 level)? Solve this problem explicitly using all five steps of hypothesis testing and illustrate your answer with a sketch showing the comparison distribution, the cutoff (or cutoffs), and the score of the sample on this distribution.
    b. Figure the 95% confidence intervals.
    c. Explain what you have done and your conclusions to a person who has never had a course in statistics.

22. A learning psychologist was interested in whether providing a stationary pattern of small lights on the ceiling and walls of a darkened laboratory would decrease the time it took for rats to learn a maze. (She was wondering if the rats would be able to use the stationary cues to aid in their navigation.) From her previous research she knew that on the average it took a rat 38 trials, with a standard deviation of 6, to learn a particular maze, and that the distribution is normal. She then tested a group of 10 rats in the changed laboratory and found their average number of trials to learn the maze was 36.

    a. Was this difference significant at the .05 level? Solve this problem explicitly using all five steps of hypothesis testing and illustrate your answer with a sketch showing the comparison distribution, the cutoff (or cutoffs), and the score of the sample on this distribution.
    b. Figure the 99% confidence intervals.
    c. Explain what you have done and your conclusions to a person who has never had a course in statistics.

111

23. A social psychologist was interested in the effect of dressing informally on student course ratings. She knew from previous courses that her average ratings were 3.25 (on a 4-point scale) with a standard deviation of .3. During the target semester, she dressed very casually. In a course with 30 students, her average rating was 3.1. (These data are fictitious.)

   a. Was this significantly different at the .05 level? Solve this problem explicitly using all five steps of hypothesis testing and illustrate your answer with a sketch showing the comparison distribution, the cutoff (or cutoffs), and the score of the sample on this distribution.

   b. Explain what you have done and your conclusions to a person who has never had a course in statistics.

24. For each of the following hypothetical studies, explain what a Type I and Type II error would be, and what each would mean.

   a. A study comparing the mean test score for a class using a new learning technique (expected to improve test scores) with the average score on the same test.

   b. A study testing whether chimpanzees injected with a new drug learn to use symbolic communication faster than the normal chimp.

25. A school psychologist was wondering how the preschoolers at the school where he worked compared to other preschoolers who have taken a standardized problem-solving test. He therefore administered the test to all the preschool children and found that their average was significantly higher than the mean for the general population (the Z score +1.97) at the .05 level. How would the psychologist interpret these findings and report them to a group of people unfamiliar with statistics?

Note. There is no section on using SPSS with this chapter because none of the procedures covered are easily implemented using standard computerized statistical packages. (The material in this chapter is mainly preparation for carrying out procedures that are widely used, however, and for which the computer can be very helpful.)

Chapter 8
Making Sense of Statistical Significance

Learning Objectives

To understand, including being able to carry out any necessary procedures or computations:

■ The computation of effect size and its uses.
■ Effect size conventions.
■ Meta-analysis and its advantages and disadvantages
■ Decision errors: Type I errors, Type II errors, and possible correct and erroneous outcomes of hypothesis testing
■ What is statistical power?
■ Calculating power for a study with a single sample and a known population.
■ Power tables.
■ Influences on power.
■ The relation of power to effect size and each of its components
■ Relation of sample size to power.
■ Relation of significance level to power.
■ Relation of using one- versus two-tailed tests to power.
■ Role of power when designing a study.
■ Issues regarding the possibility of "proving" the null hypothesis.
■ Issues regarding the comparative advantage of emphasizing effect size versus statistical significance in interpreting the result of a completed study.
■ Ways to increase power of a planned study (and the advantages and disadvantages of each).
■ Role of power in evaluating results of a study (for both when a study is and is not significant).
■ How power and effect size are discussed in research articles.

Chapter Outline

I. Effect Size

A. It can be thought of as the amount the two population distributions do not overlap. It is how "big" the effect of the experimental procedure is.

B. One measure of effect size (d) is the difference between the two means divided by the population standard deviation: $d = (\mu_1 - \mu_2) / \sigma$.

    1. This is called the *standardized effect size*.
    2. It is also known as *Cohen's d*.

C. The general importance of effect size.

    1. Note that the computation of effect size does not use the standard deviation of the distribution of means (σ_M), but of the original population of individual cases (σ).
    2. Dividing the mean difference by the standard deviation of the population of individual cases standardizes the difference in the same way that a Z score gives us a standard metric for comparison to other scores, even other scores on different scales.
    3. Because it provides a standard metric for comparison, especially by using the standard deviation of the population of individual cases, we bypass the dissimilarity from study to study of different sample sizes, making comparison even easier and effect size even more of a standard metric.

4. Thus, knowing the effect size of a study permits us to compare results with effect sizes found in other studies, even other studies using different sample sizes.

5.   Equally important, knowing effect size can permit us to compare studies using different measures which may have scales with quite different means and variances.

6. Even within a particular study, we can apply our general knowledge of what is a small or large effect size.

D. Effect size conventions: Developed by Cohen, based on what is typically found in psychology research.

1. Small effect size.
   a. About 85% overlap of the two populations.
   b. $d = .2$: That is, the predicted mean is about two-tenths of a standard deviation higher than the mean of the known population.
   c. An example is the difference in height between 15- and 16-year-old girls.

2. Medium effect size.
   a. About 67% overlap of the two populations.
   b. $d = .5$: That is, the predicted mean is about half a standard deviation higher than the mean of the known population.
   c. An example is the difference in height between 14- and 18-year-old girls.

3. Large effect size.
   a. About 53% overlap of the two populations.
   b. $d = .8$: That is, the predicted mean is about eight-tenths of a standard deviation higher than the mean of the known population.
   c. An example is the difference in height between 13- and 18-year-old girls.

II. Meta-analysis is a statistical method for combining the results of independent studies.

A. It is used primarily in articles which review the experiments conducted in a particular area of research.

B. A meta-analytic review of the literature involves two steps.
1. One first locates all the studies conducted on a given topic.
2. One then statistically combines the results (usually using effect sizes) of these studies.

C. Reviews of the research literature using meta-analysis are an alternative to the traditional "narrative" literature-review article that describes and evaluates each study and then attempts to draw some overall conclusion.

D. The number of articles using meta-analysis has increased dramatically in recent years

E. They are most common in the more applied areas of psychology.

III. Decision Errors

A. Decision errors are when the right procedures lead to the wrong decisions.
1. Type 1 error occurs when significant results are obtained when the research hypothesis is not true.   Alpha (α) is the probability of a Type I error (it is the same as the significance level, usually .01 or .05).
2. A Type II error occurs when the study does not give significant results even if the research hypothesis is true.   Beta (ß) is the probability of a Type II error.

B. Relation of Type I and Type II errors
1. Decreasing the likelihood of a Type 1 error increases the likelihood of a Type II error.
2. Similarly, decreasing the likelihood of a Type II error increases the likelihood of a Type I error.
3. Most researchers compromise by using a 1% or 5% significance level.

C. Review of possible correct and erroneous decisions in hypothesis testing.
  1. The research hypothesis is actually true and the hypothesis-testing procedure results in rejecting the null hypothesis (a correct decision). Probability of this outcome = power.
  2. The research hypothesis is actually false and the hypothesis-testing procedure results in rejecting the null hypothesis (a Type I error). Probability of this outcome = α.
  3. The research hypothesis is actually true and the hypothesis-testing procedure results in failing to reject the null hypothesis (a Type II error). Probability of this outcome = β.
  4. The research hypothesis is actually false and the hypothesis-testing procedure results in failing to reject the null hypothesis (a correct decision). Probability of this outcome = $1 - \alpha$.

IV. What Is Statistical Power?

A. The probability that a study will yield significant results if the research hypothesis is true.

B. In contrast, if the research hypothesis is not true, one would not want to get significant results (that would be a Type I error).

C. Also in contrast, even if the research hypothesis is true, the study may not necessarily give significant results–the particular sample that happens to be selected from the population studied may not turn out to be extreme enough to provide a clear case for rejecting the null hypothesis (this would be a Type II error).

V. Calculating Statistical Power

A. The procedures considered below are for studies involving the mean of an actual sample compared to a known population, and where the distributions of means can be assumed to be normal and to come from populations with the same standard deviation.

B. Logic of computing power.
  1. The cutoff on the comparison distribution (determined in the steps of hypothesis testing) is the score or point at which, if a mean of the actual sample were greater than it, this would be grounds for rejecting the null hypothesis.
  2. This cutoff is usually stated as a Z score.
  3. But one can determine the raw-score equivalent to this Z score–that is, the raw score at which, if a mean of the actual sample were greater than it, this would be grounds for rejecting the null hypothesis.
  4. Now consider the distribution of means predicted by the research hypothesis (this is something we have not considered before).
     a. It will have a different mean than the comparison distribution–for example, if a higher score is predicted by the research hypothesis, the mean of this distribution will be higher than that of the comparison distribution.
     b. To figure power one must make an explicit prediction of the mean of this distribution.
  5. Power is the percentage of cases on the distribution of means based on the *research* hypothesis that fall above the raw-score cutoff value, which was originally computed using the comparison distribution (which is based, of course, on the null hypothesis). This same raw-score cutoff point is thus positioned in quite different places on the two distributions.
  6. Note that the computation of power has nothing to do with the actual outcome of the experiment–in fact, it is ordinarily computed in advance of actually conducting the study to help determine whether the study has enough power to be conducted or whether the procedures of the proposed study should first be adjusted in some way to make it more powerful.

C. Systematic steps of computing power.
    1. Gather the needed information.
        a. The mean (μ_M) and standard deviation (σ_M) of the comparison distribution.
        b. The predicted mean of the population that receives the experimental intervention (how to do this is discussed later in the chapter).
    2. In the usual way, find the cutoff (which is always found in tables and is in Z-score terms) needed on the comparison distribution in order to reject the null hypothesis. This is the same as you do in the first three steps of hypothesis testing.
    3. Convert this Z score to a raw score using the mean and standard deviation (still of the comparison distribution): raw cutoff = $(Z)(\sigma_M) + (\mu_M)$.
    4. Determine the Z score corresponding to this raw-score cutoff on the distribution of means for the population that receives the experimental manipulation. That is, Z = (raw cutoff - mean of predicted distribution) / σ_M.
    5. Using the normal curve table, determine the probability of getting a score more extreme than this new Z score; this is power.
    6. Beta is the remaining probability (1 - power).
D. Power tables.
    1. The procedures required for more complicated hypothesis-testing situations (the situations covered in the remainder of this text) follow the same logic but involve considerable additional work to carry out by hand–nor is it usually feasible to do it by computer.
    2. However, statisticians have prepared power tables that much simplify the process.
    3. The fundamental logic on which these tables are based is exactly what you have learned here, and using the tables requires exactly the same information that is needed to figure power directly.
    4. In later chapters of this text, whenever you learn a new hypothesis-testing procedure, you will also be furnished with power tables (and instructions how to use them). (An index of these tables is provided in Appendix A of the text.)

VI. Influences on Power
A. Primary influences.
    1. Effect size.
    2. Sample size.
B. Secondary influences.
    1. Level of statistical significance (α).
    2. Two-tailed versus one-tailed tests.
    3. Type of hypothesis-testing procedure used.

VII. Determining the Power of a Study and Effect Size
A. The larger the effect size, the greater the power.
B. The larger the difference between the two means (and thus the more offset the two distributions are from each other, minimizing their overlap), the greater the effect size.
C. The smaller the population standard deviation (and thus the less overlap because each distribution is narrower), the greater the effect size.
D. How to determine the predicted mean of the distribution based on the research hypothesis.
    1. Estimate it from previous similar research.
    2. Calculate it from a precise theory.
    3. Determine the smallest difference that would be practically or theoretically interesting (method of the minimum meaningful difference).

E. If you know the effect size (for example, based on Cohen's conventions) and the population standard deviation, it is possible to figure the expected mean difference by solving the effect size formula for $(\mu_1 - \mu_2)$.

VIII. Determining the Power of a Study and Sample Size
A. The larger the sample size, the greater the power.
B. This is because the variance of the distribution of means is based on the population variance divided by the sample size–the larger the sample size, the smaller the variance, and the smaller the variance, the less overlap of the distributions of means.
C. Determining needed number of participants to attain a given level of power.
   1. One reason the influence of sample size on power is so very important is that the number of participants is something the researcher can often control prior to the experiment.
   2. The number of participants needed for a given level of power can be found by turning the steps of computing power on their head.
      a. Begin with a desired level of power (often 80% is used).
      b. Then calculate how many participants are needed to get that level of power.
   3. In practice researchers use special tables for this purpose (subsequent chapters of the text provide such tables for each new hypothesis testing procedure).

IX. Other Influences on Power
A. Significance level (α).
   1. The less stringent the significance level (for example, .05 versus .01), the more power.
   2. This is because the cutoff for a less stringent significance level will not be as extreme.
B. Two-tailed versus one-tailed tests.
   1. One-tailed tests have more power (for results in the predicted direction).
   2. This is because the cutoff in the predicted direction is less extreme (since all the α percentage is at that end, instead of being divided in half).
C. Type of hypothesis-testing procedure.
   1. Sometimes a researcher has a choice of more than one statistical procedure to apply to a given set of results, and each has its own power.
   2. Sometimes there may be more than one type of research design available, such as between-subjects versus within-subjects (see Appendix A), and each of these also has its own effect on power.

X. Role of Power When Designing a Study
A. If a researcher checks and finds that the power of a planned experiment is low, it is clear that even if the research hypothesis is true, this study is not likely to yield significant results in support of that research hypothesis. Thus the researcher must seek practical ways to modify the study to increase the power to an acceptable level.
B. What is an acceptable level of power?
   1. 80% is a widely used convention.
   2. If a study is very difficult or costly to conduct, a researcher might want even higher levels (such as 90% or even 95%) before undertaking the project.
   3. If a study is very easy and inexpensive to conduct, a researcher might be willing to take a chance with a somewhat lower level of power (such as 60% or 70%).
   4. The acceptable level of power also depends on how difficult and costly it is to increase power.

XI. How to Increase the Power of a Planned Study
   A. Increasing expected difference between population means.
      1. If the original prediction is the most accurate available, arbitrarily changing it would undermine the accuracy of the power calculation.
      2. However, it is sometimes possible to change the way the experiment is being conducted (for example, by increasing the intensity of the experimental manipulation) so that the researcher would have reason to expect a larger mean difference.
      3. Disadvantages of this approach.
         a. Can be difficult or costly to implement.
         b. Can create circumstances implementing the experimental treatment that are unrepresentative of those to which the results are intended to be generalized.
   B. Decreasing the population standard deviation.
      1. Conduct the study using a population that is less diverse than the one originally planned—however, this limits the scope of the population to which the results can be generalized.
      2. Use conditions of testing that are more constant (such as controlled laboratory conditions) and measures that are more precise—this is a highly recommended approach.
   C. Increasing sample size.
      1. The most commonly used, straightforward way to increase power.
      2. In some cases, however, there may be limits to the number of participants available or great costs in recruiting or testing additional numbers.
   D. Using a less stringent significance level—however, this increases the risk of a Type I error, and thus should be used cautiously.
   E. Using a one-tailed test—however, one runs the various risks discussed in Chapter 6 with one-tailed tests, most notably the possibility of having to deal with opposite-to-predicted results.
   F. Using a more sensitive hypothesis-testing procedure—when choices are available (and there are no offsetting disadvantages), one should always use the procedure that gives greatest power.
XII. Role of Power in Evaluating Results of a Study
   A. When a result is significant.
      1. Statistical significance is a necessary prerequisite to considering a result as either theoretically or practically important.
      2. For a result to be practically important, however, in addition to statistical significance, it should be of a reasonable effect size.
      3. It is easy for a study with a very small effect size, having little practical importance, to still come out significant—if the study has reasonable power due to other factors, especially a large sample size.
      4. But if the sample was small, you can assume a significant result is probably also practically important.
      5. When comparing two studies, the effect sizes and not the significance levels obtained should be compared (since the significance levels could be due to different sample sizes and not to different underlying effects in the populations).
   B. When a result is not significant.
      1. If the power of the study was low.
         a. Failing to get a significant result is especially inconclusive.
         b. The non-significant outcome could be because the research hypothesis was false, or it could be because the research hypothesis was true but the study had too little power to come out significant.

2. If the power of the study was high.
   a. Failing to get a significant result suggests more strongly that the research hypothesis (as specified with a specific mean difference) is false.
   b. This does not mean that all versions of the research hypothesis are false (it is possible that the experimental manipulation does make a difference, but a much smaller one than was hypothesized when computing power).

XIII. Controversies

A. Can you "prove" the null hypothesis?
   1. The traditional principle is that when the results are not strong enough to reject the null hypothesis, the implication is that the results are inconclusive–not that the null hypothesis is true.
   2. This is because, no matter how much power an experiment has, it is always possible that there is a real effect.
   3. Thus, in general, it is best to avoid conducting studies in which your prediction is that the populations do not differ.
   4. However, you can use statistical results to provide a convincing case that whatever difference exists must be very, very small.
      a. Specify a specific small amount of difference.
      b. Use that small difference as the predicted effect size.
      c. Conduct a study that has very high power in spite of that small effect size.
      d. If the study fails to achieve significance even with this amount of power, then you have what amounts to a significance at the level of 1 minus your power. If there is any difference in the populations, it is less than the small difference you initially specified.
   5. This procedure is rarely practical because of the very large number of participants needed for a high power experiment with a small effect size.

B. Effect size versus statistical significance.
   1. Some psychologists argue that significance tests are misleading for several reasons.
      a. They are highly influenced by sample size, so that a large sample can produce significance with an unimportant underlying effect and a small sample can fail to give significance even with a large underlying effect.
      b. They give an all-or-none outcome based on an arbitrary α.
   2. These opponents to current procedure instead offer several reasons for emphasizing effect size.
      a. It has neither of the above disadvantages.
      b. It directly indicates the importance of the underlying effect.
      c. It permits direct comparison among (and the accumulation of results across) studies.
   3. However, there are also counter-arguments in favor of significance tests.
      a. If a result is not significant, it should not be taken seriously regardless of its effect size, since we are not sure the effect did not just arise by chance.
      b. There are times when even a very small effect size is important.
      c. In theoretically-oriented research, usually what matters most is our confidence in the pattern of results being consistent with a theory and not the effect size of those results (which may depend largely on the details of the set-up of the experiment).
   4. In general, psychologists in applied areas should and usually do give more emphasis to effect size (but still use significance tests as well), while psychologists in more theoretical areas tend to rely mainly on significance, though occasionally making use of effect size to compare results across studies.

XIV. Power and Effect Size as Discussed in Research Articles
    A. Power is not often mentioned directly in research articles (its greater role is in the planning of research and in interpreting research results).
    B. Power is occasionally mentioned in the context of justifying the number of participants used in a study.
    C. Authors are also likely to mention effect size when comparing results of studies or parts of studies (or in meta-analysis articles).

Formula

Effect size (d)

        Formula in words: The difference between the hypothesized and known population means, divided by the population standard deviation.

        Formula in symbols: $d = \mu_1 - \mu_2 / \sigma$

          μ_1 is the mean of Population 1 (the hypothesized mean for the population that is exposed to the experimental manipulation).

          μ_2 is the mean of Population 2 (which is also the mean of the comparison distribution).

          σ is the standard deviation of Population 2 (and assumed to be the standard deviation of both populations).

How to Figure Power for a Study Involving a Single Sample of More than One Subject and a Known Population

1. Gather the needed information.
    A. The mean (μ_M, same as μ_2) and standard deviation (σ_M) of the comparison distribution (these can be computed from μ_2 and σ or σ^2, which are usually given as part of the problem).
    B. The predicted mean of the population that receives the experimental intervention can be determined in one of several ways:
        1. It may be given in the problem.
        2. One can determine the minimum meaningful difference.
        3. One can use theory or previous research.
        4. One can use the effect size conventions.
          a. Determine whether effect size is small (.2), medium (.5), or large (.8).
          b. Substitute this effect size (.2, .5, or .8), the mean of the known population (μ_2), and the standard deviation of the known population (σ) into the formula for effect size – $d = (\mu_1 - \mu_2)/\sigma$ – and solve for μ_1.
    C. Draw a picture of the two distributions of means, one above the other, with the means of each at the appropriate places.

2. **Figure the raw-score cutoff point on the comparison distribution to reject the null hypothesis.**

   A. Find the cutoff in Z-score terms (that is, carry out Steps 1 to 3 of the usual hypothesis-testing procedure).

   1. Identify the characteristics of the comparison distribution.

      a. Its mean is the same as the mean of the population of individual cases from which the samples are taken: $\mu_M = \mu_2$.

      b. Its standard deviation is the square root of the result of dividing the variance of the distribution of the population of individual cases by the number of cases in the samples being selected: $\sigma_M = \sqrt{(\sigma^2/N)}$. ($N$ is the number of cases in each sample.)

      c. Its shape must be normal or approximately normal (which will be the case if either the population is normal or the sample size is greater than 30), or this problem can't be done.

   2. Decide on the significance level (1% or 5%).

   3. Decide about whether this is a one-tailed or two-tailed test.

   4. Determine the percentage of cases between the mean and where the appropriate percentage begins on the normal curve.

      a. If a one-tailed test, this is 50% minus the significance level.

      b. If a two-tailed test, this is 50% minus 1/2 the significance level.

   5. Look up the Z corresponding to this percentage in the *% Mean to Z* column in the normal table–this is the cutoff Z.

   B. Convert this to a raw score (or to two raw-scores if a two-tailed test is used) using the mean and standard deviation of this distribution:

   $$\text{raw cutoff} = (Z)(\sigma_M) + (\mu_M).$$

   C. Draw in the raw cutoff on Population 2's distribution of means–label the area more extreme than it as alpha (α).

3. **Figure the Z score for this point , but on the distribution of means for the population that receives the experimental manipulation (population 1).**

   A. $Z = $ (raw cutoff - mean of predicted distribution) $/ \sigma_M$.

   B. If a two-tailed test, be sure to do this for both cutoffs.

   C. Draw in the cutoff on Population 1's distribution of means; label the area beyond it in the predicted direction as power.

4. **Using the normal curve table, figure the probability of getting a score more extreme than that Z score.**

Outline for Writing Essays for Computing Power for Studies Involving a Single Sample of More than One Subject and a Known Population

The reason for your writing essay questions in the practice problems and tests is that this task develops and then demonstrates what matters so very much–your comprehension of the logic behind the computations. (It is also a place where those better at words than numbers can shine, and for those better at numbers to develop their skills at explaining in words.)

Thus, to do well, be sure to do the following in each essay: (a) give the reasoning behind each step; (b) relate each step to the specifics of the content of the particular study you are analyzing; (c) state the various formulas in nontechnical language, because as you define each term you show you understand it (although once

you have defined it in nontechnical language, you can use it from then on in the essay);
(d) look back and be absolutely certain that you made it clear just *why* that formula or
procedure was applied and *why* it is the way it is.

The outlines below are *examples* of ways to structure your essays. There are
other completely correct ways to go about it. And this is an *outline* for an answer–you
are to write the answer out in paragraph form. Examples of full essays are in the answers
to Set I Practice Problems in the back of the text.

These essays are necessarily very long for you to write (and for others to grade).
But this is the very best way to be sure you understand everything thoroughly. One
shortcut you may see on a test is that you may be asked to write your answer for someone
who understands statistics up to the point of the new material you are studying. You can
choose to take the same shortcut in these practice problems (maybe writing for someone
who understands right up to whatever point you yourself start being just a little unclear).
But every time you write for a person who has never had statistics at all, you review the
logic behind the entire course. You engrain it in your mind. Over and over. The time is
never wasted. It is an excellent way to study.

I. **Explain the logic of hypothesis testing and associated terminology (as per the
    outline for essays in Chapter 7 of this *Study Guide*), focusing on the particular
    study you are working on.**
II. **Explain the concept of power–the probability of getting significant results if the
    research hypothesis is true.**
III. **Computation of power.**
   A. State the Z score cutoff on the comparison distribution (determined in the steps of
    hypothesis testing, as you have explained in describing those steps), being sure to
    explain how it was arrived at.
   B. Convert the cutoff Z to a raw score and draw a picture of the distribution showing
    the raw-score cutoff and the area beyond it (shading this area and labeling it "area
    in which the result would be significant").
   C. Explain the idea of a distribution of means predicted by the research hypothesis
    (that is, the distribution expected for the group exposed to the experimental
    manipulation).
     1. Note that it will have a different mean than the comparison distribution and state what your
       prediction is.
     2. Describe your basis for predicting that mean.
      a. Given in the problem.
      b. Based on theory or previous research.
      c. Based on minimum meaningful effect size.
     3. Note that we assume it will have the same standard deviation and will also be a normal
       curve.
     4. Draw a diagram of the predicted distribution, drawing it above the comparison distribution,
       with the scale of numbers matching and in the same location across the page as that of the
       distribution of means below (forcing the center of the curve you draw above to be offset).
   D. Mark the raw-score cutoff on the distribution of means for the population exposed
    to the experimental manipulation.
   E. Power is the area more extreme in the predicted direction than this cutoff. (Shade
    this area in the upper curve, and label it power.)

F. Since this upper distribution is a normal curve, and the proportion of cases above any point on a normal curve is known and available on a table, this proportion can be computed.
1. Find the Z-score equivalent to the raw-score cutoff using the mean and standard deviation for the distribution of means based on the research hypothesis. (This is necessary since the normal curve table uses Z scores.)
2. Using the normal curve table, find the percentage of cases more extreme than this Z score.
3. State your percentage and mark it on the graph.

IV. **Indicate whether this level of power would be sufficient to conduct the study or whether modifications should be made to increase power. (Use 80% as a benchmark.)**

Chapter Self-Tests

Multiple-Choice Questions

1. Statistical power can be defined as

a. the effect that the result of the study will have on the area of applied psychology.
b. the probability of rejecting the null hypothesis if in fact the null hypothesis is true.
c. having a large enough effect size in order to always get a significant result.
d. the probability that the study will yield a significant result if the research hypothesis is true.

2. You can calculate power by

a. comparing the population distribution to a distribution made up of samples drawn from the rejection region in the predicted direction.
b. determining the probability of a Type I error and subtracting it from 1.
c. creating a hypothetical comparison distribution which would be false if the null hypothesis were true and plotting the sample mean on this distribution.
d. calculating the area of the distribution expected under the research hypothesis that corresponds to the rejection region on the distribution expected under the null hypothesis.

3. In real-life research today, when psychology researchers determine power they usually use

a. a standard computer program.
b. a computational formula.
c. a power table.
d. the computational procedure described in this chapter.

4. If in a planned experiment the population distribution expected under the research hypothesis and the known population have almost no overlap at all, the planned experiment has

a. a large effect size.
b. a moderate effect size.
c. a small effect size.
d. no statistical importance.

5. How does the number of participants affect power?

    a. By allowing the experimenter to remove results that are not extreme and so to significantly decrease variance.
    b. By reducing the amount of variance in each of the distributions of means, and thereby further separating these two distributions.
    c. By adding the effect of extreme scores to the population variance.
    d. By limiting the difference between the sample and population means.

6. When the standard deviation of the population of individual cases is low, this makes power

    a. low.
    b. high.
    c. irrelevant–the chances of getting a significant result are almost nil.
    d. none of the above–the standard deviation of the population of individual cases has nothing to do with power.

7. Two similar studies each investigated the effectiveness of a different job training program. If you wanted to compare the effectiveness of the two programs based on the results of these studies, it would be best to compare their

    a. power.
    b. effect size.
    c. significance levels.
    d. Z scores on the comparison distribution.

8. What effect does using a .05 level of significance instead of a .01 level have on power?

    a. It increases power.
    b. It decreases power.
    c. It has no effect on power.
    d. It increases power if a one-tailed test is used but has no effect on power if a two-tailed test is used.

9. Consider the relationship of power to a nonsignificant result. If the power of the experiment was high,

    a. a nonsignificant result does not give us any indication regarding the research hypothesis.
    b. the researcher has probably spent a great deal of effort in altering the effect size.
    c. it is likely that there is only a small effect size, if any.
    d. it is likely that there was an error in calculating power.

10. Research designed to test an abstract theory is MORE likely than applied research to rely exclusively on

    a. effect size.
    b. statistical significance.
    c. the minimum meaningful difference.
    d. Cohen's kappa for estimating effect size.

11. When the study does not give significant results, even though the research hypothesis is true, a _____ error occurs.
    a. Type I
    b. Type II
    c. rejection
    d. calculation

Fill-In Questions

12. d is a symbol for _____.

13. If the predicted mean of the known population is 9, the hypothesized mean for the population exposed to the experimental manipulation is 15, and the standard deviation of the population of individual cases is 12, according to Cohen's conventions, this is a _____ effect size.

14. _____ is a procedure used to combine results of studies reported in many separate research studies.

15. _____ is the probability of rejecting the null hypothesis when in fact it is true.

16. _____ is the probability of failing to reject the null hypothesis when in fact it is false.

17. In a particular planned study, the cutoff Z score for significance has a raw score of 16 on the comparison distribution (that is, scores of 16 or higher would be sufficient to reject the null hypothesis). The distribution of means for Population 1 is predicted by the researcher to have a mean of 19 and a standard deviation of 3. What is the power of this study? (Use the normal curve approximation rules.) _____

18. In another planned study, the cutoff Z score for significance has a raw score of 138 on the comparison distribution. The distribution of means for Population 1 is predicted by the researcher to have a mean of 152 and a standard deviation of 7. What is the power of this study? (Use the normal curve approximation rules.) _____

19. To determine the power of a planned study of a new procedure for increasing typing speed, a researcher uses the _____, figuring that unless the procedure being studied increases average typing speed by at least 10 words per minute, it is not worth using.

20. Using more accurate measurement in a study increases power by its direct effect in reducing _____.

21. Increasing the number of participants in a study increases power by reducing _____.

Problems and Essays

22. A consumer psychologist is planning a study of children's buying habits of candy. At a particular summer camp where this psychologist has previously done research, it is known that the amount spent on candy at the camp store by the children during a one-week period is roughly normally distributed with a mean of $3.80 and a standard deviation of $1.50. (The camp store is the only source of candy anywhere near the camp and records of all purchases are automatically kept because children have an account at the store that they use rather than actually carrying money.) In this study 25 randomly selected children at the camp will be given a special lecture on the effects of candy on teeth and general health. Then how much candy they buy at the camp store during the following week will be analyzed from the store records. The researchers are realistic and expect that such a lecture will have, at best, only a modest effect. But unless the effect is at least an average reduction of $.25, such lectures would be considered ineffective.

    a. Assuming the researcher will use the .05 significance level, what is the power of this study?

    b. Explain your answer to a person who has never had a course in statistics.

    c. What is the predicted effect size?

    d. Describe four things the researchers could do to try to increase the power of the study and say why each might work.

23. A psychologist is interested in whether memory is affected by sadness. On the particular memory task the researcher is planning to use, it is known that scores of college students are approximately normally distributed with a mean of 68 and a standard deviation of 12. In this study the researcher plans to test a group of 30 students after they have just viewed a very sad movie. Based on a theory that people will concentrate on the memory task in order not to think about the sad movie, the researcher predicts that this group will score about 6 points higher than the usual participants (that is, that they will score about 74 on the average).

    a. Assuming the researcher will use the .01 significance level, what is the power of this study?

    b. Explain your answer to a person who has never had a course in statistics.

    c. What is the predicted effect size?

    d. Describe four things the researchers could do to try to increase the power of the study and say why each might work.

24. A study is reported in which baseball players are compared to the general public on how much they like chewing gum. The result was that the null hypothesis was not rejected; no significant difference was found. In this study 500 baseball players were tested, and in general the power was very high. What should you conclude from all this about whether baseball players like chewing gum more than people in general? Why?

25. A study reports that a particular kind of training workshop reduces burnout among school counselors. This was a large study, involving thousands of school counselors, and the study employed very accurate measures and generally had very high power. The result was that the null hypothesis was rejected at the .05 level of significance (one-tailed). What should you conclude from all this about the impact of the workshop? Why?

26. Identify the four possible outcomes of a research study.

Note. There is no section on using SPSS with this chapter because, in general, it is figured from tables. However, SPSS can be used to figure power.

Chapter 9
Introduction to the *t* Tests

Learning Objectives

To understand, including being able to carry out any necessary procedures or computations:
- ■ Estimated population variance based on scores in the sample.
- ■ The *t* test for a single sample and a known population mean.
- ■ Purpose of the *t* distribution and how it is different from a normal curve.
- ■ The *t* table.
- ■ The *t* test for dependent means.
- ■ The normal-population-distribution assumption for the *t* test for dependent means and the conditions in which it is safe and not safe to violate it.
- ■ Effect size for a study using a *t* test for dependent means, including whether it is a small, medium, or large effect, based on Cohen's conventions.
- ■ Power table for the *t* test for dependent means.
- ■ Number-of-participants table for the *t* test for dependent means.
- ■ Limitations of a pretest-posttest design.
- ■ *t* tests for dependent means as reported in psychology research articles.

Chapter Outline

I. The *t* Test for a Single Sample

A. Hypothesis testing with a single sample and a population for which the mean is known but not the variance works the same way as you learned in Chapter 7, except that you estimate the population variance (for Step 2) and you use a different table to determine the cutoff point (Step 3).

B. Estimating population variance from the sample information.
1. Since a sample represents its population, its variance is representative of the population's variance.
2. However, the variance of a random sample, on the average, will be slightly smaller than the variance of the population from which that sample is taken. (That is, the sample's variance is a *biased* estimator of the population's variance.)
3. To figure an *unbiased* estimate of the population variance, divide the sum of squared deviations in the sample by the number of scores in the sample minus one.
4. The formula is $S^2 = \Sigma(X-M)^2/(N-1) = SS/(N-1)$.
5. The number you divide by in computing the estimated population variance (N-1) is the degrees of freedom. Thus $S^2 = SS/df$.
6. Once you know S^2, you figure the standard deviation of the comparison distribution in the usual way, except for using S^2 instead of σ. That is $S_M^2 = S^2/N$; $S_M = \sqrt{S_M^2}$.

C. Shape of the comparison distribution when using an estimated population variance: The *t* distribution.
1. When carrying out the hypothesis testing process using an estimated population variance, here is less true information and more room for error.

128

2. Thus, extreme scores are more likely to occur in the distribution of means than would be found in a normal curve. (And the smaller the N, the more likely.)
3. The appropriate comparison distribution follows instead a mathematically defined curve called a t distribution.
4. t distributions differ according to the degrees of freedom when figuring S^2.
5. The more degrees of freedom on which the t distribution is based, the closer it is to a normal curve.

D. Determining the cutoff sample score for rejecting the null hypothesis: Using the t table.
1. Appendix A of this book (and most statistics books) gives a simplified table of t distributions which includes only the crucial cutoff scores.
2. To use the t table you need to know the degrees of freedom, the significance level, and whether it is a one- or two-tailed test.

E. Determining the Score of Your Sample Mean on the Comparison Distribution: The t Score.
1. Step 4 of the hypothesis testing process, determining the score of your sample's mean on the comparison distribution, is done exactly the same way with a t test.
2. However, the resulting score is called a t score instead of a Z score.
3. Thus, $t = (M - \mu)/S_M$.

II. The t Test for Dependent Means
A. A more common situation for a t test involves studies in which there are two scores for each of several participants--often a before and after score or when each participant is tested under two different circumstances.
1. These are called repeated-measures or within-subjects designs.
2. The hypothesis testing procedure is called a t test for dependent means.

B. A t test for dependent means is conducted in exactly the same way as the t test for a single sample (above), except you use difference scores and you assume the population mean (of difference scores) is zero.

C. Difference scores:
1. A difference score is figured by subtracting, for each participant, one score from the other (for example, the before score from the after score).
2. Using difference score converts two sets of scores into one.
3. Once the difference score has been figured for each participant, the entire hypothesis testing procedure is carried out using difference scores.

D. The population of difference scores (Population 2, the one to which the population represented by your sample will be compared) is ordinarily assumed to have a mean of zero. (This makes sense because we are comparing our sample's population to one in which there is, on the average, no difference.)

III. Assumptions of the t Test
A. The comparison distribution will be a t distribution only if the population of individual cases (or difference scores, if conducting a t test for dependent means) from which we drew our sample follows a normal curve.
B. Otherwise the appropriate comparison distribution will follow some unknown, other shape.
C. Thus, a normal population distribution is an *assumption* of the t test.
D. Unfortunately, it is rarely possible to tell whether the population is normal based on the information in your sample.

E. Fortunately, results are reasonably accurate when the population distribution is fairly far from normal. (The t test is said to be *robust* over moderate violations of the assumption of a normal population distribution.)

F. Thus, psychologists use the t test so long as neither of the following is the case:
  1. There is reason to expect a very large discrepancy from normal.
  2. The population is highly skewed and a one-tailed test is being used.

IV. Effect Size and Power for the t Test for Dependent Means

A. Effect size:
  1. Effect size for the t test for dependent means is figured in the same way as we did in Chapter 8: $d = (\mu_1 - \mu_2)/\sigma$.
  2. Since the mean of Population 2 is ordinarily assumed to be zero and the standard deviation (σ) is of the populations of difference scores, the formula reduces to $d = \mu_1/\sigma$, with both terms relating to difference scores.
  3. Note: To figure effect size you divide by σ (or its estimate S), and not by σ_M (or S_M).
  4. Cohen's rules of thumb for effect sizes are the same as for the situation in Chapter 8: A small effect size is .20, a medium effect size is .50, and a large effect size is .80.

B. Power:
  1. The text provides a table (Table 9.9) that gives the approximate power for the .05 significance level for small, medium, and large effect sizes and one- or two-tailed tests.
  2. This power table is especially useful when interpreting the practical importance of a nonsignificant result in a published study.

C. Planning sample size: The text provides a table (Table 9.10) that gives the approximate number of participants needed to achieve 80% power for estimated small, medium, and large effect sizes using one- and two-tailed tests for the .05 significance levels. (Eighty percent is a common figure used by researchers for the minimum power needed to make it worth conducting a study.)

D. Studies using difference scores often have considerably larger effect sizes for a given amount of expected difference than other kinds of research designs.

V. Controversies

A. The main controversies about the t test have to do with its relative advantages and disadvantages in comparison to various alternatives. These alternatives are discussed in Chapter 15.

B. Research designs in which the same participants are tested before and after some experimental intervention, without any kind of control group that does not undergo the same procedure, is a weak research design. (Even if such a study produces a significant difference, it leaves many alternative explanations for why that difference occurred.)

VI. How t Tests for Dependent Means Are Described in Research Articles

A. Research articles may describe t tests in the text following a standard format. For example: $t(24) = 2.8, p < .05$.

B. Alternatively, they may present the means of the different groups on a table, often using stars to indicate the level of significance for each comparison.

Formulas

I. Unbiased estimate of the population variance (S^2) for a t test for a single sample or a t test for dependent means

Formula in words: Estimated population variance is the sum of deviations of the scores in the sample from the sample's mean, divided by the degrees of freedom (the number of cases in the sample minus one).

Formula in symbols: $S^2 = \Sigma(X-M)^2/(N-1) = SS/N-1 = SS/df$

$\Sigma(X-M)^2$ or SS is the sum of squared deviations from the mean of the sample.

N is the number of scores in the sample (or number of pairs of scores).

df is the degrees of freedom.

II. Degrees of freedom (df) for a t test for a single sample or a t test for dependent means

Formula in words: Degrees of freedom are the number of difference scores minus one.

Formula in symbols: $df=N-1$

III. Estimated population standard deviation (S)

Formula in words: Estimated population standard deviation is the square root of the estimated population variance.

Formula in symbols: $S = \sqrt{S^2}$

IV. Variance of the distribution of means based on an estimated population variance (S^2_M)

Formula in words: Variance of the distribution of means based on an estimated population variance is the estimated population variance divided by the number of scores (or difference scores) in the sample.

Formula in symbols: $S^2_M = S^2/N$

S^2 is the variance of the population of individual scores (or of difference scores in a t test for dependent means).

N is the number of scores (or difference scores) in the sample.

V. Standard deviation of the distribution of means based on an estimated population variance (S_M)

Formula in words: Standard deviation of the distribution of means based on an estimated population variance is the square root of the variance of the distribution of means based on an estimated population variance.

Formula in symbols: $S_M = \sqrt{S_M^2}$.

VI. *t* score for a *t* test for a single sample or a *t* test for dependent means

Formula in words: *t* score is the difference between the mean of the sample and the known population mean, divided by the standard deviation of the distribution of means based on an estimated population variance.

Formula in symbols: $t = (M - \mu)/S_M$

M is the mean of the sample of scores (or the mean of the sample of difference scores).

μ is the mean of the population to which the sample's population is being compared (Population 2). In the case of a *t* test for dependent means, μ is usually assumed to be 0.

VII. Effect size (*d*) for *t* test for a single sample or for a *t* test for dependent means

Formula in words: A standard measure of effect size (*t*) is the difference between the hypothesized and known population means, divided by the population standard deviation.

Formula in symbols: $d = (\mu_1 - \mu_2) / \sigma$.

μ_1 is the hypothesized (or, if the study is completed, actual) mean of the population which the sample represents. (In a *t* test for dependent means, μ_1 is a mean of difference scores.)

μ_2 is the known mean of the population of scores (or difference scores) to which the sample's population is to be compared. (In a *t* test for dependent means, μ_2 is usually considered to be 0.)

σ is the standard deviation of the scores (or difference scores) in the population. It may be estimated as S.

VIII. Alternative, simplified formula for effect size (*d*) for a *t* test for dependent means when μ_2 is considered to be 0

Formula in words: A standard measure of effect size (*t*) for the *t* test for dependent means can be figured by taking the hypothesized population mean difference score, divided by the standard deviation of the population of difference scores.

Formula in symbols: $d = \mu_1 / \sigma$

How to Conduct a *t* Test for a Single Sample
(Based on Table 9.4 in the Text)

1. Restate the question into a null and a research hypothesis about populations.
2. Determine the characteristics of the comparison distribution:
   A. The mean is the same as the known population mean.
   B. The standard deviation is figured as follows:
     1. Figure estimated population variance: $S^2 = SS/df$
     2. Figure variance of the distribution of means: $S_M^2 = S^2/N$.
     3. Figure standard deviation: $S_M = \sqrt{S_M^2}$.
   C. Shape will be a *t* distribution with *N*-1 degrees of freedom.

3. **Determine the cutoff sample score on the comparison distribution at which the null hypothesis should be rejected.**
    A. Determine the degrees of freedom, desired significance level, and whether to use a one-tailed or two-tailed test.
    B. Look up the appropriate cutoff on a t table.
4. **Determine the score of your sample's mean on the comparison distribution:** $t = (M-\mu)/S_M$.
5. **Compare the scores in 3 and 4 to decide whether or not to reject the null hypothesis.**

How to Conduct a t Test for Dependent Means
(Based on Table 9.7 in the Text)

1. **Restate the question into a null and a research hypothesis about populations.**
2. **Determine the characteristics of the comparison distribution:**
    A. Convert each participant's two scores into difference scores. Carry out the remaining steps using these difference scores.
    B. Figure the mean of the difference scores.
    C. Assume the population mean is zero--$\mu=0$.
    D. Figure the estimated population variance of difference scores: $S^2 = SS/df$.
    E. Figure the variance of the distribution of means of difference scores: $S_M^2 = S^2/N$.
    F. Figure the standard deviation of the distribution of means of difference scores:
    $$S_M = \sqrt{S_M^2}.$$
    G. Note that it will be a t distribution with $df = N-1$.
3. **Determine the cutoff sample score on the comparison distribution at which the null hypothesis should be rejected.**
    A. Determine desired significance level and whether to use a one-tailed or two-tailed test.
    B. Look up the appropriate cutoff on a t table.
4. **Determine the score of your sample on the comparison distribution:**
    $t = (M-\mu)/S_M$.
5. **Compare the scores in 3 and 4 to decide whether or not to reject the null hypothesis.**

Outlines for Writing Essays

The reason for your writing essay questions in the practice problems and tests is that this task develops and then demonstrates what matters so very much--your comprehension of the logic behind the computations. (It is also a place where those better at words than numbers can shine, and for those better at numbers to develop their skills at explaining in words.)

Thus, to do well, be sure to do the following in each essay: (a) give the reasoning behind each step; (b) relate each step to the specifics of the content of the particular study you are analyzing; (c) state the various formulas in nontechnical language, because as you define each term you show you understand it (although once you have defined it in nontechnical language, you can use it from then on in the essay); (d) look back and be absolutely certain that you made it clear just *why* that formula or procedure was applied and *why* it is the way it is.

The outlines below are *examples* of ways to structure your essays. There are other completely correct ways to go about it. And this is an *outline* for an answer--you are to write the answer out in paragraph form. Examples of full essays are in the answers to Set I Practice Problems in the back of the text.

These essays are necessarily very long for you to write (and for others to grade). But this is the very best way to be sure you understand everything thoroughly. One shortcut you may see on a test is that you may be asked to write your answer for someone who understands statistics up to the point of the new material you are studying. You can choose to take the same shortcut in these practice problems (maybe writing for someone who understands right up to whatever point you yourself start being just a little unclear). But every time you write for a person who has never had statistics at all, you review the logic behind the entire course. You engrain it in your mind. Over and over. The time is never wasted.   It is an excellent way to study.

t Test for a Single Sample (in which each participant is measured once)

I. Restate the question into a research hypothesis and a null hypothesis about populations. (Step 1 of hypothesis testing.)

A. State in ordinary language the hypothesis testing issue: Does the average of the scores of the group of persons studied represent a higher (or lower or different) mean than would be expected if this group of persons had just been a randomly selected example of people in general--that is, does this set of people studied represent a different group of people from people in general?

B. Explain language (to make the rest of essay easier to write by not having to repeat long explanations), focusing on the meaning of each term in the concrete example of the study at hand.

    1. Populations.

    2. Sample.

    3. Mean.

    4. Research hypothesis.

    5. Null hypothesis.

    6. Rejecting the null hypothesis to provide support for the research hypothesis.

II. Determine the characteristics of the comparison distribution. (Step 2 of hypothesis testing.)

    A. Explain the principle that the comparison distribution is the distribution (pattern of spread of the means of scores) that represents what we would expect if the null hypothesis were true and our particular mean were just randomly sampled from this population of means.

    B. Note that because we are interested in the mean of a sample of more than one case, we have to compare our actual mean to a distribution not of individual cases but of means.

    C. Give an intuitive understanding of how one might construct a distribution of means for samples of a given size from a particular population.
        1. Select a random sample of the given size (number of participants) from the population and figure its mean.
        2. Select another random sample of this size from the population and figure its mean.
        3. Repeat this process a very large number of times.
        4. Make a distribution of these means.
        5. Note that this procedure is only to explain the idea and would be too much work and unnecessary in practice.

    D. There is an exact mathematical relation of a distribution of means to the population the means are drawn from, so that in practice the characteristics of the distribution of means can be determined directly from knowledge of the characteristics of the population and the size of the samples involved.

    E. The mean of a distribution of means.
        1. It is the same as the mean (average) of the scores in the known population of individual cases.
        2. State what it is in the particular problem you are working on.
        3. Explanation.
           a. Each sample is based on randomly selected values from the population.
           b. Thus, sometimes the mean of a sample will be higher and sometimes lower than the mean of the whole population of individuals.
           c. There is no reason for these to average out higher or lower than the original population mean.
           d. Thus the average of these means (the mean of the distribution of means) should in the long run equal the population mean.

    F. The standard deviation of a distribution of means.
        1. The spread of a distribution of means will be less spread out than the population of individual cases from which the samples are taken.
           a. Any one score, even an extreme score, has some chance of being selected in a random sample.
           b. However, the chance is less of several extreme scores being selected in the same random sample, particularly since in order to create an extreme sample mean they would have to be scores which were extreme in the same direction.
           c. Thus, there is a moderating effect of numbers. In any one sample, the deviants tend to be balanced out by middle cases or by deviants in the opposite direction, making each sample tend towards the middle and away from extreme values.
           d. With fewer extreme values for the means, the variation among the means is less.
        2. The more cases in each sample, the less spread out is the distribution of means of that sample size: With a larger number of cases in each sample, it is even harder for extreme cases in that sample not to be balanced out by middle cases or extremes in the other direction in the same sample.

3. Explain the idea of standard deviation.
   a. It is a standard measure of how spread out a distribution is.
   b. Roughly, it is the average amount scores vary from the mean.
   c. Exactly speaking, it is the square root of the average of the squares of the amount that each score differs from the mean.
4. The standard deviation of the distribution of means is found by a formula that divides the average of squared deviations from the mean of the population by the number of participants in the sample (thus making it smaller in proportion to the number of participants in the sample), and taking the square root of this result.
5. Computing this standard deviation requires knowing the variation in the population, and this is not known. But it can be estimated.
   a. Whatever the distribution your particular scores come from, it is reasonable to assume that the variation among your particular group is representative of the variation in that larger distribution of scores.
   b. A sample's variation is on the average slightly less than the population it comes from because it is less likely to include scores that are far from its mean.
   c. Thus, a special adjustment is made that exactly corrects for this: Instead of taking the average of the squared deviations--the sum of squared deviations divided by the number of participants--one instead divides the sum of squared deviations by one less than the number of participants in the sample.
6. Describe the steps of computing the estimated population variance and the standard deviation of the distribution of means for your example, stating the final result.

G. The shape of the distribution of means.
   1. The distribution tends to be bell shaped, with most cases falling near the middle and fewer at the extremes, due to the same basic process of extremes balancing each other out that we noted in the discussion of the standard deviation--middle values are more likely and extreme values less likely.
   2. Specifically, it can be shown that it will follow a precise shape called a *t* distribution.
   3. Actually there are different *t* distributions according to the amount of information that goes into estimating the variation in the distribution from the sample, the number you divide by in making the estimate (the number of participants minus one).
   4. Also, the shape of the comparison distribution is only a precise *t* distribution if the population of individual scores follows a precise shape called a normal curve (also bell shaped) that is widely found in nature. Note that in the problem you are told that the distribution of the population is a normal curve so that this condition is met in your case.

III. Determine the cutoff sample score on the comparison distribution at which the null hypothesis should be rejected. (Step 3 of hypothesis testing.)

A. Before you figure out how extreme your particular sample's mean is on this distribution of means, you want to know how extreme it would have to be to decide it was too unlikely that it could have been a randomly drawn mean from this comparison distribution of means.

B. Since the shape of the comparison distribution follows a mathematically defined formula, you can use a table to tell you how many standard deviations from the mean your score would have to be to be in the top so many percent.

C. Note that the number of standard deviations from the mean on this *t* distribution is called a *t* score. (Explaining this term makes writing simpler later on.)

D. To use these tables, you have to decide the kind of situation you have; there are two considerations.
   1. Are you interested in the chances of getting this extreme of a mean, one that is extreme in only one direction (such as only higher than for people in general) or in both? (Explain which is appropriate for your study.)

136

2. Just how unlikely would the extremeness of a particular mean have to be? The standard figure used in psychology is less likely than 5% (though 1% is sometimes used to be especially safe). (Say which you are using in your study--if no figure is stated in the problem and no special reason given for using one or the other, the general rule is to use 5%.)

    E. State the cutoff for your particular problem.

IV. Determine the score of your sample on the comparison distribution. (Step 4 of hypothesis testing.)

    A. The next step is to find where your actual sample's mean would fall on the comparison distribution, in terms of a t score.

    B. State this t score.

V. Compare the scores in 3 and 4 to decide whether or not to reject the null hypothesis. (Step 5 of hypothesis testing.)

    A. State whether your mean (from Step 4) does or does not exceed the cutoff (from Step 3).

    B. If your mean exceeds the cutoff.
       1. State that you can reject the null hypothesis.
       2. State that by elimination, the research hypothesis is thus supported.
       3. State in words what it means that the research hypothesis is supported (that is, the study shows that the particular experimental manipulation appears to make a difference in the particular thing being measured).

    C. If your score does not exceed the cutoff.
       1. State that you can not reject the null hypothesis.
       2. State that the experiment is inconclusive.
       3. State in words what it means that the study is inconclusive (that is, the study did not yield results which give a clear indication of whether or not the particular experimental manipulation appears to make a difference in the particular variable being measured).
       4. Explicitly note that even though the research hypothesis was not supported in this study, this is not evidence that it is false--it is quite possible that it is true but it has only a small effect which was not sufficient to produce a mean extreme enough to yield a significant result in this study.

t Test for dependent means (two scores for each participant)

I. Restate the question into a research hypothesis and a null hypothesis about populations. (Step 1 of hypothesis testing.)

    A. Note that the entire problem involves difference (or change) scores.

    B. State in ordinary language the hypothesis testing issue: Does the average of the difference scores of the group of persons studied represent a higher (or lower or different) mean amount of difference than would be expected if this group of persons had just been a randomly selected sample of people in general in whom there is no difference?

C. Explain language (to make rest of essay easier to write by not having to repeat long explanations), focusing on the meaning of each term in the concrete example of the study at hand.
    1. Populations.
    2. Sample.
    3. Mean.
    4. Research hypothesis.
    5. Null hypothesis.
    6. Rejecting the null hypothesis to provide support for the research hypothesis.

II. Determine the characteristics of the comparison distribution. (Step 2 of hypothesis testing.)

A. Explain the principle that the comparison distribution is the distribution (pattern of spread of the means of difference scores) that represents what we would expect if the null hypothesis were true and our particular mean were just randomly sampled from this population of means of difference scores.

B. Note that because we are interested in the mean of a sample of more than one case, we have to compare our actual mean to a distribution not of individual cases but of means.

C. Give an intuitive understanding of how one might construct a distribution of means for samples of a given size from a particular population.
    1. Select a random sample of the given size (number of participants) from the population and figure its mean.
    2. Select another random sample of this size from the population and figure its mean.
    3. Repeat this process a very large number of times.
    4. Make a distribution of these means.
    5. Note that this procedure is only to explain the idea and would be too much work and unnecessary in practice.

D. There is an exact mathematical relation of a distribution of means to the population the means are drawn from, so that in practice the characteristics of the distribution of means can be determined directly from knowledge of the characteristics of the population and the size of the samples involved.

E. The mean of a distribution of means.
    1. It is the same as the mean (average) of the scores in the known population of individual cases--which is presumed to have a mean of zero because it represents a population in which there is on the average no difference, and no difference means zero difference.
    2. Explain why the mean of the distribution of means is the same as the mean of the population of individual cases.
      a. Each sample is based on randomly selected values from the population.
      b. Thus, sometimes the mean of a sample will be higher and sometimes lower than the mean of the whole population of individuals.
      c. There is no reason for these to average out higher or lower than the original population mean.
      d. Thus the average of these means (the mean of the distribution of means) should in the long run equal the population mean (which is zero).

F. The standard deviation of a distribution of means.
    1. The spread of a distribution of means will be less spread out than the population of individual cases from which the samples are taken.
      a. Any one difference score, even an extreme score, has some chance of being selected in a random sample.

138

b. However, the chance is less of several extreme difference scores being selected in the same random sample, particularly since in order to create an extreme sample mean they would have to be difference scores which were extreme in the same direction.

c. Thus, there is a moderating effect of numbers. In any one sample, the deviants tend to be balanced out by middle cases or by deviants in the opposite direction, making each sample tend towards the middle and away from extreme values.

d. With fewer extreme values for the means, the variation among the means is less.

2. The more cases in each sample, the less spread out is the distribution of means of that sample size: With a larger number of cases in each sample, it is even harder for extreme cases in that sample not to be balanced out by middle cases or extremes in the other direction in the same sample.

3. Explain the idea of standard deviation.

a. It is a standard measure of how spread out a distribution is.

b. Roughly, it is the average amount difference scores vary from the mean.

c. Exactly speaking, it is the square root of the average of the squares of the amount that each difference score differs from the mean of the difference scores.

4. The standard deviation of the distribution of means is found by a formula that divides the average of squared deviations from the mean of the population by the number of participants in the sample (thus making it smaller in proportion to the number of participants in the sample) and taking the square root of this result.

5. Computing this standard deviation requires knowing the amount of variation in the population, and this is not known. But it can be estimated.

a. Whatever the distribution your particular difference scores come from, it is reasonable to assume that the variation among your particular group is representative of the variation in the larger distribution of difference scores.

b. A sample's variation is on the average slightly less than the population it comes from because it is less likely to include difference scores that are far from its mean.

c. Thus, a special adjustment is made that exactly corrects for this: Instead of taking the average of the squared deviations--the sum of squared deviations divided by the number of participants--one instead divides the sum of squared deviations by one less than the number of participants in the sample.

6. Describe the steps of computing the estimated population variance and the standard deviation of the distribution of means for your example, stating the final result.

G. The shape of the distribution of means.

1. The distribution tends to be bell-shaped, with most cases falling near the middle and fewer at the extremes, due to the same basic process of extremes balancing each other out that we noted in the discussion of the standard deviation--middle values are more likely and extreme values less likely.

2. Specifically, it can be shown that it will follow a precise shape called a *t* distribution.

3. Actually there are different *t* distributions according to the amount of information that goes into estimating the variation in the distribution from the sample, the number you divide by in making the estimate (the number of participants minus one).

4. Also, the shape of the comparison distribution is only a precise *t* distribution if the population of individual difference scores follows a precise shape called a normal curve (also bell-shaped) that is widely found in nature. Note that in the problem you are told that the distribution of the population is a normal curve so that this condition is met in your case.

III. Determine the cutoff sample score on the comparison distribution at which the null hypothesis should be rejected. (Step 3 of hypothesis testing.)

A. Before you figure out how extreme your particular sample's mean difference score is on this distribution of means of difference scores, you want to know how extreme it would have to be to decide it was too unlikely that it could have been a randomly drawn mean from this comparison distribution of means.

B. Since the shape of the comparison distribution follows a mathematically defined formula, you can use a table to tell you how many standard deviations from its mean (of zero) your difference score would have to be in order to be in the top so many percent.

C. Note that the number of standard deviations from the mean on this t distribution is called a t score. (Explaining this term makes writing simpler later on.)

D. To use these tables you have to decide the kind of situation you have; there are two considerations.

    1. Are you interested in the chances of getting this extreme a mean that is extreme in only one direction (such as only higher than for people in general) or in both? (Explain which is appropriate for your study.)

    2. Just how unlikely would the extremeness of a particular mean have to be? The standard figure used in psychology is less likely than 5% (though 1% is sometimes used to be especially safe). (Say which you are using in your study--if no figure is stated in the problem and no special reason given for using one or the other, the general rule is to use 5%.)

E. State the cutoff for your particular problem.

IV. **Determine the score of your sample on the comparison distribution. (Step 4 of hypothesis testing.)**

A. The next step is to find where your actual sample's mean difference score would fall on the comparison distribution, in terms of a t score.

B. State this t score.

V. **Compare the scores in 3 and 4 to decide whether or not to reject the null hypothesis. (Step 5 of hypothesis testing.)**

A. State whether your mean (from Step 4) does or does not exceed the cutoff (from Step 3).

B. If your mean exceeds the cutoff.

    1. State that you can reject the null hypothesis.

    2. State that, by elimination, the research hypothesis is thus supported.

    3. State in words what it means that the research hypothesis is supported (that is, the study shows that the particular experimental manipulation appears to make a difference in the particular thing being measured).

C. If your score does not exceed the cutoff.

    1. State that you can not reject the null hypothesis.

    2. State that the experiment is inconclusive.

    3. State in words what it means that the study is inconclusive (that is, the study did not yield results which give a clear indication of whether or not the particular experimental manipulation appears to make a difference in the particular thing being measured).

    4. Explicitly note that even though the research hypothesis was not supported in this study, this is not evidence that it is false--it is quite possible that it is true but it has only a small effect which was not sufficient to produce a mean extreme enough to yield a significant result in this study.

Chapter Self-Tests

Multiple-Choice Questions

1. In the formula $SS/N-1$, "$N-1$" is known as

   a. the transformation coefficient.
   b. the transformed denominator.
   c. the degrees of freedom.
   d. the denominator transformation term (DTT).

2. When estimating the variance of a population from the sample, you divide by the sample size minus one, because using the sample size directly

   a. does not correct for squaring the deviations.
   b. underestimates the population variance.
   c. fails to take into account the sample size.
   d. creates too little "bias."

3. When testing the null hypothesis for a study with a single sample with 10 scores and an unknown population variance, the cutoff score on the comparison distribution will be ___ the cutoff on a normal curve.

   a. more extreme than
   b. the same as
   c. less extreme than
   d. either more or less extreme than or the same as (depending on the population variance)

4. In a study of memory, an experimenter found that 10 participants who used imagery to learn a list of 20 words remembered on average 18.4 words. If the sum of squared deviations from the sample's mean is 6, what is the estimated population variance?

   a. $1.6/18.4 = 0.09$.
   b. $6/9 = 0.67$.
   c. $18.4/10 = 1.84$.
   d. There are not enough data to estimate the population variance.

5. If a study yields a t score of 2.46, and the cutoff t score was 2.36, should you reject the null hypothesis? Why or why not?

   a. Yes, because the figured t score is more extreme than the cutoff score.
   b. No, because the figured t score is more extreme than the cutoff score.
   c. No, because the figured t score is too close to the cutoff t score to be significant.
   d. This can not be determined without knowing the degrees of freedom.

6. A group of students take the SAT, then take an SAT prep class, then take the SAT again. To test the null hypothesis that there is no difference in students' SAT scores from before to after taking the prep class, which population mean would be used?

   a. Zero.
   b. The original (before) SAT score of the test group.
   c. The second (after) SAT score of the test group.
   d. The national mean SAT score.

7. A counselor claims that after attending three sessions with her, clients score higher on a Satisfaction With Life scale than they do before counseling. Her null hypothesis is that there is no difference in clients' scores after counseling. If the cutoff t score is 2.0 and the standard deviation of the comparison distribution is 1.5, by how many points do clients' scores have to change in order to justify rejecting the null hypothesis?

   a. 1.5.
   b. 2.0.
   c. 2.5.
   d. 3.0.

8. Which of the following is an assumption you must make before you can use the t test?

   a. The sample is normally distributed.
   b. The sample is skewed.
   c. The population is normally distributed.
   d. The population is skewed.

9. Suppose you are doing research on the general intelligence of people with eidetic memory (that is, people who have exact visual memory), and participants are so hard to come by that you are limited to 10 participants. If in fact there is a medium effect size in the population, and you are testing your hypothesis with a t test for dependent means, two-tailed, at the .05 level, what is the power of this study? Refer to Table 9.9 in the text for your answer.

   a. .09.
   b. .15.
   c. .32.
   d. .46.

10 A research article reports results of a study using a t test for dependent means as "$t(16) = 2.67, p < .05$." This means

   a. the result is not significant.
   b. there were 16 participants.
   c. the t score was 16.
   d. the t score was 2.67.

Fill-In Questions

11. When estimating the population variance from the sample variance, the amount of information in the sample that is free to vary is called the _____.

12. When conducting a t test for a single sample, in the formula $(M - \mu)/S_M$, μ is the _____.

13. When figuring the variance of the distribution of means in a *t* test problem, you divide the estimated population variance by _____.

14. If an assumption which is necessary to conduct a statistical analysis can be violated without seriously jeopardizing the results of the analysis, the test is said to be _____ over that assumption.

15. With a *t* test for dependent means, an effect size of _____ is considered to be large.

16. Studies using difference scores often have _____ effect sizes than other types of studies.

17. A research design in which participants are tested and then re-tested is weak unless the group studied is compared to a(n) _____.

18. A *t* distribution differs from a normal distribution in that there the tails contain a proportion of the cases.

19. To find the score at which the null hypothesis will be rejected, you look on a table of *t* distributions. But first you need to know whether it is a one- or two-tailed test, the degrees of freedom in the sample, and the _____.

20 With sample sizes of 30 or more, a *t* distribution becomes almost indistinguishable from a(n) _____.

Problems and Essays

21. A psychologist is interested in whether people who live in noisy parts of a city have worse hearing. To test this, she administers hearing tests to six randomly selected healthy eighteen year olds who have grown up in one of the noisiest parts of the city. Their scores on the hearing test are 16, 14, 18, 18, 20, and 16. This test was designed so that healthy 18 year olds should score 20. (The variance is not known.)
    a. What should the psychologist conclude? Solve this problem explicitly using all five steps of hypothesis testing and illustrate your answer with a sketch showing the comparison distribution, the cutoff (or cutoffs), and the score of the sample on this distribution.
    b. Explain your computations and the logic of what you have done to a person who has never had a course in statistics.

22. A social psychologist was interested in the effect of positive feedback on self-esteem. She gave 6 participants positive feedback about an essay they wrote, and then measured self-esteem. The average self-esteem measure of students at that college is 7, and the variance is unknown. The students in this (fictional) study scored as follows: 9, 8, 5, 5, 2, 8.
    a. What should the psychologist conclude about the effect of providing positive feedback (using the .05 level)? Solve this problem explicitly using all five steps of hypothesis testing and illustrate your answer with a sketch showing the comparison distribution, the cutoff (or cutoffs), and the score of the sample on this distribution.
    b. Explain what you have done to a person who has never had a course in statistics.

23. A cognitive psychologist theorizes that people will be able to form sentences with pleasant words quicker than with unpleasant words. To test her hypothesis, she creates a list of equal numbers of pleasant and unpleasant words, trying to select words of approximately equal difficulty, putting the words in random order in the list. Participants are then asked to form a sentence using each word, as soon the word is shown to them on a computer screen. A special timing device records how long it takes from the time the word appears on the screen until the participant starts speaking the sentence. Five participants are used, and the average time it takes each participant to do the pleasant and unpleasant words are shown in the table below.

   a. Is the time it takes participants to come up with a sentence different for the two kinds of words? What should the psychologist conclude about the effect of providing positive feedback (using the .05 level)? Solve this problem explicitly using all five steps of hypothesis testing and illustrate your answer with a sketch showing the comparison distribution, the cutoff (or cutoffs), and the score of the sample on this distribution.

   b. Explain your procedures and the logic of what you have done to a person who has never had a course in statistics.

Mean Reaction Time (in Seconds)

Subject	Pleasant	Unpleasant
1	.44	.51
2	.33	.51
3	.60	.74
4	.59	.77
5	.68	.55

24. A (fictional) psychologist wanted to know if her anxiety-reduction program was effective in reducing test anxiety. The average test anxiety level at her college was 12, and the variance unknown. Five participants were trained in her anxiety reduction method, and then their test anxiety level was measured. The results were as follows:

Subject	Before	After
1	13	10
2	14	17
3	9	11
4	15	8
5	16	8

   a. Does her program significantly reduce test anxiety (at the .05 level) Solve this problem explicitly using all five steps of hypothesis testing and illustrate your answer with a sketch showing the comparison distribution, the cutoff (or cutoffs), and the score of the sample on this distribution.

   b. Explain what you have done to a person who has never had a course in statistics.

25. A developmental psychologist has created a special exercise program intended to improve hand-eye coordination of toddlers. As a first test of the effectiveness of this set of exercises, he arranges for a group of 38 toddlers to participate in the program, testing their hand-eye coordination on a standard test before and after several weeks using the program. In the report of the results of this study, he writes: "Mean scores for the 38 toddlers increased from 61.32 to 68.93, $t(37) = 3.21, p < .01$, one-tailed." Explain this result, including the underlying computations that went into it, to a person who has never had a course in statistics.

26. An instructor of a speed reading course claimed that students could increase their reading speed without lowering their reading comprehension. A skeptical student decided to test this. She tested a group of 9 volunteers on their comprehension of a story before and after the class. She also noted their reading speeds, which an analysis showed to be significantly greater after the class, $t(8)=3.5$, $p<.01$. Their scores on the comprehension tests are listed below. Do the data support the claim of the instructor, that reading comprehension does not decrease?

Participants' *Reading Comprehension Scores*

SUBJECT	BEFORE	AFTER
1	87	85
2	84	82
3	75	71
4	80	78
5	97	91
6	92	91
7	88	89
8	67	71
9	70	70

Explain to a person who has never had a course in statistics: (a) the meaning of the reading speed result and (b) how you figured (including its logic) and what you found, in the analysis of the comprehension scores.

Using SPSS (11.0 for Windows) with this Chapter

If you are using SPSS for the first time, before proceeding with the material in this section, read the Appendix on Getting Started and the Basics of Using SPSS.

You can use SPSS to carry out a *t* test for dependent means. (It is also possible to carry out a *t* test for a single sample using SPSS, but as noted in the chapter, this procedure is rarely used in practice and was covered mainly as a step towards introducing you to the more widely used *t* tests.) You should work through the example, following the procedures step by step. Then look over the description of the general principles involved and try the procedures on your own for some of the problems listed in the Suggestions for Additional Practice. Finally, you may want to try the suggestions for using the computer to deepen your understanding.

I. Example
  A. Data: Hand-eye coordination scores for nine surgeons, each measured under both quiet and noisy conditions (fictional data), from the example in the text. The scores for the surgeons, under quiet conditions first, are 18, 12; 21, 21; 19, 16; 21, 16; 17, 19; 20, 19; 18, 16; 16, 17; and 20, 16.
  B. Follow the instructions in the SPSS Appendix for starting up SPSS.
  C. Enter the data as follows.
    1. Type 18 and press enter. Then click on the next box on the same line and type 12 and enter. This will put the subject's two scores on the same line next to each other.

2. Click on the first box on the next line and type 21 and enter. Then click on the second box on the second line and type 21 and enter (the quiet score and the noisy score for the second surgeon).
3. Type the scores for the remaining subjects, on each line one subject's quiet and noisy score, in that order.
4. To name the two variables, click on the first box in the first column (labeled VAR00001). This will bring up the Define Variable dialogue box. Delete the default variable name and type in QUIET in the Variable Name text box. Click on OK. This will close the dialogue box and return you to the data window. Repeat this for the second variable replacing VAR0002 with NOISY.

Your screen should look like Figure SG9-1.

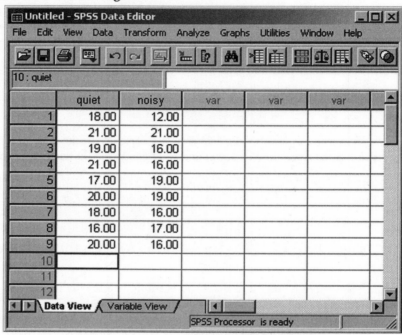

Figure SG9-1

D. Carry out a *t* test for dependent means as follows.
  Analyze
    Compare Means >
      Paired Samples T-test
        [Highlight QUIET so that it appears in the Current Selections box. Highlight NOISY so that it appears in the current selections box. Click on the arrow so that both variables appear in the Paired Variables box.]
        OK

The results should appear as Figure SG9-2 below.

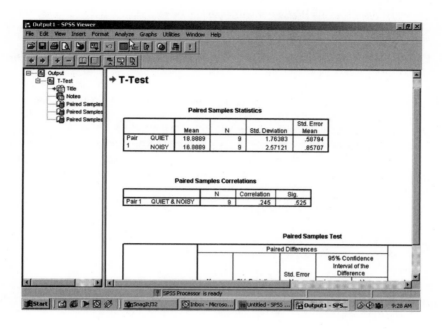

Figure SG9-2

E. Inspect the result.

1. The first table provides information about the two variables.
   a. The first column gives the variable names.
   b. The second column gives the mean of each variable.
   c. The third column gives the **Number of pairs** (that is, the number of difference scores).
   d. The fourth column gives the standard deviation of each variable. (Note that the standard deviation is an estimated population standard deviation, S, based on the sample--that is, it uses the N-1 formula.)
   e. The fifth column, **Std. Error of Mean**, is the standard deviation of the distribution of means, S_M, corresponding to each variable (based on an estimated population variance). These are not usually used as part of a t test for dependent means.
2. The second table describes the correlation between the two variables, which you ignore since your interest is in the difference between these two variables not the extent to which highs go with highs and lows with lows.
3. The third table gives the outcome of the t test.
   a. The first column gives the mean of the difference scores, in this case, **2.0000**, the same as calculated in the text.
   b. The next column, **SD**, gives the estimated population standard deviation of the difference scores, which it lists as **2.739**. This figure, when squared, comes out to exactly what was computed in the text for S^2 (7.5).

147

c. The third column, **SE of Mean**, gives the standard deviation of the distribution of means (of difference scores), which it lists as **.913**, the same (within rounding error) as was computed in the text.

d. The next column begins **95% Confidence Interval**. (This is the raw scores corresponding to the t scores at the bottom 2.5% and the top 2.5% of the t distribution. This was not covered in the text.)

e. The last column gives the computed t score, which it lists as **2.19**. (The text, using rounded-off figures, computed 2.20.)

f. The next column gives the degrees of freedom, **8**. This is the same as computed in the text.

g. Finally, the last column, **2-tail Sig**, gives the probability, the exact chance, of getting a t score this extreme on this particular t distribution. In this example, the computer reports **.060**. Since the significance level was set in advance at .05, this result does not reach significance. (Note that the figure given is for a two-tailed test, which is appropriate in the example. But if you were using a one-tailed test, you would consider the result significant at the .05 level if this number were .10 or less. To put this another way, the particular result of .060 means that there is .030 higher than 2.191 and .030 lower than -2.191.)

F. Print out the result.

G. Save your lines of data as follows.

> File
>> Save Data
>>> [Name your data file and designate the drive you want the data saved in.]
>>>> OK

II. Systematic Instructions for Computing the t Test for Dependent Means

A. Start up SPSS.

B. Enter the data as follows.

1. Type 18 and press enter. Then click on the next box on the same line and type 12 and enter. This will put the subject's two scores on the same line next to each other.

2. Click on the first box on the next line and type 21 and enter. Then click on the second box on the second line and type 21 and enter (the quiet score and the noisy score for the second surgeon).

3. Type the scores for the remaining subjects, on each line one subject's quiet and noisy score, in that order.

4. To name the two variables, click on the first box in the first column (labeled VAR00001). This will bring up the Define Variable dialogue box. Delete the default variable name and type in QUIET in the Variable Name text box. Click on OK. This will close the dialogue box and return you to the data window. Repeat this for the second variable replacing VAR0002 with NOISY.

C. Carry out the t-test for dependent means as follows.

> Analyze
>> Compare Means >
>>> Paired Samples T-test
>>>> [Highlight QUIET so that it appears in the Current Selections box. Highlight NOISY so that it appears in the current selections box. Click on the arrow so that both variables appear in the Paired Variables box.]
>>>> OK

148

D. Save your lines of data as follows.

    File

     Save Data

      [Name your data file and designate the drive you want the data saved in.]

      OK

III. Additional Practice

(Compute a *t* test for dependent means for each of these data sets and compare your results to those in the text.)

A. Text example: Data in Table 9-5 for husbands' communication quality scores before and after marriage (from Olthoff & Aron, 1993).

B. Practice problems in the text.
1. Set I: 5 & 6.
2. Set II: 17, 18, & 19.

IV. Using the Computer to Deepen Your Knowledge

A. The effect of increasing the mean of the difference scores.
1. Use SPSS to compute the *t* test for dependent means using the surgeon example, but adding 2 to each Noisy score. (You can do this by creating a variable with a **COMPUTE** instruction, such as **COMPUTE NOIPLUS2 = NOISY + 2.**)
2. Conduct another *t* test for dependent means using the original data, but this time adding 6 to the first three Noisy scores and nothing to the others. (To do this, you will actually have to change the scores as entered.)
3. Compare the two outcomes: Both have a larger mean difference, but the increase in the *t* score is much greater in the first case. Why is this? (Hint: Consider the variance of the difference scores.)

B. Correlation and the *t* test for dependent means.
1. Examine the correlation reported in the output for the original data and for each of the adjusted data sets in A above (that is, first with adding 2 to each Noisy score and then with adding 6 to a third of them).
2. Compare the correlations and their relation to the effects of these changes in data to the *t* test results.
   a. Notice that the size of the correlation is not directly related to the size of the *t* test result (the two procedures are measuring different things).
   b. Notice that the adding of 6 to a third of the scores creates a lower correlation than adding 2 to all of them. Why is this? Consider its relation to the results of the *t* tests and to variance in the difference scores.

C. The importance of matching.
1. Rearrange the Noisy scores so that all the same numbers are in the Noisy column, but they are not paired with the same subject's Quiet scores. Then compute a *t* test for dependent means.
2. Try another rearrangement and compute a *t* test for dependent means.
3. Compare these two results to the original.

Chapter 10
The *t* Test for Independent Means

Learning Objectives

To understand, including being able to conduct any necessary computations:

- The principle of the distribution of differences between means.
- The mean of the distribution of differences between means.
- The variance of the distribution of differences between means.
- The shape of the distribution of differences between means.
- The steps in conducting a *t* test for independent means.
- Assumptions for the *t* test for independent means (and the conditions under which it is safe to violate them).
- Effect size of a study using the *t* test for independent means.
- Power of a study using the *t* test for independent means.
- The problem of too many *t* tests.
- How results of studies using *t* tests for independent means are reported in research articles.

Chapter Outline

I. The *t* Test for Independent Means
   A. Used in studies with two samples.
   B. Follows the usual steps of hypothesis testing.
   C. Only differences from a *t* test for dependent means is that the comparison distribution is a distribution of differences between means and the *t* score is based on this distribution.

II. The Distribution of Differences Between Means
   A. It is the comparison distribution in a *t*-test for independent means.
   B. It can be understood as being constructed in four steps.
   1. Construct a distribution of means for each of the two populations.
   2. Randomly select one mean from each distribution of means.
   3. Subtract one from the other.
   4. Repeat a large number of times to create a distribution of these differences.
   C. If the null hypothesis is true, its mean is zero–since the two populations, and hence the two distributions of means, have the same mean, differences between means randomly drawn from these should average out to zero.
   D. Its variance.
   1. A single overall estimate is made of the variance of the populations, since it is assumed the population variances are equal.
      a. If sample sizes are equal, this pooled population variance estimate is the average of the estimates for the two populations–$S_{Pooled}^2 = (S_1^2 + S_2^2) / 2$.
      b. If samples sizes are different, pooled population variance estimate is based on an average which first weights each estimate by the degrees of freedom on which it is based: $S_{Pooled}^2 = [df_1/(df_1+df_2)][S_1^2] + [df_2/(df_1+df_2)][S_2^2]$.
   2. The variance of each distribution of means is the pooled estimate divided by the corresponding sample size: $S_{M1}^2 = S_{Pooled}^2 / N_1$ and $S_{M2}^2 = S_{Pooled}^2 / N_2$.

3. Variance of the distribution of differences between means is the sum of the variances of the two distributions of means (because the variance of each contributes to its variance): $S_{\text{Difference}}^2 = S_{M1}^2 + S_{M2}^2$.

4. The standard deviation of the distribution of the difference between means is the square root of its variance: $S_{\text{Difference}} = \sqrt{S_{\text{Difference}}^2}$.

E. Its shape.
  1. A t distribution (because we are using estimated population variances).
  2. Its degrees of freedom are the sum of the degrees of freedom for the two samples (because each contributes to the pooled estimate of the variance): $df_{\text{Total}} = df_1 + df_2$.

F. The t score on this distribution is the difference between the two sample means divided by the standard deviation of this distribution: $t = (M_1 - M_2)/S_{\text{Difference}}$.

III. Assumptions of the t Test for Independent Means

A. Normal population distributions.
  1. Violation of this assumption is a problem mainly if the two populations are thought to have dramatically skewed distributions, and in opposite directions.
  2. The test is especially robust to violations if a two-tailed test is used and if the sample sizes are not extremely small.

B. Equal population variances.
  1. The test is fairly robust to even fairly substantial differences in the population variances if there are equal numbers in the two groups.
  2. If the two estimated population variances are quite different, *and* if the samples have different numbers of cases, a modification of the usual t test procedure (not covered in this text) is sometimes used.

C. It is difficult in practice to determine whether the assumptions hold.

D. Some procedures that can be applied when the assumptions are clearly violated are described in Chapter 15. For example, some computer programs can perform the procedure without assuming equal variances.

E. Participants needed to achieve 80% power for estimated small, medium, and large effect sizes using one- and two-tailed tests, all using the .05 significance level.

IV. Effect Size and Power for the t Test for Independent Means

A. Effect size.
  1. Estimated $d = (\mu_1 - \mu_2) / \sigma$.
  2. For a completed study, estimate effect size as $d = (M_1 - M_2) / S_{\text{Pooled}}$.
  3. Cohen's convention: Small $d = .20$; medium $d = .50$; large $d = .80$. (Same as for t test for dependent means.)

B. Power.
  1. Table 10.5 in the text gives approximate power for the .05 significance level for small, medium, or large effect sizes and one- or two-tailed tests.
  2. Power when sample sizes are not equal.
    a. For any given number of participants, power is greatest when participants are divided into two equal groups.
    b. The power is equivalent to a study with equal sample sizes in which each of those equal sizes is the harmonic mean of the actual unequal sample sizes: $N' = [(2)(N_1)(N_2)]/[N_1 + N_2]$.

151

C. Planning sample size: Table 10.6 in the text gives the approximate number of participants needed to achieve 80% power for estimated small, medium, and large effect sizes using one- and two-tailed tests, all using the .05 significance level.

V. Controversies: Too Many *t* Tests

A. If you conduct a large number of *t* tests, the chance of any one of them coming out significant at, say, the 5% level is really greater than 5%.

B. The controversy is about how to deal with this problem.

C. Solutions are complicated in most research situations for two reasons.
   1. Each test is not independent of the others.
   2. Some tests are more important than others.

VI. How *t* Tests for Independent Means are Described in Research Articles

A. They are usually reported in the article text by giving the two sample means (and sometimes the *SD*s), followed by the standard format for any *t* test–for example: $t(38) = 4.72, p < .01$.

B. Sometimes they are reported in tables which give the means (and sometimes *SD*s), using stars to indicate significance levels.

Formulas

I. Pooled estimate of population variance (S_{Pooled}^2)

Formula in words: Weighted average of estimates for each population; that is, each estimate contributes the proportion to the overall estimate that its degrees of freedom are to the total degrees of freedom.

Formula in symbols: $S_{\text{Pooled}}^2 = [df_1/(df_1+df_2)][S_1^2] + [df_2/(df_1+df_2)][S_2^2]$

   S_1^2 is the unbiased estimate of the variance of Population 1.

   S_2^2 is the unbiased estimate of the variance of Population 2.

   Note: Each $S^2 = \Sigma(X-M)^2/df = SS/df$ (see Chapter 9).

   df_1 is the degrees of freedom for the sample from Population 1.

   df_2 is the degrees of freedom for the sample from Population 2.

   Note: Each $df = N-1$.

II. Variance of each population's distribution of means (S_{M1}^2 and S_{M2}^2)

Formula in words: The pooled population variance estimate divided by the corresponding sample size

Formulas in symbols: $S_{M1}^2 = S_{\text{Pooled}}^2 / N_1$ and $S_{M2}^2 = S_{\text{Pooled}}^2 / N_2$

   N_1 is the number of participants in the sample representing Population 1.

   N_2 is the number of participants in the sample representing Population 2.

III. Variance of the distribution of differences between means ($S_{\text{Difference}}^2$)

Formula in words: Sum of the variances of the two distributions of means.

Formula in symbols: $S_{\text{Difference}}^2 = S_{M1}^2 + S_{M2}^2$

IV. Standard deviation of the distribution of the differences between means ($S_{\text{Difference}}$)

Formula in words: The square root of the variance of the distribution of differences between means.

Formula in symbols: $S_{\text{Difference}} = \sqrt{S_{Difference}^2}$.

V. Degrees of freedom for a *t* test for independent means (df_{Total})

Formula in words: Sum of the degrees of freedom in the two samples.

Formula in symbols: $df_{\text{Total}} = df_1 + df_2$

VI. *t* score for a *t* test for independent means

Formula in words: the difference between the two sample means divided by the standard deviation of the distribution of differences between means.

Formula in symbols: $t = (M_1 - M_2)/S_{\text{Difference}}$

M_1 is the mean of the sample representing Population 1.

M_2 is the mean of the sample representing Population 2.

VII. Effect size for a *t* test for independent means (*d*)

Formula in words: the hypothesized difference between the population means divided by the population standard deviation.

Formula in symbols: $d = (\mu_1 - \mu_2) / \sigma$

μ_1 is the mean of Population 1.

μ_2 is the mean of Population 2.

σ is the standard deviation of each of the populations.

VIII. Estimated effect size for a *t* test for independent means (d) for a completed study

Formula in words: the observed difference between the sample means divided by the pooled estimate of the population standard deviation.

Formula in symbols: $d = (M_1 - M_2) / S_{\text{Pooled}}$

S_{Pooled} is the pooled estimate of the population standard deviation

$$(S_{\text{Pooled}} = \sqrt{S^2_{Pooled}}\,).$$

IX. Harmonic mean sample size (*N'*)

Formula in words: Twice the product of the two sample sizes divided by the sum of the sample sizes.

Formula in symbols: $N' = [(2)(N_1)(N_2)] / [N_1+N_2]$

How to Conduct a *t* Test for Independent Means
(Based on Table 10.4 in the Text)

1. **Restate the question into a null and a research hypothesis about populations.**
2. **Determine the characteristics of the comparison distribution.**
   A. Its mean will be 0.
   B. Its standard deviation is figured as follows.
      1. Figure estimated population variances based on each sample (that is, figure two estimates).
      2. Figure pooled estimate of population variance: $S_{\text{Pooled}}^2 = [df_1/(df_1+df_2)][S_1^2] + [df_2/(df_1+df_2)][S_2^2]$. Note: $df_1=N_1-1$ and $df_2=N_2-1$.
      3. Figure variance of each distribution of means: $S_{M1}^2 = S_{\text{Pooled}}^2/N_1$ and $S_{M2}^2 = S_{\text{Pooled}}^2/N_2$.
      4. Figure variance of distribution of differences between means: $S_{\text{Difference}}^2 = S_{M1}^2 + S_{M2}^2$.

5. Figure standard deviation of distribution of differences between means:

$$S_{\text{Difference}} = \sqrt{S^2_{Difference}} \ .$$

    C. Determine its shape: It will be a t distribution with df_{Total} degrees of freedom ($df_{\text{Total}} = df_1 + df_2$).

3. Determine the cut-off sample score on the comparison distribution at which the null hypothesis should be rejected.

    A. Determine the degrees of freedom (df_{Total}), desired significance level, and whether to use a one- or two-tailed test.

    B. Look up the appropriate cut-off on a t table; if exact df is not given, use df below.

4. Determine your sample's score on the comparison distribution: $t = (M_1 - M_2)/S_{\text{Difference}}$.

5. Compare the scores in 3 and 4 to decide whether or not to reject the null hypothesis.

Outline for Writing Essays for Hypothesis Testing Problems Involving the Means of Two Independent Samples

(t test for Independent Means)

    The reason for your writing essay questions in the practice problems and tests is that this task develops and then demonstrates what matters so very much–your comprehension of the logic behind the computations. (It is also a place for those of you who are better at words than numbers to shine. And for those better at numbers to develop their skills at explaining in words.)

    Thus, to do well you need to be sure to do the following in each essay: (a) give the reasoning behind each step; (b) relate each step to the specifics of the content of the particular study you are analyzing; (c) state the various formulas in nontechnical language, because as you define each term you show you understand it (although once you have defined it in nontechnical language, you can use it from then on in the essay); (d) look back and be absolutely certain that you made it clear just why that formula or procedure was applied and why it is the way it is.

    The outlines below are *examples* of ways to structure your essays. There are other completely correct ways to go about it. And this is an *outline* for an answer–you must write the answer out in paragraph form. Examples of full essays are in the answers to Set I Practice Problems in the back of the text.

    These essays are necessarily very long for you to write (and for others to grade). But this is the very best way to be sure you understand everything thoroughly. One shortcut you may see on a test is to write your answer for someone who understands statistics up to the point of the new material you are studying. You can choose to take the same shortcut in these practice problems (maybe writing for someone who understands right up to whatever point you yourself start being just a little unclear). But every time you write for a person who has never had statistics at all, you review the logic behind the entire whole course. You engrain it in your mind. Over and over. The time is never wasted.   It is an excellent way to study.

I. Reframe the question into a research hypothesis and a null hypothesis about populations. (Step 1 of hypothesis testing.)

    A. State in ordinary language the hypothesis testing issue: Do the two groups of persons studied represent larger groups or "populations" of people whose averages are different?

    B. Explain language (to make rest of essay easier to write by not having to repeat long explanations each time), focusing on the meaning of each term in the concrete example of the study at hand.

        1. Populations.

        2. Sample.

        3. Mean.

        4. Research hypothesis.

        5. Null hypothesis.

        6. Rejecting the null hypothesis to provide support for the research hypothesis.

II. Determine the characteristics of the comparison distribution. (Step 2 of hypothesis testing.)

    A. Explain the principle that the comparison distribution is the distribution (pattern of spread of differences between means of scores of two groups) that represents what we would expect if the null hypothesis were true and our particular two groups each consist of randomly selected scores from populations that have the same mean.

    B. Thus, the comparison distribution is the distribution of differences between means of two groups where the two groups really are not from two different populations, but the two populations are one and the same.

    C. Note that because we are working with a difference between means of two groups, we have to compare our actual difference between the means of two groups to a distribution not of individual cases, but of differences between means of two groups.

    D. Give an intuitive understanding of how one might construct a distribution of differences between means of two groups.

        1. Create a distribution of means based on the population the first group represents.

            a. Select a random sample of the size (number of participants) of your first group from the population it represents and figure its mean.

            b. Select another random sample of this size from this population and figure its mean.

            c. Repeat this process a very large number of times.

            d. Make a distribution of these means.

        2. Create a distribution of means based on the population the second group represents.

        3. Select one mean from each distribution of means and find the difference (subtract the one from the other).

        4. Repeat this process many times.

        5. Make a distribution of these differences.

        6. Note that this procedure is only to explain the idea, and would be too much work and unnecessary in practice.

    E. There is an exact mathematical relation of a distribution of differences between means to the population the means are drawn from, so that in practice the characteristics of the distribution of means can be determined directly from knowledge of the characteristics of the population and the size of the samples involved.

F. Since we are still assuming the null hypothesis is true, the mean of a distribution of differences between means is zero because the distributions of means from each will have the same mean, and differences between means taken from them should average out to zero.

G. The standard deviation of a distribution of differences between means is a measure of the amount of spread or variation in the differences. (Define variance and standard deviation in lay language.) This standard deviation is figured in steps.

1. Estimate the variation in each of the populations which each group represents.
   a. Whatever the distribution a particular group's scores come from, it is reasonable to assume that the variation among the scores in your particular group is representative of the variation in that larger distribution of scores.
   b. A sample's variation is on the average slightly less than the population it comes from because it is less likely to include scores that are far from its mean.
   c. Thus, a special adjustment is made that exactly corrects for this: Instead of taking the average of the squared deviations–the sum of squared deviations divided by the number of participants–one instead divides the sum of squared deviations by one less than the number of participants in the sample.

2. Describe the computations (and state results) for your two groups.

3. Average the estimates to get a more accurate pooled estimate.
   a. Normally we assume the two populations have the same amount of variation.
   b. The averaging is done so as to give weight to each estimate in proportion to the information it contributes (which is the number of cases minus one).
   c. Describe the computations and state the results.

4. Figure the variance of each distribution of means.
   a. The spread of each distribution of means will be less spread out than the population of individual cases from which the samples are taken because of the following reasoning.
      i. Any one score, even an extreme score, has some chance of being selected in a random sample.
      ii. However, the chance is less of very many extreme scores being selected in the same random sample (what is required to create an extreme sample mean), particularly since scores would have to be extreme in the same direction.
      iii. Thus, there is a moderating effect of numbers: In any one sample the deviants tend to be balanced out by middle cases or by deviants in the opposite direction, making each sample tend towards the middle and away from extreme values.
      iv. With fewer extreme values for the means, the variation among the means is less.
   b. The more cases in each sample, the less spread out is the distribution of means of that sample size: With a larger number of cases in each sample, it is even harder for extreme cases in that sample not to be balanced out by middle cases or extremes in the other direction in the same sample.
   c. The variance of each distribution of means is found by a formula that divides the estimated population variance by the number of participants in the group representing it (thus making it smaller in proportion to the number of participants in the group).
   d. Describe the computations and state the results.

5. Find the standard deviation of the distribution of differences between means.
   a. The variance in each distribution of means contributes to the variance in the differences between the means.
   b. The variance of the distribution of means, in fact, comes out to the sum of the variances of the two distributions of means. Its standard deviation is the square root of this result.
   c. Describe the computations and state the results.

156

H. The shape of the distribution of differences between means.
1. The distribution tends to be bell-shaped, with most cases falling near the middle and fewer at the extremes, due to the same basic process of extremes balancing each other out that we noted in the discussion of the standard deviation–middle values are more likely and extreme values less likely.
2. Specifically, it can be shown that it will follow a precise shape called a *t* distribution.
3. Actually there are different *t* distributions according to the amount of information that goes into estimating the variation in the distribution from the sample, which is the sum of the numbers you divide by in making the estimates (one less than the number of participants in the first group plus one less than the number of participants in the second group).
4. But the shape of the comparison distribution is only a precise *t* distribution if both populations of individual scores follow a precise shape called a normal curve (also bell-shaped) that is widely found in nature. Note that in the problem you are told that the distributions of the populations are normal curves so that this condition is met in your case.

III. Determine the cutoff sample score on the comparison distribution at which the null hypothesis should be rejected. (Step 3 of hypothesis testing.)

A. Before you figure out how extreme the particular difference between the means of your two groups is on this distribution of differences between means, you want to know how extreme your difference would have to be to decide it was too unlikely that it could have been a randomly drawn mean from this comparison distribution.

B. Since the shape of the comparison distribution follows a mathematically defined formula, you can use a table to tell you how many standard deviations from the mean your score would have to be in order to be in the top so many percent.

C. Note that the number of standard deviations from the mean on this *t* distribution is called a *t* score. (Explaining this term makes writing simpler as you go along.)

D. To use these tables you have to decide the kind of situation you have, and there are two considerations.
1. Are you interested in the chances of getting this extreme of a difference between means that is extreme in only one direction (such as only higher for one group than the other) or in either? (Explain which is appropriate for your study.)
2. Just how unlikely would the extremeness of a particular mean have to be? The standard figure used in psychology is less likely than 5% (though 1% is sometimes used to be especially safe). (Say which you are using in your study–if no figure is stated in the problem and no special reason given for using one or the other, the general rule is to use 5%.)

E. State the cutoff for your particular problem.

IV. Determine the score of your sample on the comparison distribution. (Step 4 of hypothesis testing.)

A. Find where the actual difference your two groups' means would fall on the comparison distribution, in terms of a *t* score.

B. State this *t* score.

V. Compare the scores obtained in Steps 3 and 4 to decide whether to reject the null hypothesis. (Step 5 of hypothesis testing.)

A. State whether your difference between means (from Step 4) does or does not exceed the cutoff (from Step 3).

B. If your difference between means exceeds the cutoff, you write out the following.
   1. You can reject the null hypothesis.
   2. By elimination, the research hypothesis is thus supported.
   3. Say what it means that the research hypothesis is supported. (That is, the study shows that the particular experimental manipulation *appears* to make a difference in the particular thing being measured, or that people in general of the kind represented by one of your groups are probably really different or have been changed on the thing being measured from people in general of the kind represented by your other group.)
C. If your score does not exceed the cutoff, write out these points.
   1. You can not reject the null hypothesis.
   2. The experiment is inconclusive.
   3. Say what it means that the study is inconclusive. (That is, the study did not yield results which give a clear indication of whether or not the particular experimental manipulation appears to make a difference in the particular thing being measured; or that it is not clear based on this study whether people in general of the kind represented by one of your groups are really different or have been changed on the thing being measured from people in general of the kind represented by your other group.)
   4. Explicitly note that even though the research hypothesis was not supported in this study, this is not evidence that it is false–it is quite possibly true but the thing studied has only a small effect, not sufficient to produce a mean extreme enough to yield a significant result in this study.

Chapter Self-Tests

Multiple-Choice Questions

1. A distinguishing feature of the *t* test for independent means is

   a. dependent populations are treated as if they are unrelated.
   b. the difference between the means of two independent samples is evaluated.
   c. variance is not used in this procedure.
   d. the variance of the parent populations is unrelated to the variance of the samples.

2. When conducting a *t* test for independent means using a two-tailed test, the null hypothesis typically states that

   a. the mean of Population 1 is the same as the mean of Population 2.
   b. the mean of Population 1 is different from the mean of Population 2.
   c. the variance of Population 1 is less than or the same as the variance of Population 2.
   d. the variance of Population 1 is different from the variance of Population 2.

3. In a *t* test for independent means, because there are two samples we end up with two estimates of the population variance. If the sample sizes are different, the two estimates are combined by

   a. directly averaging the two estimates into one number.
   b. finding a weighted average.
   c. pooling the raw data of each sample, then finding the variance of the new super sample.
   d. finding the difference of the two estimates (that is, the estimate for Population 1 minus the estimate for Population 2), and using a special table to look up the new estimate based on that difference.

4. The distribution of differences between means has a mean of

 a. the population variance divided by N.
 b. the pooled mean of the sample means.
 c. 0.
 d. 1.

5. The variance of a distribution of differences between means is

 a. the smallest of the two variances of the two distributions of means.
 b. the largest of the two variances of the two distribution of means.
 c. the average of the variances of the two distributions of means.
 d. the sum of the variances of the two distributions of means.

6. In the formula $t = (M_1 - M_2)/S_{\text{Difference}}$, the "$M$'s" refer to

 a. the means of the two populations.
 b. the means of the distribution of means.
 c. the hypothesized means of the two populations.
 d. the means of the two samples.

7. A study compares the scores of men and women on a scale measuring how important beauty is to the participant. If there are 20 women and 15 men, what proportion of the pooled estimate of the population variance will come from men?

 a. $15/20 = 75\%$
 b. $(15-1)/(20-1) = 14/19 = 74\%$
 c. 50%
 d. $(15-1)/((20-1)+(15-1)) = 14/33 = 42\%$.

8. When conducting a t test for independent means, if the assumption of normality is seriously violated, you should

 a. not be concerned because the t test for independent means is highly robust even under extreme violations of the assumptions.
 b. use a procedure other than the t test for independent means.
 c. proceed, but interpret your results with caution.
 d. proceed ONLY if the population variances are not skewed.

9. In a study with 30 participants total (divided into a control group and an experimental group), which of the following cases would be the most powerful?

 a. The experimental group has 20 participants and the control group has 10.
 b. Both groups have 15 participants.
 c. The control group has 20 participants and the experimental group has 10.
 d. The control group has 29 participants and the experimental group has 1 participant.

10. Which of the following is part of the process of computing a t test for independent means?

 a. Each sample's standard deviation is divided by its sample size to find the standard deviation of its population's distribution of means.
 b. The population variance, which is known, is used to find the variance of the two samples.
 c. The population variance is estimated, then that estimate is used to find the variance of each of the distributions of means.
 d. An estimate of the population mean, based on pooled sample means, is translated into a t score, and then compared to a t distribution.

Fill-In Questions

11. In a study of the effects of a particular drug on creativity, participants were evaluated while taking part in a creative task. During the task 10 participants were under the influence of the drug and 10 participants were not. A t test for _____ would be conducted to analyze the data.

12. "$Sp^2 = (S^2_1 + S^2_2) / 2$" is a formula used for the pooled estimate of the population variance when sample sizes are _____.

13. The formula, "S_{Pooled}^2/N_2," is used to figure the variance of Sample 2's _____.

14. When the variances of the distribution of means for both samples are added together, the result is the variance of _____.

15. In the formula "$t = (M_1 - M_2)/S_{Difference}$," $S_{Difference}$ is the _____ of the distribution of differences between means.

16. & 17. The assumptions for a t test for independent means require that the populations are both _____ and have the same _____.

18. When computing the effect size (d) of a completed experiment, based on the actual observed data, the difference between the observed means is divided by _____.

19. There is _____ (more, less, about equal) power in a study in which there are 5 participants in Sample 1 and 15 in Sample 2 than in a study with 10 participants in each sample.

20. A study with 15 participants in one condition and 10 in the other, using a t test for independent means, yielded a t of 3.21, which was significant at the .01 significance level, one-tailed. Write these results in the standard format (using appropriate symbols, etc.) as they would be reported in the text of a research article. _____.

Problems and Essays

21. As a senior thesis a psychology major examines the effects of self-defense training on self-confidence. (This is a new program and it is not clear whether it will increase self-confidence, decrease it, or make no difference.) Five of ten volunteers are randomly selected to receive self-defense training. The other five receive no special training. At the end of the training period, all participants complete a self-confidence questionnaire.

   a. Is there a difference in self-confidence between the two groups, according to the data below (use the .01 significance level)? Solve this problem explicitly using all five steps of hypothesis testing and illustrate your answer with a sketch showing the comparison distribution, the cutoff (or cutoffs), and the score of the sample on this distribution.

   b. Explain your analysis to a person who has never had a course in statistics.

Self-Confidence Scores For Participants Who Do and Do Not Receive Self-Defense Training

TRAINING	NO TRAINING
15	14
18	16
14	19
17	18
15	13

22. A social psychologist conducted a study of whether she could produce a placebo effect on intelligence. (A "placebo" is an inactive drug or a fake treatment. A "placebo effect" occurs when a participant reacts to a placebo as if it were a real drug or treatment.) She randomly divided seven participants into two groups. All seven were given pills (known to have no true effect) to take at the start of the experiment in which they were told that they would first be given some questionnaires, including an intelligence test, for background information, and then would undergo some physiological testing to measure effects of the "vitamin" on levels of red blood cells. Three of the participants were randomly assigned to be told that these pills would take an hour to have any effect, and if they noticed anything at all from them even then, it would be some tingling in the feet. The other four were told that this vitamin has been found to enhance alertness and mental agility during the first hour and then to have no special effect except possibly some tingling in the feet. The table below shows the scores on the intelligence test.

   a. Based on these data, is intelligence test performance increased by a placebo pill? (Use the .05 significance level.) Solve this problem explicitly using all five steps of hypothesis testing and illustrate your answer with a sketch showing the comparison distribution, the cutoff (or cutoffs), and the score of the sample on this distribution.

   b. Explain your conclusion and procedure to a person who has never had a course in statistics.

161

Intelligence Scores of Placebo Group and Control Group

PLACEBO	CONTROL
85	89
97	76
105	99
74	

23. A researcher wanted to know if there were gender differences in statistics grades. She selected 5 men and 5 women and compared their (fictional) scores (100 points possible). They were as follows: Men : 71, 81, 79, 91, 82; Women: 80, 84, 76, 92, 84.

    a. Is there a difference in performance based on gender (use the .05 level of significance). Solve this problem explicitly using all five steps of hypothesis testing and illustrate your answer with a sketch showing the comparison distribution, the cutoff (or cutoffs), and the score of the sample on this distribution.

    b. Explain your conclusion and procedure to a person who has never had a course in statistics.

24. Do people who are health-conscious get better grades? To address this question, a researcher first assessed the degree of health consciousness (using a questionnaire) of a group of college students. Of those, the top 15 and the bottom 15 were selected, forming the High Health-Conscious (HHC) group and the Low Health Conscious (LHC) group, respectively. The researcher reported: "The HHC group was not found to have a significantly higher GPA than the LHC group (HHC M=3.2, SD=.33; LHC M=3.0, SD=.68; $t(28) = 1.06$)." Explain and interpret these results to a person who is not familiar with statistics.

25. A personality psychologist is interested in whether introverts and extraverts differ in their sensitivity to light. Forty introverts and forty extraverts are each measured in a series of visual tasks and the results are shown in the table below. (Each is a measure of sensitivity, with higher numbers indicating greater sensitivity.) Explain and interpret these results to a person not familiar with statistics.

Means of Introverts and Extraverts on Perceptual Sensitivity Measures

	Introverts	Extraverts	t
Light Intensity-A	4.16	13.21	0.78
Light Intensity-B	1422.12	1238.63	4.21**
Color Contrast	107.16	94.16	1.91*
Adaptation-A	.0024	.0013	2.68**
Adaptation-B	1.81	1.93	-1.07

$*p < .05$ $**p < .01$

Using SPSS (11.0 FOR Windows) with this Chapter

     If you are using SPSS for the first time, before proceeding with the material in this section read the Appendix on Getting Started and the Basics of Using SPSS.

You can use SPSS to carry out a *t* test for independent means. You should work through the example, following the procedures step by step. Then look over the description of the general principles involved and try the procedures on your own for some of the problems listed in the Suggestions for Additional Practice. Finally, you may want to try the suggestions for using the computer to deepen your understanding.

I. Example

A. Data: Employee performance after several months on the job of seven participants randomly assigned to a special job skills program and seven participants randomly assigned to the standard job skills program (fictional data), from the example in the text. The scores for those receiving the special program are 6, 4, 9, 7, 7, 3 and 6. The scores for those receiving the standard program are 6, 1, 5, 3, 1, 1, and 4.

B. Follow the instructions in the SPSS Appendix for starting up SPSS.

C. Enter the data as follows.

    1. Type **1** and enter. Then click on the next box on the same line and type **6** and enter. The 1 stands for the special program, and the 6 stands for the performance score of the first subject in that special program. (This system is used because SPSS assumes that all scores on the same line are for the same subject-thus, you do not lay out the column for each condition.)

    2. Type the program and performance scores for the remaining subjects in the special program.

    3. Type **2** and enter. Then click on the next box on the same line and type **6** and enter (the **2** is being used to stand for the standard program, the **6** is for the performance score of the first subject in the standard program.

    4. Type the scores of the remaining subjects.

    5. To name the two variables, click on the Variable View tab. In the first row of the first column type in PROGRAM under the column titlted "Name." Repeat this process in the second row for the second variable using the variable name PERFORM. The screen should now appear as shown in Figure SG10-1.

D. Carry out the *t* test for independent means as follows:

    1. Analyze

        Compare Means >

        Independent-Samples T Test

            [Highlight PERFORM and move it into the Test Variable(s) box.

            Highlight PROGRAM and move it into the Grouping Variable

                box.

            Define Groups

                    [Type in 1 for Group 1 and 2 for Group 2. Your screen should

                    now look like Figure SG10-2]

                        Continue

                            OK

    2. The result should look like Figure SG10-3.

Figure SG10-1

Figure SG10-2

164

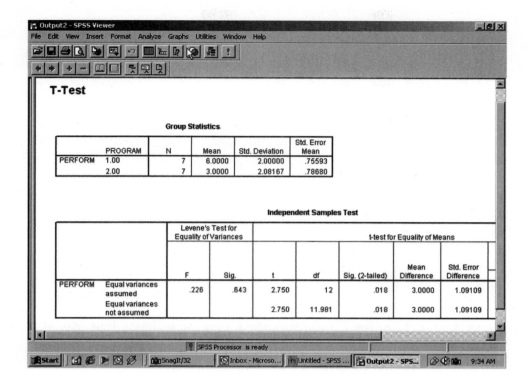

Figure SG10-3

E. Inspect the result.
    1. The first table provides information about the two variables.
        a. The first column gives the levels of the grouping variable (that is, **1** or **2**, corresponding to the numbers used for the special and standard programs, respectively).
        b. The second, third and fourth columns give, respectively, the number of cases, mean, and estimated population standard deviation for each grouping. That is, these numbers correspond to what in the text are called N_1 and N_2; M_1 and M_2; and S_1 and S_2.
        c. The fifth column, **Std. Error Mean**, is the standard deviation of the distribution of means, S_M for each grouping. Note that these are based on each population variance estimate and not on the pooled estimate–so they are not quite the same for each group as the square root of the S_M^2 computed in the text.
    2. The next line, **Levene's Test for Equality of Variances** is a significance test of the null hypothesis that the *variances* of the two populations are the same. This test is important mainly as a check on whether it is reasonable to proceed with the ordinary t test for independent means with its assumption that the population variances are equal. If this test is significant (that is, if the **P** is less than .05), this assumption is brought into question. However, in the example, the result is clearly not significant (**.643** is well above .05) so we have no special reason to doubt the assumption of equal population variances.
    3. The bottom table is labeled *t* **test for Equality of Means**.
        a. The first row (the one labeled **Equal**) gives results of the ordinary t test for independent means that assumes equal population variances.

165

b. Notice in the first column (of the first row) that the *t* score, degrees of freedom, and standard deviation of the distribution of differences between means (what SPSS labels as **SE of Diff**) are the same as computed in the text for this example, within rounding error.

c. The column labeled **2-tail Sig** gives the probability, the exact chance, of getting a *t* score this extreme on this particular *t* distribution. In this example, the computer reports **.018**. Since the significance level was set in advance at .05, this result is clearly significant. (Note that the figure given is for a two-tailed test, which is appropriate in the example. But if you were using a one-tailed test, you would consider the result significant at the .05 level if this number were .10 or less. To put this another way, the particular result of .018 means that there is .009 of the curve higher than 2.75 and .009 lower than -2.75.)

d. The last column, labeled **95% CI for Diff**, refers to what is called the "95% confidence interval." (It refers to the raw scores corresponding to the *t* scores at the bottom 2.5% and the top 2.5% of the *t* distribution.

e. The second row of the bottom table, labeled **Equal Variances Not Assumed**, gives the results of a special *t* test which does not require the assumption of equal population variances.

F. Print out the result.

G. Save your lines of data as follows.

      File
      Save Data
        [Name your data and designate the drive you would like your data saved in]
        OK

II. Systematic Instructions for Computing the *t* Test for Independent Means

A. Start up SPSS.

B. Enter the data as follows, with one variable consisting of either a 1 or a 2, representing which group a subject is in, and the other variable consisting of the scores on the measured variable.

1. Type **1** and enter. Then click on the next box on the same line and type **6** and enter. The 1 stands for the special program, and the 6 stands for the performance score of the first subject in that special program. (This system is used because SPSS assumes that all scores on the same line are for the same subject-thus, you do not lay out the column for each condition.)

2. Type the program and performance scores for the remaining subjects in the special program.

3. Type **2** and enter. Then click on the next box on the same line and type **6** and enter (the **2** is being used to stand for the standard program, the **6** is for the performance score of the first subject in the standard program.

4. Type the scores of the remaining subjects.

5. To name the two variables, click on the Variable View tab. In the first row of the first column, type in Program under the column titled "Name." Repeat this process in the second row for the second variable using the variable name Perform.

C. Carry out the *t* test for independent means as follows:

1. Analyze
    Compare Means >
    Independent-Samples T Test
        [Highlight PERFORM and move it into the Test Variable(s) box.
        Highlight PROGRAM and move it into the Grouping Variable box.
            Define Groups
                [Type in 1 for Group 1 and 2 for Group 2]
                Continue
                    OK

2. Print out a copy of the result.

3. Inspect the result, attending especially to the first line of the bottom table (the row labeled Equal) which describes the computations for an ordinary *t* test for independent means, with its assumption of equal population variances.

D. Save your lines of data as follows:

    File
      Save Data
        [Name your data file and designate the drive you would like your data saved in]
          OK

III. Additional Practice

(For each data set compute a *t* test for independent means and compare your results to those in the text).

A. Text example: Data in Table 10-1 for a manipulation check on the relation of the work situation of the mothers of adolescent boys to perceived academic competence (from Moorehouse & Sanders, 1992).

B. Practice problems in the text.

   1. Set I Question 5; Set II Question 15 from Chapter 10.

IV. Using the Computer to Deepen Your Knowledge

A. The *t* test for independent means versus the *t* test for dependent means.

   1. Use SPSS to compute a *t* test for independent means using the surgeon example from Chapter 9–you will have to retype in the data setting this up as if the Quiet and Noisy scores were from two different groups of people. Notice that the resulting *t* is considerably lower.

   2. Now try to set up the *t* test computed in this chapter (the new job program example) as a *t* test for dependent means, by arbitrarily pairing the score of the first subject in the new-program group with the score of the first subject in the standard-program group, and continuing in that fashion over all the scores. (This would not even be possible if there were different numbers of subjects in the group.) Notice that the *t* is not much higher than the *t* test for independent means. (Also note the correlation.)

   3. Try another *t* test for dependent means with the same job-program example, but this time pairing the subjects in the two groups differently. (Again, note the correlation.)

   4. What is the principle operating here? (Hint: When two sets of scores are from the same people, they tend to be correlated.)

B. Effect of variance on the *t* test for independent means.

   1. Compute the *t* test in the example again, but this time use as data for the special-program group three 5s, three 7s, and one 6. This will keep the mean the same, but will much reduce the variance of the scores.

   2. Compute another *t* test, but this time use all 6s for the special-program group. This still keeps the mean of this group the same, but reduces the variance to zero.

   3. Compare these results (including the original finding). What accounts for the differences?

Chapter 11
Introduction to the Analysis of Variance

Learning Objectives

To understand, including being able to conduct any necessary computations:

- When it is appropriate to use an analysis of variance.
- The within-group estimate of the population variance.
- The between-group estimate of the population variance.
- The F ratio.
- The F distribution and using an F table.
- The steps in conducting a one-way analysis of variance.
- Assumptions for the analysis of variance (and the conditions under which it is safe to violate them).
- Planned comparisons and the Bonferroni procedure.
- Omnibus tests versus planned comparisons
- How results of studies using analysis of variance are reported in research articles

Chapter Outline

I. **Basic Logic of the Analysis of Variance**
   A. This can be used in studies with three or more samples.
   B. Follows the usual steps of hypothesis testing.
   C. The null hypothesis is that the three or more populations being compared all have the same mean.
   D. Population variance can be estimated by averaging variance estimates from all samples. This is called the *within-group* estimate of the population variance.
   E. Population variance can also be estimated based on variation among means of samples. This is called a *between-group* estimate of the population variance.
      1. When the null hypothesis is true.
         a. All populations have same mean.
         b. Any variation among means of your particular samples thus can only represent variation among individual scores in the populations.
         c. Thus, variance of individual scores can be estimated from variation among samples.
      2. When the research hypothesis is true.
         a. The populations have different means.
         b. Any variation among means of your particular samples thus can represent both variation among individual scores in the populations *plus* variation between the population means.
         c. When a between-group estimate is figured in this case, it reflects both sources of variation.
   F. Decisions regarding the null and research hypotheses involve comparing the within-group and between-group estimates of the population variance.
      1. When the null hypothesis is true, the two should be about the same.
      2. When the research hypothesis is true, the between-group estimate should be larger than the within-group estimate.
      3. In terms of proportions (between-group divided by within-group), the proportion should be about 1 when the null hypothesis is true and greater than 1 when it is not.
      4. This proportion is called the *F Ratio*.

168

G. The F distribution and the F table.
1. Statisticians have developed the mathematics of an F distribution–the probabilities of getting Fs of various sizes under the null hypothesis.
2. Tables are available indicating how extreme the F ratio calculated from your samples has to be in order to reject the null hypothesis at various standard significance levels.
3. You can think of F in terms of an analogy to the signal-to-noise ratio in engineering, in which the signal is like the variation among means and the noise like the variation of individual scores.

II. **Analysis of Variance Procedures**
A. Within-group population variance estimate.
1. Figure population variance estimates from the data in each sample–$S^2=SS/df$.
2. Since all populations are assumed to have equal variances, if sample sizes are equal then these estimates can be combined by a straightforward averaging.
3. This is called the *within group variance* or *mean squares within* and is symbolized as S_{Within}^2 or MS_{Within}.
B. Between-group population variance estimate.
1. Estimate the variance of the distribution of means, based on the means of your particular samples: Treating each mean as a number, apply the usual formula for estimated population variance.
2. Extrapolate from the estimated variance of the distribution of means to an estimated variance of the population of individual scores: Multiply by the size of each sample (just the opposite of the dividing you do when going from a population of individual cases to a distribution of means).
3. This is called the *between-group variance* or *mean-squares between* and is symbolized as $S_{Between}^2$ or $MS_{Between}$.
C. The F ratio is the between-group variance estimate divided by the within-group variance estimate.
D. The F distribution.
1. Think of it as constructed by taking one random sample from each of several populations with the same mean, computing an F ratio, repeating this process many times, and constructing a distribution of these F ratios.
2. In practice, there is an exact mathematical F distribution.
3. The F distribution is not symmetrical, but is positively skewed because it is a ratio of variances (which must always be positive).
4. Using the F table requires a numerator degrees of freedom (number of groups minus 1) and a denominator degrees of freedom (sum of degrees of freedom over all the groups–number of participants in each group minus one).

III. **Hypothesis Testing with the Analysis of Variance: Follows same standard five steps.**

IV. **Assumptions in the Analysis of Variance**
A. Same as in t test: normal populations with equal variance.
B. Also as with the t test, the analysis of variance of the kind considered in this chapter is generally robust to moderate violations.
C. Violation of normality is a problem when there is reason to believe populations are strongly skewed in different directions or your sample size is quite small.
D. Violation of equal variances is a problem when the largest variance estimate of any group is 4 or 5 times that of the smallest.
E. If assumptions are seriously violated, alternative procedures (described in Chapter 15) are available.

V. Planned Comparisons
A. The overall analysis of variance does not test which specific population means are different from which.
B. Planned comparisons are procedures for significance testing for comparisons among specific population means.
C. Planned comparisons.
1. These are a subset of all possible comparisons that the researcher specifies in advance of the study.
2. A major problem is keeping overall probability of falsely rejecting any null hypothesis at an acceptable level while testing many comparisons.
3. A common approach to planned comparisons, the Bonferroni procedure, uses a more stringent significance level for each comparison, so that the overall chance of any one of the comparisons being significant is still reasonably low.
4. The general principle in the Bonferroni procedure is to use the true significance level desired divided by the number of planned comparisons conducted.

VI. Controversy: Overall F Versus Targeted Planned Comparisons
A. A controversial recommendation is to ignore the overall analysis of variance results in favor of specific planned comparisons.
B. Linear contrasts are often used in this context. They test a more complex particular predicted relationship, such as one that specifies the pattern of means expected for several groups.

VII. How Analyses of Variance are Described in Research Articles
A. They are usually reported in the article text by giving the sample means (and sometimes the SDs), followed by a standard format for reporting Fs–for example, $F(3,67) = 5.21$, $p < .01$. The first number in parenthesis is the numerator degrees of freedom, the second number is the denominator degrees of freedom.
B. Planned comparisons and linear contrasts are usually described directly. They are a common procedure with post hoc comparisons is to report means in tables with subscripted letters such that those having the same letter are not significantly different from each other.

Formulas

I. Within-group estimate of the population variance when sample sizes are equal (S_{Within}^2 or MS_{Within})

Formula in words: Average of population variance estimates figured from each sample.

Formula in symbols: S_W^2 or $MS_{Within} = (S_1^2 + S_2^2 + ... + S_{Last}^2) / N_{Groups}$

S_1^2 is the unbiased estimate of the variance of Population 1.

S_2^2 is the unbiased estimate of the variance of Population 2.

S_{Last}^2 is the unbiased estimate of the variance of the population corresponding to the last group.

Note: Each $S^2 = \Sigma(X-M)^2/df = SS/df$ (see Chapter 9) refers to where you are supposed to fill in the corresponding figures for the populations between 2 and the last.

N_{Groups} is the number of groups.

II. Variance of the distribution of means estimated from sample means (S_M^2)

Formula in words: Sum of squared deviations of each sample's mean minus the overall mean of all participants, divided by the degrees of freedom for this estimate (the number of groups minus one).

Formula in symbols: $S_M^2 = \Sigma(M\text{-}GM)^2/df_{\text{Between}}$

M is the mean of each sample.

GM is the grand mean–the overall mean of all scores (also, when sample sizes are equal, the mean of the means–$GM = \Sigma M/N_{\text{Groups}}$).

df_{Between} is the degrees of freedom in the between-group estimate–the number of groups minus 1 (that is, $df_{\text{Between}} = N_{\text{Groups}}\text{-}1$).

III. Between-group estimate of the population variance when sample sizes are equal (S_{Between}^2 or MS_{Between})

Formula in words: Variance of the distribution of means times the sample size.

Formulas in symbols: S_{Between}^2 or $MS_{\text{Between}} = (S_M^2)(n)$

n is the number of scores in each sample.

IV. The F ratio

Formula in words: The between-group estimate of the population variance divided by the within-group estimate of the population variance.

Formulas in symbols: $F = S_{\text{Between}}^2/S_{\text{Within}}^2$ or $F = MS_{\text{Between}}/MS_{\text{Within}}$

V. Numerator degrees of freedom or between-groups degrees of freedom (df_{Between})

Formula in words: The number of groups minus 1.

Formula in symbols: $df_{\text{Between}} = N_{\text{Groups}}\text{-}1$

VI. Denominator degrees of freedom or within-groups degrees of freedom (df_{Within})

Formula in words: The sum of the degrees of freedom for all of the groups.

Formula in symbols: $df_{\text{Within}} = df_1 + df_2 + \ldots + df_{\text{Last}}$

df_1 is the degrees of freedom for the first sample.

df_2 is the degrees of freedom for the second sample.

df_{Last} is the degrees of freedom for the last sample.

Note: Each $df = N - 1$ (see Chapter 9).

How to Conduct a One-Way Analysis of Variance
(with Equal Sample Sizes)
(Based on Table 11-6 in the Text)

1. **Restate the question into a research hypothesis and a null hypothesis about populations.**
2. **Determine the characteristics of the comparison distribution.**
   A. The comparison distribution will be an F distribution.
   B. The numerator degrees of freedom is the number of groups minus 1: $df_{Between} = N_{Groups} - 1$.
   C. The denominator degrees of freedom is the sum of the degrees of freedom in each group (the number of cases in the group minus 1): $df_{Within} = df_1 + df_2 + \ldots + df_{Last}$.
3. **Determine the cutoff sample score on the comparison distribution at which the null hypothesis should be rejected.**
   A. Determine the desired significance level.
   B. Look up the appropriate cutoff on an F table, using the degrees of freedom calculated above.
4. **Determine the score of your sample on the comparison distribution. (This will be an F ratio.)**
   A. Figure the between-groups population variance estimate ($S_{Between}^2$ or $MS_{Between}$).
      1. Figure the means of each group.
      2. Figure a variance estimate based on the means of the groups: $S_M^2 = \Sigma(M-GM)^2/df_{Between}$.
      3. Convert this estimate of the variance of a distribution of means to an estimate of the variance of a population of individual scores by multiplying by the number of cases in each group: $S_{Between}^2$ or $MS_{Between} = (S_M^2)(n)$.
   B. Figure the within-groups population variance estimate (S_W^2 or MS_{Within}).
      1. Figure population variance estimates based on each group's scores: For each group, $S^2 = SS/df$.
      2. Average these variance estimates: S_W^2 or $MS_{Within} = (S_1^2+S_2^2+\ldots+S_{Last}^2) / N_G$.
   C. Figure the F ratio: $F = S_{Between}^2/S_{Within}^2$ (or $F = MS_{Between}/MS_{Within}$)
5. **Compare the scores in III and IV to decide whether to reject the null hypothesis.**

How to Conduct Planned Comparisons

1. **Estimate the variance of the distribution of means:** Sum the sample means' squared deviations from the grand mean and divide by the number of means minus 1.

    A. $S_M{}^2 = \sum(M - GM)^2/df_{Between}$

2. **Figure the estimated variance of the population of individual scores:** Multiply the variance of the distribution of means by the number of scores in each group.

    A. $S_{Between}{}^2 = (S_M{}^2)(n)$

How to Figure the Bonferroni Correction

1. **Divide the true desired significance level by the number of planned comparisons.**

Outline for Writing Essays on the Logic and Computations for Conducting a One-Way Analysis of Variance (with Equal Sample Sizes)

The reason for your writing essay questions in the practice problems and tests is that this task develops and then demonstrates what matters so very much–your comprehension of the logic behind the computations. (It is also a place where those better at words than numbers can shine, and for those better at numbers to develop their skills at explaining in words.)

Thus, to do well, be sure to do the following in each essay: (a) give the reasoning behind each step; (b) relate each step to the specifics of the content of the particular study you are analyzing; (c) state the various formulas in nontechnical language, because as you define each term you show you understand it (although once you have defined it in nontechnical language, you can use it from then on in the essay); (d) look back and be absolutely certain that you made it clear just *why* that formula or procedure was applied and *why* it is the way it is.

The outlines below are *examples* of ways to structure your essays. There are other completely correct ways to go about it. And this is an *outline* for an answer–you are to write the answer out in paragraph form. Examples of full essays are in the answers to Set I Practice Problems in the back of the text.

These essays are necessarily very long for you to write (and for others to grade). But this is the very best way to be sure you understand everything thoroughly. One shortcut you may see on a test is that you may be asked to write your answer for someone who understands statistics up to the point of the new material you are studying. You can choose to take the same shortcut in these practice problems (maybe writing for someone who understands right up to whatever point you yourself start being just a little unclear). But every time you write for a person who has never had statistics at all, you review the logic behind the entire course. You engrain it in your mind. Over and over. The time is never wasted. It is an excellent way to study.

I. Restate the question into a null and a research hypothesis about populations. (Step 1 of hypothesis testing.)

State in ordinary language the hypothesis testing issue.

A. The interest in these groups is as representatives, or "samples," of larger groups, or "populations," of particular types of individuals (such as those exposed to various experimental manipulations).

B. Thus you construct a scenario in which the populations do not differ, then do computations based on that scenario to see how likely it is such populations would produce samples of scores whose averages are as different from each other as are the averages of the particular samples in this study.

II. Determine the characteristics of the comparison distribution. (Step 2 of hypothesis testing.)

A. Explain logic of overall approach.

1. We make and compare two estimates of the variation within these populations (which are assumed to be the same).
2. If the scenario of no difference is true, then an estimate based on the variation among the averages of the samples should give the same result as an estimate based on the average variation within each sample.
3. But if the scenario is false (and the population averages differ), then this will increase the estimate based on the differences among the averages of the samples but will not affect the estimate based on the variation within them.
4. Thus, if the scenario of no difference is true, the ratio of the two estimates (one based on differences divided by one based on variation within) should be about 1. If the scenario is false, the ratio should be greater than one.

B. Explain F distribution.

1. Statisticians have determined the probability of getting samples which produce ratios of different sizes under the conditions in which the scenario of no difference is true.
2. The probabilities depend on how many groups there are, and how many participants within each group.

III. Determine the cutoff sample score on the comparison distribution at which the null hypothesis should be rejected. (Step 3 of hypothesis testing.)

A. Procedure: Determine significance level and look up cutoff on an F table.

B. Explanation.

1. Begin by figuring out how large this ratio of the two variation estimates would have to be in order to decide that the probability was so low that it is unlikely that the scenario of no difference could be true.
2. There are standard tables that indicate the size of these ratios associated with various low probabilities.
3. To use these tables you have to decide the kind of situation you have. There are two considerations.
   a. How many groups and how many participants in each group. (State the numbers for your study.)
   b. Just how unlikely would a ratio have to be to decide the whole scenario on which these tables are based (the scenario of no difference) should be rejected? The standard figure used in psychology is less likely than 5% (though 1% is sometimes used to be especially safe). (Say which you are using in your study–if no figure is stated in the problem and no special reason given for using one or the other, the general rule is to use 5%.)
5. State the cutoff F ratio for your situation.

174

IV. Determine the score of your sample on the comparison distribution. (Step 4 of hypothesis testing.)

    A. Estimate the populations' variances based on scores within the samples.

        1. Procedure: Figure $S^2 = SS/df$ for each, then $S_{Within}^2 = (S_1^2 + S_2^2 + ... + S_{Last}^2) / N_{Groups}$.

        2. Explanation.

            a. The variation in a sample ought to be representative of the population it comes from.

            b. State variance formula in lay terms, noting a reason for squaring–to eliminate signs that would cancel each other out.

            c. State unbiased variance formula in lay terms, noting a reason for dividing by N-1 instead of N–to adjust for the tendency of sample variance to be smaller than population variance.

            d. In doing this kind of problem, we assume that all populations have equal variation (unless we have reason to think otherwise).

            e. Thus we can average the estimates of the variation of the populations to get a better overall estimate.

    B. Estimate the variance of the distribution of means.

        1. Procedure: $S_M^2 = \Sigma(M\text{-}GM)^2/df_{Between}$.

        2. Explanation.

            a. Purpose: Intermediate step to computing the population's variation based on the variation among averages of samples.

            b. Think of a population of averages of samples taken at random from a population.

            c. The variation among the averages of these samples ought to reflect the variation among the individual cases in the population (the more variation in one, the more variation in the other).

            d. If the scenario of no difference among population averages is true, then taking one sample from each population is the same as taking the samples all from the same population.

            e. Thus you can make an estimate of the variation in this population based on the variation among the averages of your sample.

            f. Remind the reader of the variance formula and unbiased variance formula already described.

    C. Estimate the populations' variances based on variation among the averages of the samples:

        1. Procedure: $S_{Between}^2 = (S_M^2)(n)$.

        2. Explanation.

            a. The variation in a distribution of averages is less than in a distribution of individual scores (note that the exact relation is in proportion to the number of scores in each sample).

            b. Thus to estimate a population's variation based on the variation in a distribution of averages of samples taken from it, you multiply by the size of each sample.

    D. Figure the ratio of the two variance estimates.

        1. Procedure: $F = S_{Betwen}^2/S_{Within}^2$

        2. Explanation and purpose: This is where you figure the crucial ratio of variation estimates for your particular samples by dividing the estimate based on variation between groups by the estimate based on the variation within.

V. Compare the scores in Steps 3 and 4 to decide whether or not to reject the null hypothesis. (Step 5 of hypothesis testing.)

    A. Note whether or not your F ratio exceeds the cutoff and draw the appropriate conclusion.

        1. Reject the null hypothesis: The variation among the averages of your particular samples is so great that it seems unlikely that their populations are the same. So they seem to be different and the null hypothesis seems untrue.

2. Fail to reject the null hypothesis: The result is inconclusive. On the one hand, these results were not extreme enough to persuade you that the variation was due to the populations being different. On the other hand, it is still possible that they really are different, but because of the people who happened to be selected to be in your samples from the populations, this difference did not show up.

B. Be sure to state your conclusion in terms of your particular measures and situation, so it is clear to a lay person just what the real bottom line of the study is.

Chapter Self-Tests

Multiple-Choice Questions

1. When conducting an analysis of variance,

   a. the null hypothesis is that the populations have the same means.
   b. the sample variances are assumed to be the same.
   c. population variances must differ by no more than 1 *SD*.
   d. preliminary *t* tests are often conducted between the different populations.

2. Which of the following is true about the within-group estimate of the population variance in analysis of variance:

   a. it is unaffected by whether or not the null hypothesis is true.
   b. it reflects the variance caused by experimental conditions.
   c. if the research hypothesis is true, it is larger than the true variance.
   d. its size is a reliable indicator of effect size.

3. When calculating an analysis of variance, if the research hypothesis is in fact true, then

   a. the *F* ratio will always be significant.
   b. the between-group variance estimate is likely to be bigger than the within-group variance estimate.
   c. the within-group variance estimate is likely to be bigger than the between-group estimate.
   d. small sample sizes are sufficient to detect small differences among the variance of sample means.

4. Suppose IQ was tested with children divided into three groups according to their parents' parenting styles. Within the group of children of each parenting style, the IQ scores would

   a. be equal, because within-group variance is always 0.
   b. be equal, because the IQ's of different children within a parenting style grouping are more alike than they are different.
   c. vary, due to differences among the parenting styles.
   d. vary, reflecting variation normally found within the population of children of each parenting style.

5. When conducting an analysis of variance with groups of equal size, the overall estimate of the population variance, based on the variation within groups,

   a. can only be calculated when the variance of the samples are assumed to be equal.
   b. is used to determine the between-group variance.
   c. is estimated by averaging the individual estimates within each group.
   d. is exactly the square root of the sample size minus one.

6. Which of the following is the correct formula for S_M^2?

    a. $\Sigma(M\text{-}GM)/df_{\text{Between}}$.
    b. SS_T/df_{Between}.
    c. $\Sigma(M\text{-}\mu)/df$.
    d. $(M\text{-}\mu)/S^2$.

7. If there are 5 cases in each sample, and the estimated variance of the distribution of means is 8, then MS_{Between} (or S_{Betweem}^2) is

    a. $8/5 = 1.6$.
    b. $8 \times 5 = 40$.
    c. $8^2/5 = 12.8$.
    d. $8/(5\text{-}1) = 2$.

8. One characteristic of the F distribution is that

    a. there is an inherent bias toward increased positive findings for an alpha level of .01.
    b. the degrees of freedom of the F ratio's numerator solely determines which F distribution is used as a comparison distribution.
    c. its range is -1 to $+\infty$.
    d. it is positively skewed (the long tail to the right).

9. After conducting an analysis of variance, if a researcher wanted to present his findings for publication and he had used 8 participants in each group, what should the "___" be in "$F(3,\_\_\_) = 4.93, p < .05$"?

    a. 8.
    b. 11.
    c. 28.
    d. 32.

Fill-In Questions

10. When conducting an analysis of variance, the null hypothesis is that population means are _____ .

11. When conducting an analysis of variance, the _____-group estimate of the population variance should always be pretty accurate, regardless of whether the null hypothesis is true or not.

12. When conducting an analysis of variance and the null hypothesis is true, then the ratio of the between-group variance estimate to the within-group variance estimate should be about _____ .

13. In the signal-to-noise analogy used to clarify analysis of variance, the between-group variance is likened to _____ .

14. In a one-way analysis of variances, "$\Sigma(M\text{-}GM)/df_{\text{Between}}$" is the formula for _____ .

15. In a one-way analysis of variance the between-group variance is figured by first finding the estimate of the variance of the _____ , then multiplying this estimate by the sample size.

16. When conducting an analysis of variance, one assumption that must be met is that the variance is the same in each _____.

17. Although there are circumstances where the reverse is true, in general when participants are selected so that the averages of the groups come out the same (on such variables as intelligence, age, etc.), the power of such a design is _____ ("greater than," "less than," or "the same as") the power of a study in which the participants are just randomly assigned to groups regardless of their scores on these variables.

Problems and Essays

18. A social psychologist interested in the effects of media violence arranged to have 15 children watch a popular children's television program that included a lot of violence. Five were randomly assigned to watch the show on a small-screen television set, five on a standard screen set, and five on a large-set. Immediately after, each child was left in a room with various toys, and the number of seconds of play (during a short observation period) with violent toys was systematically recorded.

    a. Do the data below (which are fictional) suggest that the size of screen on which children watch a violent show makes any difference in the subsequent amount of play with violent toys? (Use the .05 significance level.) Solve this problem explicitly using all five steps of hypothesis testing and illustrate your answer with a sketch showing the comparison distribution, the cutoff (or cutoffs), and the score of the sample on this distribution.
    b. Figure planned comparisons for Small versus Standard, Small versus Large, and Standard versus Large. Test the significance of each of these contrasts using an overall .05 level (that is, each contrast should be tested at a Bonferroni corrected level based on an overall level of .05).
    c. Explain your analysis to a person who has never had a course in statistics.

   Time Playing with Violent Toys After Watching a Violent Program on Televisions of Different-Sized Screens

SMALL	STANDARD	LARGE
65	76	45
68	54	58
59	59	56
54	60	64
57	52	48

19. A researcher was interested in how different groups perceive psychologists. She asked college students, psychologists, lawyers, and people in the general public how important they thought psychologists were to the current United States society (1=Not important, 10=Very important).

    a. Do the data below (which are fictional) suggest that the different groups have differing opinions? (Use the .01 significance level.) Solve this problem explicitly using all five steps of hypothesis testing and illustrate your answer with a sketch showing the comparison distribution, the cutoff (or cutoffs), and the score of the sample on this distribution.
    b. Figure a planned comparisons for each pair, and test the significance of each of these contrasts using an overall .01 level (that is, each contrast should be tested at a Bonferroni corrected level based on an overall level of .01).
    c. Explain your analysis to a person who has never had a course in statistics.

178

Importance of Psychologists According to College Students,
Psychologists, Lawyers, and General Public

COLLEGE	PSYCHOLOGISTS	LAWYERS	PUBLIC
4	6	5	4
3	7	6	4
6	5	7	5

20. A (fictional) psychologist was interested in how persons from different majors scored on an aptitude test he devised.   He selected 5 people from each of the following majors: English, Psychology, and Business.

a. Do the data below suggest that the groups differ on this aptitude test? (Use a .05 level of significance.) Solve this problem explicitly using all five steps of hypothesis testing and illustrate your answer with a sketch showing the comparison distribution, the cutoff (or cutoffs), and the score of the sample on this distribution.

b. Figure a planned comparisons for each pair, and test the significance of each of these contrasts using an overall .01 level (that is, each contrast should be tested at a Bonferroni corrected level based on an overall level of .05).

c. Explain your analysis to a person who has never had a course in statistics.

English	Psychology	Business
7	7	11
4	5	6
11	4	3
8	8	9
2	4	8

21. A health psychologist wanted to examine the relation of social support provided by people in different categories of relationship to the ability of a person to cope with a serious illness. The researcher identified 80 women, all of about the same age and suffering from the same serious illness, 20 of whom during the illness only had had contact with their husband; 20, only contact with their children; 20, only contact with a close woman friend; and 20, only contact with their parents. The (fictional) mean reported level of coping was 4.21 (S^2=3.0) for the husband-only group, 3.81 (S^2=2.0) for the children-only group, 5.29 (S^2=4.0) for the friend-only group, and 2.16 (S^2=3.0) for the parent-only group.

a.   According to these data, is the type of relationship with the person who provides social support associated with different amounts of coping? (Use the .05 level.) .)   Solve this problem explicitly using all five steps of hypothesis testing and illustrate your answer with a sketch showing the comparison distribution, the cutoff (or cutoffs), and the score of the sample on this distribution.

b.   Explain your analysis to a person who has never had a course in statistics.

22. A personality psychologist hypothesized that working adults in the general population, college students, and high school students would differ in their levels of satisfaction with life. She administered a Satisfaction With Life Index to 20 participants in each group. She reported her results as follows: "The means were 6.52 (SD = .87) for working adults, 5.47 (SD = 1.13) for college students, and 4.80 (SD = 1.87) for the high school students. The difference was significant, $F(2, 57) = 8.04, p < .01$." Explain and interpret these results to a person who has never had a course in statistics.

179

Using SPSS (11.0 for Windows) with this Chapter

If you are using SPSS for the first time, before proceeding with the material in this section read the Appendix on Getting Started and the Basics of Using SPSS.

You can use SPSS to carry out the kind of analysis of variance described in this chapter (as well as more advanced analyses of variance). But SPSS requires the raw data to conduct the analysis of variance–it is not set up to handle a problem in which you already have the means and standard deviations.

You should work through the example, following our procedures step by step. Then look over the description of the general principles involved and try the procedures on your own for some of the problems listed in the Suggestions for Additional Practice. Finally, you may want to try the suggestions for using the computer to deepen your understanding.

I. Example
    A. Data: Ratings of a defendant's guilt by participants randomly assigned to groups that receive either information that the defendant has a criminal record, information that the defendant has a clean record, or no information about the defendant's criminal record (fictional data), from the example in the text. The ratings for those in the Criminal Record group are 10, 7, 5, 10, and 8; for those in the Clean Record group, 5, 1, 3, 7, 4, and for those in the No Information group, 4, 6, 9, 3, and 3.
    B. Follow the instructions in the SPSS Appendix for starting up SPSS.
    C. Enter the data as follows.
        1. Type **1** and press enter. Then click on the next box on the same line and type **10** and enter. This will put the subjects two scores on the same line next to each other. The **1** stands for the Criminal Record group (which is arbitrarily labeled **1**, and the **10** is the rating of guilt given by the first subject in the Criminal Record group).
        2. Type the data in the same way for each of the remaining subjects, using **1** for those in the Criminal Record Group, **2** for those in the Clean Record Group and **3** for those in the No Information group.
        3. To name the two variables, click on the Variable View tab. In the first row of the first column type in INFOTYPE under the column titlted "Name." Repeat this process in the second row for the second variable using the variable name GUILT. The screen should now appear as shown in Figure SG11-1.
    D. Carry out the analysis of variance.
        1. Analyze
            Compare Means
                One-Way ANOVA
                    [Highlight GUILT and move it into the Dependent List box. Highlight INFOTYPE and move it into the Factor box.]
                        Continue [Your screen should now appear like Figure SG11-2.]
                          Options
                            [Check Descriptives]
                              Continue
                                  OK
        2. Your results should appear as shown in Figure SG11-3.

Figure SG11-1

Figure SG11-2

181

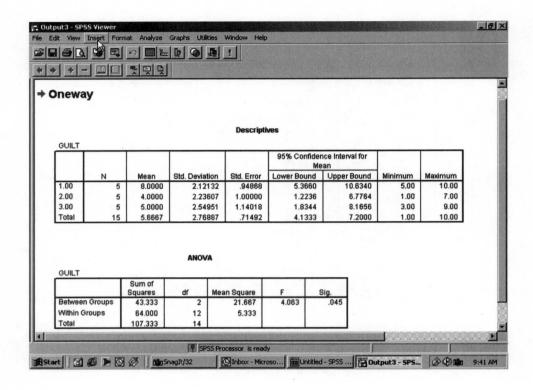

E. Inspect this screen of results.

1. The first table gives the number of cases, mean, estimated population standard deviation, and other statistics for each of the groups..

2. The second table, entitled **ANOVA**, is the analysis of variance.

3. The first column of this table lists the types of population variance estimates.

4. The second column, **Sum of Squares**, (discussed in Chapter 12).

5. The third column, **DF**, gives the degrees of freedom. In the **Between Groups** row, this corresponds to $df_{Between}$; in the **Within Groups** row, this corresponds to df_{Within}. The figures in this example, **2** and **12**, respectively, correspond to those computed in the text.

6. The fourth column, **Mean Squares**, gives the population variance estimates ($S_{Between}$ and S_{Within}), with the between-group estimate (**21.667**) given first and then the within-group estimate (**5.333**). (The text, using rounded-off figures, computed 21.7 and 5.33, respectively.)

7. The next column, **F Ratio**, gives **4.063**, which corresponds closely to the 4.07 computed using rounded figures in the text.

8. Finally, the last column, **Sig**, gives the probability–the exact chance of getting an F ratio this extreme on this particular F distribution. In this example, the probability is **.045**. Since the significance level was set in advance at .05, this result is significant.

H. Print out this screen of results by clicking on File and then Print, or by clicking on the print icon.

I. Save your lines of data as follows.
    1. File
       Save Data
         [Name your data file and designate the drive you would like your data saved in].
         OK

II. Systematic Instructions for Computing a One-Way Analysis of Variance
A. Start up SPSS.

B. Enter the data as follows, with one variable consisting of numbers (such as 1, 2, 3, etc.) representing which group a subject is in and the other variable consisting of the scores on the measured variable.

    1. Type **1** and press enter. Then click on the next box on the same line and type **10** and enter. This will put the subjects two scores on the same line next to each other. The **1** stands for the Criminal Record group (which is arbitrarily labeled **1**, and the **10** is the rating of guilt given by the first subject in the Criminal Record group).

    2. Type the data in the same way for each of the remaining subjects, using **1** for those in the Criminal Record group, **2** for those in the Clean Record group and **3** for those in the No Information group.

    3. To name the two variables , click on the Variable View tab. In the first row of the first column type in INFOTYPE under the column titlted "Name." Repeat this process in the second row for the second variable using the variable name GUILT

C. Carry out the analysis of variance as follows.
    1. Analyze
       Compare Means
         One-Way ANOVA
           [Highlight GUILT and move it into the Dependent List box. Highlight INFOTYPE and move it into the Factor box.]
             Continue
              Options
                [Check Descriptives]
                  Continue
                    OK

D. Save your lines of data as follows.
    1. File
       Save Data
         [Name your data file and designate the drive you would like your data saved in.]
         OK

III. Additional Practice.
(For each data set, conduct an analysis of variance and compare your results to those in the text).
A. Questions 2 and 3 from Chapter 11.

IV. Using the Computer to Deepen Your Knowledge
A. Impacts on the two population variance estimates.

    1. Use SPSS to compute an analysis of variance using the criminal-record example but add 3 points to every subject in the Criminal-Record group. (This increases the differences among the means of the groups but does not change the variance within any of the groups.)

    2. Compute the analysis of variance again with the original data, except this time for the two subjects in the Criminal Record group with 10s make one of them a 0 and one a 20. (This keeps the differences among the means the same, but increases the variance dramatically in the Criminal-Record group.)

3. Compute the analysis of variance yet again with the original data, except this time make all the subjects in the Criminal-Record group have 8s. (This keeps the differences among the means the same, but decreases the variance in the Criminal-Record group to 0.)

4. Compare the results of these analyses, focusing on how these modifications affect the two population variance estimates.

B. Effect of outliers on analysis of variance: Compute an analysis of variance for the criminal-record example, but change one of the scores in the Criminal-Record group to a very high number, say a 40. Compare this to the original result.

Chapter 12
The Structural Model in the Analysis of Variance.

Learning Objectives

To understand, including being able to conduct any necessary computations:

- The structural model of dividing each score's deviation from the grand mean into its deviation from its group's mean and its group's mean's deviation from the grand mean.
- The within-group estimate of the population variance determined using the structural model approach.
- The between-group estimate of the population variance determined using the structural model approach.
- Analysis of variance tables.
- The relation of the structural model approach to the Chapter 11 method.
- The analysis of variance with unequal sample sizes.
- Post hoc comparisons, including the Sheffé test
- Proportion of variance accounted for (R^2) as a measure of effect size in analysis of variance, including its relation to f.
- Power
- The independence assumption and the unit of analysis question.
- How the structural model of analysis of variance and post hoc comparisons are reported in research articles

Chapter Outline

I.   Principles of the Structural Model

A. Dividing up the overall deviation of each score from the grand mean into two parts:
1. Deviation of the score from the mean of its group.
2. Deviation of the mean of the score's group from the grand mean.

B. The sum of squared deviations of each score from the grand mean equals the sum of the squared deviations of each score from its group's mean plus the sum of the squared deviations of each score's group's mean from the grand mean.

C. Dividing each sum of squared deviation by the appropriate degrees of freedom gives the population variance estimates.
1. The between-groups population variance estimate ($S_{Between}^2$ or $MS_{Between}$) is the sum of squared deviations of each score's group's mean from the grand mean ($SS_{Between}$) divided by the degrees of freedom on which it is based ($df_{Between}$–the number of groups minus 1).
2. The within-groups population variance estimate (S_{Within}^2 or MS_{Within}) is the sum of squared deviations of each score from its group's mean (SS_{Within}) divided by the total degrees of freedom on which this is based (df_{Within}, which is the sum of the degrees of freedom for all the groups).

D. Logic of analysis of variance.
   1. If the null hypothesis is true, the division of the overall deviation into two parts should be random, making population estimates producing an F ratio of about 1.
   2. If the research hypothesis is true, the deviations of the group means from the grand mean should be greater than the deviations of the scores from their group's mean, making population estimates producing an F ratio greater than 1.

II. Analysis of Variance Tables
A. These tables are used to show analysis of variance results and are based on the structural model approach.
B. The columns give the following information.
   1. Source (type of variance estimate/deviation score).
   2. SS (sum of squared deviations).
   3. df (degrees of freedom).
   4. MS (mean squares–that is, population variance estimates).
   5. F ratio.
C. Each row refers to one of the variance estimates: between, within, and total.

III. Analysis of Variance with Unequal Sized Groups
A. Can not be done with the Chapter 11 method.
B. The structural-model approach automatically makes the necessary adjustments for unequal sample sizes.

IV. Assumptions for an Analysis of Variance with Unequal Sample Sizes
A. Same as with equal sample sizes.
B. Less robust to violations of equal population variances (than with equal sample sizes).

V. Post-hoc Comparisons
A. These are all possible comparisons among groups to explore all possible differences.
B. Various procedures are used for post hoc comparisons which attempt to keep overall chance of falsely rejecting the null hypothesis low while maintaining adequate power.
   1. Boneferroni procedure is safe but the conservative nature of the test makes achieving significance unlikely.
   2. Other procedures available include the Sheffé test and the Tukey test.
   3. The Sheffé test can be used for both simple and complex comparisons.
   4. To conduct a Sheffé test, divide the overall F ratio by the overall $df_{Between}$ and compare to the omnibus F cutoff level.

VI. Effect Size: The Proportion of Variance Accounted for (R^2)
A. Sum of squared deviations of each score's group's mean from the grand mean, divided by the sum of squared deviations of each score from the grand mean. Also known as η^2 (*eta* squared); η^2 is sometimes called the correlation ratio.
B. Minimum 0, maximum 1. Square root is a correlation (R).
C. Effect size conventions for R^2:
   1. Small = .01.
   2. Medium = .06.
   3. Large = .14.

186

VII. Power and Planning Sample Size

A. Power.

    1. Main determinants of power are effect size, sample size, significance level, and number of groups.

    2. Table 12-7 in the text gives approximate power for small, medium, and large effect sizes, for 3, 4, or 5 groups, all using the .05 significance level.

B. Planning sample size: Table 12-7 in the text gives the approximate number of participants needed to achieve 80% power for estimated small, medium, and large effect sizes, for 3, 4, or 5 groups, all using the .05 significance level.

VIII. Controversy: The Independence Assumption and Unit of Analysis.
Analysis of variance assumes that each score is independent of the others.   To avoid violating this assumption,

A. The researcher can design the study with this in mind

B. Change the unit of analysis

    1. Instead of using individual scores, the researcher could use the average score for a group

    2. However, this can greatly reduce the power of an experiment.

C. Analyze for similarities within groups

IX. Structural Model Analysis of Variance and Post Hoc Comparisons as Described in Research Articles. Most computer programs (such as SPSS) provide an ANOVA table like those described in this chapter.

A. Anova tables were common in older articles; more recent articles rarely include such tables.

B. Researchers often report post hoc comparisons among all pairs of means.

    1. Researchers commonly put small letters by the means in tables.

    2. Means with the same letter are not significantly different.

Formulas

I.   Between-group estimate of the population variance ($SS_{Between}{}^2$ or $MS_{Between}$)

Formula in words: Sum of squared deviations of each score's group's mean from the grand mean, divided by the degrees of freedom on which it is based (the number of groups minus 1).

Formulas in symbols: $S_{Between}{}^2 = \Sigma(M - GM)^2/df_{Between}$ or $MS_{Between} = S_{Between}/df_{Between}$

M is the mean of each sample.

GM is the grand mean–the overall mean of all scores.

$df_{Between}$ is the degrees of freedom in the between-group estimate–the number of groups minus 1 (that is, $df_{Between} = N_{Groups}-1$).

$SS_{Between}$ is the sum of squared deviations of each score's group's mean from the grand mean–$\Sigma(M-GM)^2$.

II. Within-group estimate of the population variance (S_{Within}^2 or MS_{Within})

Formula in words: Sum of squared deviations of each score from its group's mean, divided by the total degrees of freedom on which this is based (the number of scores in each group minus 1, summed over all groups).

Formula in symbols: $S_{Within}^2 = \Sigma(X\text{-}m)^2/df_{Within}$ or $MS_{Within} = SS_{Within}/df_{Within}$

X is each score.

df_{Within} is the degrees of freedom in the within-group estimate–the number of scores in each group minus 1, summed over all groups–$df_{Within} = df_1 + df_2 + \ldots + df_{Last}$.

SS_{Within} is the sum of squared deviations of each score minus the mean of its group–$\Sigma(X\text{-}M)^2$.

III. Proportion of variance accounted for (R^2)

Formula in words: Sum of squared deviations of each score's group's mean from the grand mean, divided by the sum of squared deviations of each score from the grand mean.

Formula in symbols: $R^2 = SS_{Between}/SS_{Total}$

SS_{Total} is the sum of squared deviations of each score from the grand mean–$\Sigma(X\text{-}GM)^2$.

Alternate formula for computing R^2 using F and degrees of freedom reported in a research article: $R^2 = (df_{Between})/([F][df_{Between}]+df_{Within})$.

How to Conduct an Analysis of Variance Using the Structural Model-Based Method

1. **Restate the question into a research hypothesis and a null hypothesis about the populations.**

2. **Determine the characteristics of the comparison distribution.**
    A. The comparison distribution will be an F distribution.
    B. The numerator degrees of freedom is the number of groups minus 1:
    $df_{Betwen} = N_{Groups} -1$.
    C. The denominator degrees of freedom is the sum of the degrees of freedom in each group (the number of cases in the group minus 1):
    $df_{Within} = df_1 + df_2 + \ldots + df_{Last}$.
    D. Check the accuracy of your computations by making sure that df_{Within} and $df_{Between}$ sum to df_{Total} (which is the total number of cases minus 1).

3. **Determine the cutoff sample score on the comparison distribution at which the null hypothesis should be rejected.**
    A. Decide the desired significance level.
    B. Look up the appropriate cutoff in an F table.

188

4. **Determine the sample's score on the comparison distribution. (This will be an F ratio.)**
   A. Figure the mean of each group and the grand mean of all scores.
   B. Figure the following deviations for each score.
      1. Its deviation from the grand mean ($X - GM$).
      2. Its deviation from its group's mean ($X - M$).
      3. Its group's mean's deviation from the grand mean ($M - GM$).
   C. Square each of these deviation scores.
   D. Figure the sums of each of these three types of deviation scores (SS_{Total}, SS_{Within} and $SS_{Between}$).
   E. Check the accuracy of your computations by making sure that
      $$SS_{Within} + SS_{Between} = SS_{Total}.$$
   F. Figure the between-group variance estimate: $SS_{Between}/df_{Between}$.
   G. Figure the within-group variance estimate: SS_{Within}/df_{Within}
   H. Figure the F ratio: $F = S_{Between}^2/S_{Within}^2$.

5. **Compare the scores obtained in Steps 3 and 4 to decide whether to reject the null hypothesis.**

Analysis of Variance Table and Symbols for the One-Way Analysis of Variance

Source	SS	df	MS	F
Between	$SS_{Between}$	$df_{Between}$	$MS_{Between}$ (or $S_{Between}^2$)	F
Within	SS_{Within}	df_{Within}	MS_{Within} (or S_{Within}^2)	F
Total	SS_{Total}	df_{Total}		

Formulas for Each Section of the Analysis of Variance Table

Source	SS	df	MS	F
Between	$\Sigma(M-GM)^2$	$N_{Groups}-1$	$SS_{Between}/df_{Between}$	$MS_{Between}/MS_{Within}$
Within	$\Sigma(X-M)^2$	*	SS_{Within}/df_{Within}	
Total	$\Sigma(X-GM)^2$	$N-1$	SS_{Total}/df_{Total}	

$$*df_1 + df_2 + ... + df_{Last}$$

Definitions of Basic Symbols

Σ is the usual sum sign–which here refers to adding up the appropriate numbers for all cases

M is the mean of a score's group

GM is the grand mean

N_{Groups} is the number of groups

X is each score

N is the total number of cases in the study

How to Conduct a Sheffé Procedure

1.   Figure the comparison in the usual way (from Chapter 11), but divide the *F* by the overall study's $df_{Between}$ and use the overall study's *F* cutoff.

Outline for Writing Essays on the Logic and Computations for Conducting a One-Way Analysis of Variance Using the Structural Model Approach

The reason for your writing essay questions in the practice problems and tests is that this task develops and then demonstrates what matters so very much–your comprehension of the logic behind the computations. (It is also a place where those better at words than numbers can shine, and for those better at numbers to develop their skills at explaining in words.)

Thus, to do well, be sure to do the following in each essay: (a) give the reasoning behind each step; (b) relate each step to the specifics of the content of the particular study you are analyzing; (c) state the various formulas in nontechnical language, because as you define each term you show you understand it (although once you have defined it in nontechnical language, you can use it from then on in the essay); (d) look back and be absolutely certain that you made it clear just *why* that formula or procedure was applied and *why* it is the way it is.

The outlines below are *examples* of ways to structure your essays. There are other completely correct ways to go about it. And this is an *outline* for an answer–you are to write the answer out in paragraph form. Examples of full essays are in the answers to Set I Practice Problems in the back of the text.

These essays are necessarily very long for you to write (and for others to grade). But this is the very best way to be sure you understand everything thoroughly. One shortcut you may see on a test is that you may be asked to write your answer for someone who understands statistics up to the point of the new material you are studying. You can choose to take the same shortcut in these practice problems (maybe writing for someone who understands right up to whatever point you yourself start being just a little unclear). But every time you write for a person who has never had statistics at all, you review the logic behind the entire course. You engrain it in your mind. Over and over. The time is never wasted. It is an excellent way to study.

I.   Reframe the question into a research hypothesis and a null hypothesis about populations. (Step 1 of hypothesis testing.)
State in ordinary language the hypothesis testing issue.
A. The interest in these groups is as representatives, or "samples," of larger groups, or "populations," of particular types of individuals (such as those exposed to various experimental manipulations).
B. Thus, you construct a scenario in which the populations do not differ and then do computations based on that scenario to see how likely it is such populations would produce samples of scores whose averages are as different from each other as are the averages of the particular samples in this study.

II. Determine the characteristics of the comparison distribution. (Step 2 of hypothesis testing.)

A. Explain logic of overall approach.
   1. We make and compare two estimates of the variance within these populations (which are assumed to be the same).
   2. If the scenario of no difference is true, then an estimate based on the variation among the averages of the samples should give the same result as an estimate based on the average variation within each sample.
   3. But if the scenario is false (and the population averages differ), then this will increase the estimate based on the differences among the averages of the samples but will not affect the estimate based on the variation within them.
   4. Thus, if the scenario of no difference is true, the ratio of the two estimates (one based on differences divided by one based on variation within) should be about 1. If the scenario is false, the ratio should be greater than one.

B. Explain F distribution.
   1. Statisticians have determined the probability of getting samples which produce ratios of different sizes under the conditions in which the scenario of no difference is true.
   2. The probabilities depend on how many groups there are and how many participants.

III. Determine the cutoff sample score on the comparison distribution at which the null hypothesis should be rejected. (Step 3 of hypothesis testing.)

A. Procedure: Determine significance level and look up cutoff on an F table.

B. Explanation.
   1. Begin by figuring out how large this ratio of the two variation estimates would have to be in order to decide that the probability was so low that it is unlikely that the scenario of no difference could be true.
   2. There are standard tables that indicate the size of these ratios associated with various low probabilities.
   3. To use these tables you have to decide the kind of situation you have. There are two considerations.
      a. How many groups and how many participants overall. (State the numbers for your study.)
      b. Just how unlikely would a ratio have to be to decide the whole scenario on which these tables are based (the scenario of no difference) should be rejected? The standard figure used in psychology is less likely than 5% (though 1% is sometimes used to be especially safe). (Say which you are using in your study–if no figure is stated in the problem and no special reason given for using one or the other, the general rule is to use 5%.)
   4. State the cutoff F ratio for your situation.

IV. Determine the score of your sample on the comparison distribution. (Step 4 of hypothesis testing.)

A. Estimate the populations' variation based on scores within the samples.
   1. Divide each score's deviation from the overall average into two components–its deviation from its group's average and its group's average's deviation from the overall average. These two deviations provide the basis for making the two estimates of the overall variation in the populations.
   2. The estimate based on the variation of each score from its group's average is influenced only by variation within each group. It is figured by squaring each such deviation (to eliminate signs) and finding a kind of average of these squared deviations. (An ordinary average would underestimate the population variation, so instead one divides the total by the number of scores in each group minus 1.)

3. The estimate based on the variation of each score's group's average from the overall average is influenced both by the variation within each of the groups and any variation between groups. It is figured by squaring each score's group's average deviation from the overall average and finding a kind of average of these deviations (in this case, you divide by the number of groups minus one–again, this is an adjustment for estimating the population variation from information in samples).

    B. Figure the ratio of these two estimates of the population variation.

V. Compare the scores obtained in Steps 3 and 4 to decide whether to reject the null hypothesis. (Step 5 of hypothesis testing.)

    A. Note whether your F ratio exceeds the cutoff and draw the appropriate conclusion.

        1. Reject the null hypothesis: The variation among the averages of your particular samples is so great that it seems unlikely that their populations are the same. So they seem to be different and the null hypothesis seems untrue.

        2. Fail to reject the null hypothesis: The result is inconclusive. On the one hand, these results were not extreme enough to persuade you that the variation was due to the populations being different. On the other hand, it is still possible that they really are different, but because of the people who happened to be selected to be in your samples from the populations, this difference did not show up.

    B. Be sure to state your conclusion in terms of your particular measures and situation, so it is clear to a lay person just what the real bottom line of the study is.

Chapter Self-Tests

Multiple-Choice Questions

1. All of the following are advantages of understanding the structural model of the analysis of variance, EXCEPT

    a. unequal sample sizes can be easily dealt with.
    b. deeper insights into the underlying logic of the analysis of variance can be obtained.
    c. the results of the analysis are more accurate even when using equal sample sizes.
    d. it will be easier to understand the results laid out in computer printouts.

2. In the structural model of the analysis of variance, the deviation of a score from the grand mean is divided into

    a. an F distribution and a distribution of deviations from the F distribution.
    b. the Master Contributing Factor and the Lesser Contributing Factor.
    c. the within-group median and the between-group median.
    d. the deviation of the score from the mean of its group and the deviation of the mean of its group from the grand mean.

3. $\Sigma(X\text{-}GM)^2 =$

    a. $\Sigma(X\text{-}M)^2 + \Sigma(M\text{-}GM)^2$.
    b. $\Sigma(X\text{-}M)^2/\Sigma M^2$.
    c. $\Sigma(M\text{-}GM)^2/\Sigma M^2$.
    d. $\Sigma(M\text{-}GM)^2 - \Sigma M^2$.

4. The within-group population variance estimate is all of the following, EXCEPT

    a. $\Sigma(X\text{-}GM)^2 + \Sigma(M\text{-}GM)^2$.

    b. the sum of squared deviations of each score from its group mean, divided by the total degrees of freedom for the groups.

    c. SS_{Within}/df_{Within}.

    d. MS_{Within}.

5. In an analysis of variance, when the null hypothesis is rejected, then

    a. the groups with the two most extreme means are likely to represent populations with different means, although that is not guaranteed.

    b. the groups with the two most extreme means always come from populations with two different means, but the other groups may or may not come from populations with different means.

    c. all of the groups come from populations with different means.

    d. all of the groups come from populations with the same mean.

6. In an analysis of variance in which you conduct four planned comparisons, each at the .01 level, if you make no special adjustments, what is the approximate overall chance that at least one of the comparisons will be significant by chance?

    a. .0025.

    b. .01.

    c. .04.

    d. .20.

7. Compared to post-hoc comparisons, planned comparisons

    a. never have more power.

    b. almost always have less power.

    c. almost always have more power.

    d. have more power unless the planned comparison is a linear contrast.

8. When conducting an analysis of variance with unequal sample sizes,

    a. violations of equal population variances are more serious than when there are equal sample sizes.

    b. violations of equal population variances are less serious than when there are equal sample sizes (provided the assumption of normal population variances is met).

    c. the assumption of normal population distributions does not apply.

    d. the assumption of equal population variances does not apply.

9. The degree to which variation in the variable that is measured is explained by the experimental manipulation (R^2)

    a. indicates the degree to which the measured variable causes an effect in the experimental manipulation.

    b. is determined by the Bonferroni procedure.

    c. is the same as the degree to which a subject's particular score is related to which group the subject is in.

    d. depends mainly on the size of the samples.

10. If a study yields 100 as a sum of squared deviations of scores from the grand mean and 25 as a sum of squared deviations of scores from their group means, then the proportion of variance accounted for is

a. $100/(100-25) = 1.3$.
b. $(100-25)/100 = .75$.
c. $25/100 = .25$.
d. $100/25 = 4.0$.

11. When the participants of a study include multiple individuals from within existing groups, the _____ assumption is likely to be violated.
a. normal distribution
b. independence
c. parametric
d. equal populations

Fill-In Questions

12. $(X-GM)^2 = (X-M)^2 +$ _____.

13-15. For questions 13-15, refer to the following data:

	GROUP A				GROUP B		
X	$(X-GM)^2$	$(X-M)^2$	$(M-GM)^2$	X	$(X-GM)^2$	$(X-M)^2$	$(M-GM)^2$
27	9	4	25	17	49	16	9
32	64	9	25	26	4	25	9
28	16	1	25	24	0	9	9
20	16	1	9				
18	36	9	9				
87	89	24	75	105	105	50	45

M = 87/3 = 29   M = 105/5 = 21

GM = (105 + 87)/8 = 24

13. $SS_{Total} =$ _____.

14. $SS_{Within} =$ _____.

15. $SS_{Between} =$ _____.

16. Fill in the missing numbers:

Source	SS	df	MS	F
Between	40	4	____	____
Within	50	25	____	
Total	____	____		

17. The most general post hoc test is the _____.

18. In _____, all possible comparisons have to be considered in evaluating the chance of getting any one of them significant.

19. For R^2, _____ is a medium effect size.

20-21. A psychology professor studied the effects of coffee on first year college students. All of the students in his class volunteered for his study, and he randomly divided them into three groups: a Caffeine group which drank two cups of regular coffee; a Decaf group which drank two cups of decaffeinated coffee (without knowing it was decaffeinated); and a No-Coffee group. Immediately afterwards a pop-quiz was given. The professor recorded the quiz scores and also the students' responses to a measure of nervousness. Use the results below to answer questions 9 and 10.

MEASURE	NO COFFEE	CAFFEINE	DECAF	$F_{(2,57)}$
Quiz Score	6.39_a	8.21_b	7.11_a	5.75**
Nervousness	68.04_a	90.03_b	92.06_b	3.48*

_____
* $p<.05$ **$p<.01$
Note: Within each row, means with different subscripts differed at the .05 level, based on the Newman-Keuls test.

20. The Quiz Score was significantly different over all groups, at the _____ significance level.

21. The Caffeine group's nervousness was significantly different from the _____ group.

Problems and Essays

22. A clinical psychologist had developed a new way of measuring depression and tested it by administering it to three groups of participants. Three participants who had been diagnosed as having severe depression scored 8.7, 9.6, and 7.5; three participants who had been diagnosed as having mild depression scored 6.6, 8.5, and 8.4; and four participants from the general public scored 2.4, 4.7, 3.9, and 4.1.

    a. Based on these data, is there a significant difference among the three groups on scores on the new measure of depression (use the .01 level)? .) Solve this problem explicitly using all five steps of hypothesis testing.
    b. Explain your conclusion and procedure to a person who has never had a course in statistics.

23. A perceptual psychologist was studying figure-ground reversal. Does the amount of working with imagery in daily life affect the rate of figure-ground reversal? Specifically, do art, math, and literature students reverse figure and ground at different rates on ambiguous pictures? Math students reported reversals at 2.6, 3.0, and 4.7 seconds; literature students at 4.3, 3.8, and 2.9 seconds; and art students at 2.9, 3.2, 1.0, 1.8, and 2.1 seconds.

    a. Based on these data, is there a significant difference in speed of figure-ground reversal for students in these three majors? (Use the .05 level.) .) Solve this problem explicitly using all five steps of hypothesis testing
    b. Explain your conclusion and procedure to a person who has never had a course in statistics.

24. A psychologist wanted to know if people from different parts of the country scored differently on a motivation scale. The (fictional) data are as follows:

East Coast: 4, 7, 9, 9

Midwest: 6, 8, 10, 7

West Coast: 8, 7, 3, 6

   a. Based on these data, is there a significant difference in motivation scores based on geographic area? (Use the .05 level). .) Solve this problem explicitly using all five steps of hypothesis testing

   b. Explain your conclusion and procedure to a person who has never had a course in statistics.

25. A developmental psychologist devised an experiment to test the learning skills of children. All children performed a task, but some of the children received no information about the task (the "None" condition), some were told a subsequent task would depend on what they learned in the first task (the "Important" condition), and some were specifically told they would not need to know the information later (the "Useless" group). Two studies were conducted, one on five year olds and the other on eight year olds. Below are the results. Answer questions 3 and 4 with these results in mind.

Mean Scores on Task Performance as a Function of Information Condition, for 5 Year Olds and 8 Year Olds

	Information Received			
Age	None	Useless	Important	$F_{(2,31)}$
5	44.33_a	40.33_{ab}	44.32_b	4.39*
8	63.80_a	52.08_b	75.61_c	18.65**

*$p<.05$ **$p<.01$

NOTE: In each row, means with different subscripts are different at the .05 level, Tukey's HSD test.

Based on these data, describe the effect of the type of information received on the task performance for five year olds to a person who is not familiar with statistics. In your description include a discussion of the logic of the structural model of the analysis of variance and of multiple comparisons.

26. Using the eight year olds as an example, explain the underlying logic of the structural model of the analysis of variance and calculate R^2, describing its underlying meaning to a person who is not familiar with statistics.

Using SPSS (11.0 for Windows) with this Chapter

If you are using SPSS for the first time, before proceeding with the material in this section read the Appendix on Getting Started and the Basics of Using SPSS.

This SPSS section for Chapter 12 begins with the Chapter 11 example. If you have not done this yet, you should first do it before reading the discussion of the interpretation of the output provided here. Then try the procedures on your own for some of the problems involving unequal sample sizes listed in the Suggestions for Additional Practice. Finally, you may want to try the suggestions for using the computer to deepen your understanding and to explore the advanced SPSS procedures, multiple comparisons.

I. Deeper Understanding of the SPSS Analysis of Variance Output

A. Figure SG12-1, below, is the output from the Chapter 11 SPSS example for the analysis of variance. (This is the same as Figure SG11-3.)

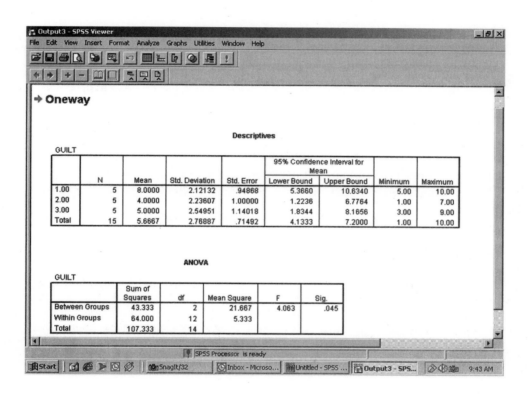

Figure SG12-1

B. The second column of the ANOVA table, labeled **Sum of Squares**, gives the **Between Groups**, **Within Groups**, and **Total** sums of squares. In the example, these are **43.333**, **64.000**, and **107.333**, respectively, corresponding closely to the figures of 43.34, 64, and 107.34 figured in the text (see Table 12-1).

II. Additional Practice

(For each data set, conduct an analysis of variance and compare your results to those in the text.)

A. Text examples.

1. Data in Table 12-3 comparing anxiety scores for three different groups of patients (fictional data based on Clark et al., 1997).

B. Practice problems in the text.

1. Set I: 4 and 5.
2. Set II: 16 and 17.

III. Using the Computer to Deepen Your Knowledge

A. Multiple t tests.

1. Use SPSS to compute three t tests for the Criminal-Record data, comparing the Criminal-Record group to the Clean-Record group, the Criminal-Record group to the No-Information group, and the Clean-Record group to the No- Information group.
2. How do these results compare to the overall analysis of variance?

B. F and R^2.

1. Double the number of scores for each condition in the criminal record example (just add another five subjects to each group with exactly the same scores) and then conduct the analysis of variance, and compute the R^2 using the sums of squares given in the output.
2. Notice that the F increases but R^2 does not change. Why? (Hint: Refer to the discussion of power and effect size.)

IV. Advanced Procedures: Multiple Comparisons

A. Several widely used multiple comparison procedures are available when you conduct a one-way analysis of variance with SPSS.

B. To carry out a multiple comparison procedure, once you have set up your ANOVA, you click on the post-hoc box and choose which type of comparison you would like to use.

1. For a Newman-Keuls test, the code is **SNK**. (This is one of the most widely used procedures for post-hoc comparisons.)
2. For Tukey's honestly significant difference test, the code is **TUKEY**. (This is another widely used procedure for post-hoc comparisons.)
3. For Scheffé's test, the code is **SCHEFFE**. (This is yet another widely used procedure for post-hoc comparisons.)
4. For the Bonferroni procedure, the code is **LSD**. (This is a widely used procedure for planned comparisons. But when used with the **ONEWAY** command it is applied to all pairwise comparisons.)

Chapter 13
Factorial Analysis of Variance

Learning Objectives

To understand, including being able to conduct any necessary computations:

- Basic logic of factorial designs.
- Terminology for describing factorial designs.
- Recognizing and interpreting interaction and main effects from a table of means.
- Graphing and interpreting graphs of results of factorial design studies.
- Application of the structural model to the two-way analysis of variance.
- Assumptions for factorial analysis of variance.
- Effect size in the two-way analysis of variance.
- Power in the two-way analysis of variance.
- Extensions of two-way analysis of variance to analyses involving more than two dimensions, unequal sample sizes, and repeated-measures.
- How results of a two-way analysis of variance are presented in research articles.

Chapter Outline

I. **Basic Logic of Factorial Designs and Interaction Effects**
   A. A *factorial design* is a study in which the influence of two or more grouping variables is studied at once by constructing groupings that include every combination of the levels of these variables.
   B. A factorial design with two grouping variables can be diagrammed as a two-dimensional chart with the levels of one variable arrayed across the rows and the levels of the other variable arrayed across the columns.
   C. A factorial design is more efficient because it permits using all participants in the study to test hypotheses for each grouping variable.
   D. A factorial design permits the researcher to test *interaction effects*–the situation in which the influence of one grouping variable differs according to the level of the other grouping variable.

II. **Terminology of Factorial Designs**
   A. The number of grouping variables is referred to as the number of *dimensions* or "*ways*" (e.g., a "two-way factorial design").
   B. A *main effect* is an effect of one variable averaged across the levels of the other grouping variable(s).
   C. In a two-way design there are two possible main effects and one possible interaction effect.
   D. A factorial design can be characterized by the number of levels in each grouping variable (e.g., "a 2 X 3 factorial design").
   E. A *cell mean* is the mean of scores in a particular combination of levels of the grouping variables.
   F. A *marginal mean* is the mean of scores in a particular level of one of the grouping variables.

1. A *row mean* is the marginal mean for one of the levels of the grouping variable whose levels are arrayed vertically in the diagram of the factorial design.
2. A *column mean* is the marginal mean for one of the levels of the grouping variable whose levels are arrayed horizontally in the diagram of the factorial design.

G. Differences in marginal means for a particular grouping variable indicate a main effect.

H. One must inspect the cell means to identify an interaction effect.

III. **Recognizing and Interpreting Interaction Effects**

A. An interaction effect is described verbally in terms of different effects of each grouping variable according to the level of the other grouping variable.

B. In a two-way factorial design study interaction effects are identified numerically from the pattern of cell means.
   1. An interaction arises when the pattern of differences across columns is not the same in each row.
   2. Equivalently, an interaction arises when the pattern of differences across columns is not the same in each row.

C. Graphing results of a two-way factorial-design study.
   1. The vertical axis of the graph represents the values of the grouping variable.
   2. The levels of one grouping variable is arrayed across the horizontal axis of the graph.
   3. For each level of the other grouping variable, a line is put in the graph connecting dots representing the cell means for its combination with each level of the other grouping variable.

D. Interpreting a bar graph of the results of a two-way factorial design study.
   1. An interaction is indicated by the bars not being parallel.
   2. A main effect for the grouping variable whose levels are represented by different bars is indicated by the lines having different average heights.
   3. A main effect for the grouping variable whose levels are arrayed across the horizontal axis is indicated by the bars having different average slopes.

E. Any combination of main and interaction effects is possible.

IV. **Basic Logic of the Two-Way Analysis of Variance**

A. The two-way analysis of variance is the statistical procedure used to test hypotheses about main and interaction effects in a two-way factorial design study.

B. In a two-way analysis of variance there are three F ratios (one for each main effect and one for the interaction effect).

C. Each F ratio represents a between-group variance estimate for its corresponding main or interaction effect, divided in each case by the same within-group variance estimate, which is based on the variation within each cell.

D. Between-group variance estimates for main effects.
   1. For the row grouping variable, based on the variation among the row means.
   2. For the column grouping variable, based on the variation among the column means.

E. Between-group variance estimate for interaction effect is based on the variation among combinations of cells other than those in the same columns or rows.
   1. In a 2 X 2 design, these are the combination of the two cells in one diagonal versus the combination of the two cells in the other diagonal.
   2. In a design with three or more levels on either dimension, there is more than one combination of cells to be considered.

V. Structural Model for the Two-Way Analysis of Variance
    A. Each score's deviation from the grand mean is divided into four components:
        1. Score's deviation from mean of its cell (used for computing within-group variance estimate).
        2. Deviation of the score's row's mean from the grand mean (used for computing row variable's between-group variance estimate).
        3. Deviation of the score's column's mean from the grand mean (used for computing column variable's between-group variance estimate).
        4. A remaining deviation (used for computing the interaction between-group variance estimate).
    B. Each variance estimate is computed by squaring each deviation, summing them over all participants, and dividing by the appropriate degrees of freedom.
    C. Computing degrees of freedom.
        1. df for each main effect: Number of levels of the variable minus 1.
        2. df for interaction effect: Number of cells, minus df for row main effect, minus df for column main effect, minus 1.
        3. df for within-group variance estimate: Sum of degrees of freedom over all cells (for each cell, df is cell's number of cases minus 1).
        4. Total degrees of freedom (df_{Total}) is the number of scores minus 1.
    D. Table for two-way analysis of variance is like that for one-way analysis (as in Chapter 12), except there is a row for each of the three between-group effects.
    E. Hypothesis testing procedure is the same as with a one-way analysis of variance, except there are research and null hypotheses to be tested for each main effect and the interaction effect.

VI. Assumptions in the Two-Way Analysis of Variance
    A. Same as with one-way analysis of variance.
    B. Assumptions apply to the populations corresponding to each cell.

VII. Power and Effect Size in the Two-Way Analysis of Variance
    A. Power and effect size calculated the same way as for a one-way analysis of variance.
    B. The proportion of variance accounted for (R^2) can be computed for each main effect and the interaction effect.
    C. R^2 is computed for each effect as the SS for that effect (SS_{Column}, SS_{Row}, or $SS_{Interaction}$) divided by the portion of SS_{Total} remaining after subtracting out the SS for each of the other two effects.
    D. R^2 for each effect can also be computed directly from Fs and degrees of freedom given in a published research report.
    E. Power (and corresponding power and sample size tables) is influenced by the number of levels of the effect and the number of levels of the effect with which it is crossed.

VIII. Extensions and Special Cases of the Factorial Analysis of Variance
    A. Three-way and higher factorial designs are a straightforward extension of two-way logic and procedures.
    B. Repeated-measures analysis of variance.

1. Arises when one or more of the grouping variables represents different measures on the same individuals (such as the same test given to the same participants before, during, and after some procedure).
2. Sometimes a repeated-measures variable is crossed with an ordinary between-subjects variable.
3. Requires special procedures.
4. There is some controversy over the appropriate procedures to use because the more traditional approach requires rigid assumptions that are often violated in practice.

IX. Controversies
A. One issue is about what to do when there are unequal number of participants in the various cells.
   1. One approach is to randomly eliminate scores from cells with too many, however this wastes power.
   2. The preferred procedure, *least-squares analysis of variance* (available on most computer programs), equalizes influence of the different cells on the main and interaction effect computation. The least-squares analysis of variance is the optimal approach. The result of using this approach is that each cell's influence on the main and interaction effects is equalized.
B. A second issue is about how to handle a situation in which one of your variables is quantitative rather than categorical. The variable can be dichotomized by making a median split of the scores, however there is debate over the appropriateness of this technique.

X. Factorial Analysis of Variance Results as Described in Research Articles
A. Cell means and Fs are given in tables or text.
B. If it is a complex analysis, a partial analysis-of-variance table may be given.
C. Graphs showing the pattern of cell means are often provided when there is a significant interaction effect.

Formulas

I. Between-group estimates of the population variance for rows (S^2_{Rows} or MS_{Rows})

Formula in words: Sum of squared deviations of each score's row's mean from the grand mean, divided by the degrees of freedom on which it is based (the number of rows minus 1).

Formulas in symbols: S^2_{Rows} or $MS_{Rows} = SS_{Rows} / df_{Rows}$

df_{Rows} is the degrees of freedom in the between-group estimate for rows. It is the number of rows minus 1: $df_{Rows} = N_{Rows}-1$.

SS_{Rows} is the sum of squared deviations of each score's row's mean from the grand mean: $\Sigma(M_{Rows}-GM)^2$.

M_{Row} is the mean of each row.

GM is the grand mean-the overall mean of all scores.

202

II. Between-group estimates of the population variance for columns ($S_{Columns}^2$ or $MS_{Columns}$)

Formula in words: Sum of squared deviations of each score's column's mean from the grand mean, divided by the degrees of freedom on which it is based (the number of columns minus 1).

Formulas in symbols: $S_{columns}^2$ or $MS_{columns} = SS_{Columns}/df_{Columns}$

$df_{Columns}$ is the degrees of freedom in the between-group estimate for columns. It is the number of columns minus 1:
$$df_{Columns} = N_{Columns} - 1$$

$SS_{Columns}$ is the sum of squared deviations of each score's column's mean from the grand mean: $\Sigma(M_{Columns} - GM)^2$.

$M_{Columns}$ is the mean of each column.

III. Between-group estimates of the population variance for the interaction ($S_{Interaction}^2$ or $MS_{Interaction}$)

Formula in words: Sum of squares of each score's remaining deviation from the grand mean (after subtracting out its deviation from its cell's mean, its row's mean's deviation from the grand mean, and its column's mean's deviation from the grand mean), divided by the degrees of freedom on which it is based (the number of cells minus the number of degrees of freedom for rows, minus the number of degrees of freedom for columns, minus 1).

Formulas in symbols: $S_{Interaction}^2 =$ or $Ms_{interaction} = SS_{Interaction}/df_{Interaction}$

$df_{Interaction}$ is the degrees of freedom in the between-group estimate for interaction. It is the number of cells minus the number of degrees of freedom for rows, minus the number of degrees of freedom for columns, minus 1:
$$df_{Interaction} = N_{Cells} - df_{Columns} - df_{Rows} - 1,$$ where N_{Cells} is the number of cells.

IV. Within-group estimate of the population variance (S_{Within}^2 or MS_{Within})

Formula in words: Sum of squared deviations of each score from its cell's mean, divided by the total degrees of freedom on which this is based (the number of scores in each cell minus 1, summed over all cells).

Formula in symbols: S_{Within}^2 or $MS_{Within} = SS_{Within}/df_{Within}$

df_{Within} is the degrees of freedom in the within-group estimate. It is the number of scores in each cell minus 1, summed over all groups: $df_{Within} = df_1 + df_2 + \ldots + df_{Last}$.

SS_{Within} is the sum of squared deviations of each score minus the mean of its cell $- \Sigma(X-M)^2$.

V. F ratios for row main effect (F_{Rows}), column main effect ($F_{Columns}$), and interaction effect ($F_{Interaction}$)

Formula in words: Population variance estimate based on the particular main or interaction effect divided by the within-group population variance estimate.

Formulas in symbols:
$F_{Rows} = S_{Rows}^2/S_{Within}^2$ or $F_{Rows} = MS_{Rows}/MS_{Within}$
$F_{Columns} = S_{Columns}^2/S_{Within}^2$ or $F_{Columns} = MS_{Columns}/MS_{Within}$
$F_{Interaction} = S_{Interaction}^2/S_{Within}^2$ or $F_{Interaction} = MS_{Interaction}/MS_{Within}$

VI. Proportion of variance accounted for by row main effect (R^2_{Rows}), column main effect (R_{Columns}^2), and interaction effect ($R^2_{\text{Interaction}}$)

Formula in words: Sum of squared deviations of each score's row, column, or row-column-combination mean from the grand mean, divided by the sum of squared deviations of each score from the grand mean after removing sums of squared deviations for the other main or interaction effects.

Formulas in symbols:

$R^2_{\text{Columns}} = SS_{\text{Columns}} / (SS_{\text{Total}} - SS_{\text{Rows}} - SS_{\text{Interaction}})$

$R^2_{\text{Rows}} = SS_{\text{Rows}} / (SS_{\text{Total}} - SS_{\text{Columns}} - SS_{\text{Interaction}})$

$R^2_{\text{Interaction}} = SS_{\text{Interaction}} / (SS_{\text{Total}} - SS_{\text{Columns}} - SS_{\text{Rows}})$

SS_{Total} is the sum of squared deviations of each score from the grand mean: $\Sigma(X-GM)^2$.

Alternate formulas for computing R^2 using F and degrees of freedom reported in a research article:

$R^2_{\text{Rows}} = (F_{\text{Row}})(df_{\text{Row}}) / ([F_{\text{Row}}][df_{\text{Row}}]+df_{\text{Within}})$

$R^2_{\text{Columns}} = (F_{\text{Column}})(df_{\text{Column}}) / ([F_{\text{Column}}][df_{\text{Column}}]+df_{\text{Within}})$

$R^2_{\text{Interaction}}=(F_{\text{Interaction}})(df_{\text{Interaction}})/([F_{\text{Interaction}}][df_{\text{Interaction}}]+df_{\text{Within}})$

How to Conduct a Two-Way Analysis of Variance
(Based on Tables 13-10 and 13-11 in the Text)

1. **Restate the question into a research hypothesis and a null hypothesis about the populations for each main effect and the interaction effect.**
2. **Determine the characteristics of the comparison distributions.**

    A. The comparison distributions will be F distributions with denominator degrees of freedom equal to the sum of the degrees of freedom in each of the cells (the number of cases in the cell minus 1): $df_{\text{Within}} = df_1 + df_2 + \ldots + df_{\text{Last}}$.

    B. The numerator degrees of freedom for F distributions varies:

    1. For the columns main effect it is the number of columns minus 1: $df_{\text{Column}} = N_{\text{Column}} - 1$.
    2. For the rows main effect it is the number of rows minus 1: $df_{\text{Row}} = N_{\text{Row}} - 1$.
    3. For the interaction effect it is the number of cells minus the degrees of freedom for columns, minus the degrees of freedom for rows, minus 1: $df_{\text{Interaction}} = N_{\text{Cells}} - df_{\text{Column}} - df_{\text{Row}} - 1$.

    C. Check the accuracy of your computations by making sure that all of the degrees of freedom add up to the total degrees of freedom: $df_{\text{Total}} = df_{\text{Within}} + df_{\text{Column}} + df_{\text{Row}} + df_{\text{Interaction}}$.

3. **Determine the cutoff sample scores on the comparison distributions at which each null hypothesis should be rejected.**

    A. Determine the desired significance levels.

    B. Look up the appropriate cutoffs in an F table.

204

4. **Determine your samples' scores on each comparison distribution. (These will be F ratios.)**
   A. Figure the mean of each cell, row, and column, and the grand mean of all scores.
   B. Figure the deviations scores of each type.

   1. Its deviation from the grand mean: $X\text{-}GM$.
   2. Its deviation from its cell's mean: $X\text{-}M$.
   3. Its row's mean's deviation from the grand mean: $M_{Row}\text{-}GM$.
   4. Its column's mean's deviation from the grand mean: $M_{Column}\text{-}GM$.
   5. Its deviation from the grand mean minus all the other deviations: Interaction deviation = $(X\text{-}GM) - (X\text{-}M) - (M_{Row}\text{-}GM) - (M_{Column}\text{-}GM)$. (Be sure to compute this deviation using unsquared deviations and to pay close attention to signs.)

   C. Square each of these deviation scores.
   D. Figure the sums of each of these five types of squared deviation scores (SS_{Total}, SS_{Within}, SS_{Row}, SS_{Column}, and $SS_{Interaction}$).
   E. Check the accuracy of your computations by making sure that the sum of squared deviations based on each score's deviation from the grand mean equals the sum of all the other sums of squared deviations: $SS_{Total} = SS_{Within} + SS_{Row} + SS_{Column} + SS_{Interaction}$.
   F. Figure the between-group variance estimate for each main and interaction effect (MS_{Column} or $S_{Column}^2 = SS_{Column}/df_{Column}$; MS_{Row} or $S_{Row}^2 = SS_{Row}/df_{Row}$; $MS_{Interaction}$ or $S_{Interaction}^2 = SS_{Interaction}/df_{Interaction}$).
   G. Figure the within-group variance estimate (MS_{Within} or $S_{Within}^2 = SS_{Within}/df_{Within}$).
   H. Figure the F ratios for each main and interaction effect ($F_{Column} = S_{Column}^2/S_{Within}^2$ or MS_{Column}/MS_{Within}; $F_{Row} = S_{Row}^2/S_{Within}^2$ or MS_{Row}/MS_{Within}; $F_{Interaction} = S_{Interaction}^2/S_{Within}^2$ or $MS_{Interaction}/MS_{Within}$).

5. **Compare the scores obtained in Steps 3 (III) and 4 (IV) to decide whether to reject the null hypothesis.**

Analysis of Variance Table and Symbols for a Two-Way Analysis of Variance

Source	SS	df	MS	F
Between				
Columns	SS_{Column}	df_{Column}	MS_{Column} (or S_{Column}^2)	F_{Column}
Rows	SS_{Row}	df_{Row}	MS_{Row} (or S_{Row}^2)	F_{Row}
Interaction	$SS_{Interaction}$	$df_{Interaction}$	$MS_{Interaction}$ (or $S_{Interaction}^2$)	$F_{Interaction}$
Within	SS_{Within}	df_{Within}	MS_{Within} (or S_{Within}^2)	
Total	SS_{Total}	df_{Total}		

Formulas for Each Section of the Analysis of Variance Table

Source	SS	df	MS	F
Between				
Columns	$\Sigma(M_{Columns}-GM)^2$	$N_{Columns}-1$	$SS_{Columns}/df_{Columns}$	$MS_{Columns}/MS_{Within}$
Rows	$(M_{Rows}-GM)^2$	$N_{Rows}-1$	SS_{Rows}/df_{Rows}	MS_{Rows}/MS_{Within}
Interaction	$\Sigma[(X-GM)-(X-M)-$ $(M_R-GM)-(M_C-GM)]^2$	$N_{Cells}-df_{Columns}-df_{Rows}-1$	$SS_{Interaction}/df_{Interaction}$	$MS_{Interaction}/MS_{Within}$
Within	$\Sigma(X-M)^2$	$df_1+df_2+...+df_{Last}$	SS_{Within}/df_{Within}	
Total	$\Sigma(X-GM)^2$	$N-1$		

Definitions of Basic Symbols

Σ is the usual sum sign–which here refers to adding up the appropriate numbers for all *cases* (not all cells)

M is the mean of a score's cell

M_{Rows} is the mean of a score's row

M_{Column} is the mean of a score's column

GM is the grand mean of all scores

N_{Cells} is the number of cells

N_{rows} is the number of rows

$N_{Columns}$ is the number of columns

X is each score

N is the total number of cases in the study

Outline for Writing Essays on the Logic and Computations for Conducting a Two-Way Analysis of Variance

The reason for your writing essay questions in the practice problems and tests is that this task develops and then demonstrates what matters so very much–your comprehension of the logic behind the computations. (It is also a place where those better at words than numbers can shine, and for those better at numbers to develop their skills at explaining in words.)

Thus, to do well, be sure to do the following in each essay: (a) give the reasoning behind each step; (b) relate each step to the specifics of the content of the particular study you are analyzing; (c) state the various formulas in nontechnical language, because as you define each term you show you understand it (although once you have defined it in nontechnical language, you can use it from then on in the essay); (d) look back and be absolutely certain that you made it clear just *why* that formula or procedure was applied and *why* it is the way it is.

The outlines below are *examples* of ways to structure your essays. There are other completely correct ways to go about it. And this is an *outline* for an answer–you are to write the answer out in paragraph form. Examples of full essays are in the answers to Set I Practice Problems in the back of the text.

These essays are necessarily very long for you to write (and for others to grade). But this is the very best way to be sure you understand everything thoroughly. One shortcut you may see on a test is that you may be asked to write your answer for someone who understands statistics up to the point of the new material you are studying. You can choose to take the same shortcut in these practice problems (maybe writing for someone who understands right up to whatever point you yourself start being just a little unclear). But every time you write for a person who has never had statistics at all, you review the logic behind the entire course. You engrain it in your mind. Over and over. The time is never wasted. It is an excellent way to study.

I. **Reframe the question into a research hypothesis and a null hypothesis about populations. (Step 1 of hypothesis testing.)**
   A. Make a chart and explain the logic of the factorial design set up.
   B. State in ordinary language the basic logic of hypothesis testing.
      1. The interest in these groups is as representatives, or "samples," of larger groups, or "populations," of particular types of individuals (such as those exposed to various experimental manipulations).
      2. Thus, you construct a scenario in which the populations do not differ and then do computations based on that scenario to see how likely it is such populations would produce samples of scores whose averages are as different from each other as are the averages of the particular samples in this study.
   C. In this case, there are *three* research hypotheses and *three* corresponding null hypotheses.
      1. Explain different ways of combining groups for row and column main effects.
      2. Explain logic of interaction effects as patterns of differences across columns varying according to level of the column variable.

II. **Determine the characteristics of the comparison distribution. (Step 2 of hypothesis testing.)**
   A. Explain logic of overall approach for testing each null hypothesis.
      1. We make and compare two estimates of the variance within these populations (which are assumed to be the same).
      2. If the scenario of no difference is true, then an estimate based on the variation among the averages of the samples (as grouped for the particular hypothesis) should give the same result as an estimate based on the average variation within each sample (in this case, within each cell).
      3. But if the scenario is false (and the population averages differ), then this will increase the estimate based on the differences among the averages of the samples but will not affect the estimate based on the variation within them.
      4. Thus, if the scenario of no difference is true, the ratio of the two estimates (the one based on variation among averages divided by the one based on variation within each cell) should be about 1. If the scenario is false, the ratio should be greater than one.
   B. Explain F distribution.
      1. Statisticians have determined the probability of getting samples which produce ratios of different sizes under the conditions in which the scenario of no difference is true.

2. The probabilities depend on how many groupings are involved in a particular comparison and how many participants within each cell.

III. Determine the cutoff sample score on the comparison distribution at which the null hypothesis should be rejected. (Step 3 of hypothesis testing.)

A. Procedure: Determine significance level and look up cutoff on an F table (using the appropriate numerator and denominator df).

B. Explanation.

1. The next step for each hypothesis is to figure out how large this ratio of the two variation estimates would have to be in order to decide that the probability was so low that it is unlikely that the scenario of no difference could be true.
2. There are standard tables that indicate the size of these ratios associated with various low probabilities.
3. To use these tables you have to decide the kind of situation you have. There are two considerations.
    a. How many groupings and how many participants in each cell. (State the numbers for your study.)
    b. Just how unlikely would a ratio have to be to decide the whole scenario on which these tables are based (the scenario of no difference) should be rejected? The standard figure used in psychology is less likely than 5% (though 1% is sometimes used to be especially safe). (Say which you are using in your study for each hypothesis–if no figure is stated in the problem and no special reason given for using one or the other, the general rule is to use 5%.)
4. State the cutoff F ratios for your situation.

IV. For each hypothesis determine the score of your sample on the comparison distribution. (Step 4 of hypothesis testing.)

A. Estimate the variation in the populations based on the various ways of grouping the scores.

1. Divide each score's deviation from the overall average into four components (each of which provides a basis for making an estimate of the population variance).
    a. Its deviation from its cell's average (basis of the estimate of the variation in the population using the variation within each cell).
    b. Its row's average's deviation from the overall average (basis of the estimate of the variation in the population using the variation among the rows).
    c. Its column's average's deviation from the overall average (basis of the estimate of the variation in the population using the variation among the columns).
    d. The remaining deviation of the score from the overall average after subtracting out each of the above (basis of the estimate of the variation in the population using the interaction of row and column effects).
2. The estimate based on the variation of each score from its cell's average is influenced only by variation within each cell.
    a. It is computed by squaring each such deviation (to eliminate signs) and finding a special kind of average.
    b. An ordinary average would slightly underestimate the population variation because a sample is less likely to have extremes from its average than is the population it represents. Thus, instead of dividing the total by the number of scores in each group, one divides by the number of scores in each group minus 1.
3. The estimates based on the variation of each score's row's, column's, or remaining deviation (for the interaction) from the overall average is influenced both by the variation among scores overall plus any systematic variation between rows, columns, or interaction groupings, respectively.

a. Each such estimate (row, column, interaction) is computed by squaring each score's deviation of the appropriate type (row, column, interaction) and finding a special kind of average.

b. In this case, the special kind of average involves dividing the total of the squared deviations by the number of groupings minus one.

B. Figure the ratios of each estimate of population variation based on row, column, or interaction deviations to the within-group variance estimate. State each of these F ratios for your study.

V. **Compare the scores obtained in Steps 3 and 4 of the hypothesis testing process to decide whether or not to reject each null hypothesis. (Step 5 of hypothesis testing.)**

A. For each of your F ratios, note whether it exceeds the cutoff and draw the appropriate conclusion.

1. Reject the null hypothesis: The variation among the averages of your particular samples (as divided in this way into rows, columns, or row-column combinations) is so great that it seems unlikely that their populations are the same. So they seem to be different and the null hypothesis seems untrue.

2. Fail to reject the null hypothesis: The result is inconclusive. On the one hand, these results were not extreme enough to persuade you that the variation among the averages of your particular samples (as divided in this way into rows, columns, or row-column combinations) was due to the populations being different. On the other hand, it is still possible that they really are different, but because of the people who happened to be selected to be in your samples from the populations, this difference did not show up.

B. Be sure to state your conclusions in terms of your particular measures and situation, so it is clear to a lay person just what the real bottom line of the study is.

Chapter Self-Tests

Multiple-Choice Questions

1. Factorial designs

   a. have replaced all other group analyses in modern psychology.
   b. are preferred by physiological psychologists, but social psychologists prefer a series of t-tests.
   c. construct groupings which include every combination of the levels of the grouping variables.
   d. yield less accurate results than analysis of variance.

2. An interaction effect

   a. occurs when the combined influence of two grouping variables could not be predicted by knowing about the influence of each separately.
   b. represents the sum of the individual influences of two grouping variables and can be computed from knowing each effect separately.
   c. represents the concordance of the measured variables.
   d. represents the lack of concordance of the measured variables.

3. A 3 X 5 X 2 factorial design has

    a. 30 possible main effects.
    b. 30 possible interaction effects.
    c. one grouping variable with three levels, one with five levels, and one with two levels.
    d. one grouping variable with three levels and one with five levels, and one measured variable with two levels.

4. To identify whether there are main effects in a factorial design, you look at

    a. interaction effects.
    b. cell means.
    c. column means and row means.
    d. t tests.

5. Comparing the pattern of cell means across one row to the pattern of cell means across another row is a method of

    a. avoiding lengthy computations.
    b. identifying interaction effects.
    c. checking on whether assumptions of equal population variances have been met.
    d. computing marginal means.

6. A psychologist assigned people to recall words after either a short or long delay, and with or without an incentive (a payment for each word recalled). The mean numbers recalled were as follows:

		Incentive		
		Yes	No	
Delay	Short	8	12	10
	Long	6	2	4
		7	7	

    Assuming all differences are significant,

    a. both the main effects and the interaction effect are significant.
    b. both the main effects but not the interaction effect are significant.
    c. the main effect for delay and the interaction are significant, but not the main effect for incentive.
    d. the main effect for incentive and the interaction are significant, but not the main effect for delay.

7. When the cell means of a 2 X 2 factorial design study are graphed,

    a. a main effect on the variable whose levels are across the horizontal axis is shown by the bars being parallel.
    b. a main effect for the variable whose levels are represented by the different bars is shown by the bars crossing.
    c. an interaction effect is shown by the average of the two bars having different heights.
    d. an interaction effect is shown by the two bars not being parallel.

8. Which of the following deviations is the basis for the between-group estimate for the interaction effect?

    a. $X\text{-}M_{Interaction}$.
    b. $GM\text{-}M_{Interaction}\text{-}M_{Column}$.
    c. $(X\text{-}GM)\text{-}(M_{Column}\text{-}GM)\text{-}(M_{Row}\text{-}GM)$.
    d. $(X\text{-}GM)\text{-}(X\text{-}M)\text{-}(M_{Column}\text{-}GM)\text{-}(M_{Row}\text{-}GM)$.

9. The formula for R^2_{Column} is
   a. $SS_{\text{Column}}/SS_{\text{Row}}$.
   b. $SS_{\text{Between}}/SS_{\text{Total}}$.
   c. $SS_{\text{Column}}/(SS_{\text{Total}}-SS_{\text{Row}}-SS_{\text{Interaction}})$.
   d. $SS_{\text{Column}}/(SS_{\text{Column}}+1)$.

10. Which of the following situations would produce an incorrect result if you applied the methods of this chapter?
    a. A design in which there are unequal numbers of cases in the cells.
    b. A design in which there are more rows than columns.
    c. A design in which there are more columns than rows.
    d. A design in which the number of rows exceeds the number of columns by a factor of four or greater.

Fill-In Questions

11. A study found that a particular style of teaching increased learning for middle class students but decreased learning for lower class students. This finding is an example of a(n) _____ effect.

12. A study on non-U.S. Canadian immigrants considered the effects of region of origin (Asia, Latin America, Europe, the Middle East, or Other) and the reason for immigrating (Political, Economic, or Other) on the participants' satisfaction with the country. This study is a two-way factorial design—specifically, a(n) _____ X _____ factorial design.

13. In a graph of the results of an analysis of variance, the vertical axis shows speed at completing a task on the computer while the horizontal axis represents different levels of experience using the computer. Two lines are drawn on the graph, one for each of two conditions—familiar task and unfamiliar task. If the lines are _____, then the effect of different levels of experience on speed at the task is the same regardless of whether the person is doing a familiar or unfamiliar task.

14. In the top row of a table of cell means, there was a 10, 12, and 14. In the bottom row, there was a 14, 12, and 10. This pattern indicates that there was a(n) _____.

15. In a two-way analysis of variance, there are three F ratios because there are three different _____-group estimates of the population variance.

16. Using the structural-model approach to compute a two-way analysis of variance requires dividing the deviation of each score's mean from the _____ mean into four components.

17. $df_{\text{Interaction}} = $ _____ $- df_{\text{Column}} - df_{\text{Row}} - 1$

18. When calculating _____ for the row effect, it is important to subtract out the proportion of variance accounted for by the column and interaction effects.

19. In a factorial analysis of variance, the power of a main effect is influenced by its effect size, the number of participants, the number of levels of the variable for that main effect, and the _____.

20. An analysis of variance was conducted in which each subject completed a task 6 times–under each combination of three different temperature conditions and two different task complexities. The analysis of these results would require a _____ analysis of variance.

Problems and Essays

21. (a) Create a study using a 2 X 2 design and fill in a table of cell means so that there are two main effects but no interaction effects. (b) Make a graph showing these results. (c) Explain the pattern of the cell means you created.

22. A school district superintendent wanted to know how well the four high schools in her district were teaching students in regular and gifted classes. She conducted a small study in which she randomly selected students from the two kinds of classes at each of the four schools and asked them to take a standardized performance test. (a) Create a table showing all the cells for such a study and make up means for the cells so that an interaction effect exists. (b) Make a graph showing these results. (c) Interpret the pattern of the cell means.

23. Assuming all differences are significant, for the following outcome (a) make a graph, (b) determine marginal means, and (c) indicate which of the effects (main and interaction) are significant.

		Levels of Grouping Variable I		
		A	B	C
Levels of	}			
Independent	} SHORT	6	6	6
Variable II	} LONG	4	6	8

24. A group of first-year students at a small private college were asked to rate how important school was to the rest of their lives. The participants were selected to include three who came from each combination of low and high income parents and three different ethnic groups. The data are below.

a. Analyze these data using a factorial analysis of variance, testing the Ethnicity main effect at the .05 significance level and the Parent's Income main effect and the interaction effect at the .01 significance level. (Be sure to include the effect size.)

b. Explain your conclusions and procedures to a person who has never had a course in statistics.

Importance of College to First-Year College Students of Varying Ethnicity and Levels of Parent's Income

	Parent's Income	
Ethnicity	Low	High
Group A	6	2
	5	3
	5	2
Group B	3	5
	2	6
	4	6
Group C	2	6
	1	9
	1	8

25. A study examined the effects of being under-, over-, or normal weight and living on the west or east coast on participants' comfort with their body weight. A two-way analysis of variance found a main effect for region, $F(1,28) = 5.91$, $p < .05$, but not for bodyweight, $F(2,28) = .41$, $p < .05$. In addition, an interaction effect was found, $F(2,28) = 8.59$, $p < .01$. (a) Figure the proportion of variance accounted for by each of the effects. (b) Explain the meaning of these results to a person who has never had a course in statistics.

26. A study reports the following results:

A two-way analysis of variance was conducted to determine the pattern of influence of being an early or late riser and the amount of TV watched (high, medium, or low) on the degree to which the participants believed the world was a safe place. Assumptions of normality and homogeneity of variance appeared to have been met. Analyses indicated that there was a significant main effect in the amount of TV watched, $F(2,24) = 53.49$, $p < 0.001$, but not in the waking patterns $F(1,24) = 2.93$, *ns* (see table for cell means). However, a significant interaction effect was found, $F(2,24) = 10.28$, $p < .001$ such that....

Subjects' Mean Perceptions of the Degree to which the World is a Safe Place as a Function of Amount of TV Watched and Being an Early or a Late Riser

	Waking Pattern	
TV	Early	Late
low	20.2	35.8
med	33.4	38.2
high	59.8	50.8

(a) Make a graph showing the results, (b) explain the meaning of the pattern of cell means (including marginal means which you have to calculate) and the significant results, and (c) discuss the interpretation of non-significant results.

213

Using SPSS (11.0 for Windows) with this Chapter

If you are using SPSS for the first time, before proceeding with the material in this section read the Appendix on Getting Started and the Basics of Using SPSS.

You can use SPSS to carry out a factorial analysis of variance. You should work through the example of a two-way analysis, following the procedures step by step. Then look over the description of the general principles involved and try the procedures on your own for some of the problems listed in the Suggestions for Additional Practice. Finally, you may want to try the suggestions for using the computer to deepen your understanding and also explore the more advanced SPSS procedure of a three-way analysis of variance.

I. Example

A. Data: A 2 X 3 experiment in which expressions of antiracist attitudes are measured under all six combinations of two Response Format conditions (Public and Private) and three Direction of Influence conditions (Antiracist, No Influence, and Nonantiracist). These are fictional data given in the text, based on an actual study by Blanchard, Lilly, & Vaughn (1991). The scores for the Public-Antiracist group are 25, 20, 23, and 24; for the Private-Antiracist group, 19, 24, 21, and 20; for the Public-No Influence group, 22, 19, 22, and 21; for the Private-No Influence group, 24, 18, 22, and 20; for the Public-Nonantiracist group, 16, 19, 13, and 16; and for the Private-Nonantiracist group, 18, 21, 16, and 17.

B. Follow the instructions in the SPSS Appendix for starting up SPSS.

C. Enter the data as follows.

1. When typing in the data, you need to give a number for each variable corresponding to the condition for the particular subject. For RFORMAT use 1 for Public and 2 for Private. For DIRINF use 1 for Antiracist, 2 for No Inflluence, and 3 for Nonantiracist.

   a. For the first subject in the group (the Public-Antiracist group), type 1 and press enter. Then click on the next box on the same line and type 1 and enter. Now click on the third box on that same line and type 25 and enter. The first 1 stands for being in the Public response format, the second **1** for being exposed to the Antiracist direction of influence, and the **25**, for the attitude score.

   b. Type the data in the same way for each of the remaining subjects, being sure to give the appropriate numbers for which conditions each subject is in. Name the variable containing the scores ATTITUDE. The data screen is shown in SG13-1.

D. Carry out the analysis of variance.

Analyze

> General Linear Model >

> > Univariate

> > > Highlight ATTITUDE and move it to the Dependent Variable box. Highlight RFORMAT and DIRINF and move to Factors box.

> > > > Continue

> > > > > OK

SG13-1

1. The first box gives information about how many subjects were included in the analysis. The second screen of results (Figure SG13-2) is the analysis of variance table laid out in the standard way, except for including some additional rows which you can ignore.
2. Print out this screen of results.

E. Save your lines of data and instructions, as follows.

File

Save

[Name your data file and designate the drive you would like your data saved in]

OK

II. Systematic Instructions for Computing a Two-Way Analysis of Variance

A. Start up SPSS.

B. Enter the data as follows, entering one line of data per subject with one variable representing which condition the subject is in on the first independent variable, a second variable representing which condition the subject is in on the second independent variable, and a third variable representing the subject's score on the dependent variable.

1. When typing in the data, you need to give a number for each variable corresponding to the condition for the particular subject. For RFORMAT use 1 for Public and 2 for Private. For DIRINF use 1 for Antiracist, 2 for No Inflluence, and 3 for Nonantiracist.

a. For the first subject in the group (the Public-Antiracist group), type 1 and press enter. Then click on the next box on the same line and type 1 and enter. Now click on the third box on that same line and type 25 and enter. The first 1 stands for being in the Public respnse format, the second **1** for being exposed to the Antiracist direction of influence, and the **25**, for the attitude score.

215

b. Type the data in the same way for each of the remaining subjects, being sure to give the appropriate numbers for which conditions each subject is in.

c. When you have typed all the subjects' data in, go back and double check for accuracy

C. Carry out the analysis of variance as follows.

              Analysis

                General Linear Model >

                    Simple Factorial

                        [Highlight ATTITUDE and move it to the Dependent Variable box. Highlight RFORMAT and DIRINF and move to Factors box.]

                        Continue

                            OK

D. Save your lines of data as follows.

          File

          Save

            [Name your data file and designate the drive you would like your data saved in]

            OK

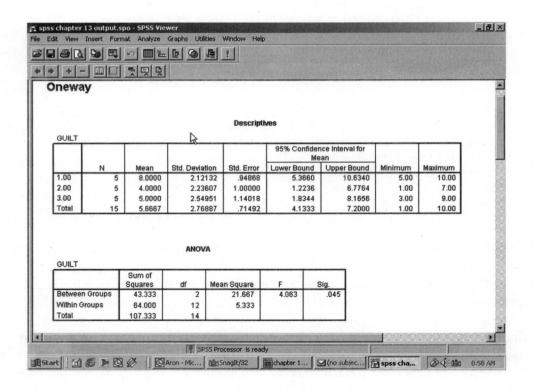

Figure 13-2

III. Additional Practice

(For each data set, conduct a two-way analysis of variance, compute cell means, and compare your results to those in the text).

A. Text example: Data from "How are you doing?" Question 5, data listed on p.480.

B. Practice problems in the text.

1. Set I: 4.
2. Set II: 19, 20.

IV. Using the Computer to Deepen Your Knowledge

A. Effects of outliers: Use SPSS to compute an two-way analysis of variance using the antiracist attitudes example, but change one of the scores in the first group to a much higher score (say a 50) and look at the impact on the main and interaction effects.

B. Eyeballing main and interaction effects.

1. Make up data for a 2 X 2 analysis of variance in which there are no main effects but there is an interaction effect. Then conduct the analysis using SPSS. (Keep your data simple, with just 2 subjects per cell, and create very large mean differences and only slight differences within cells so you can get significance with such a small N.)
2. Change the data so that there is no interaction, but two main effects.
3. Change the data again so that there is one main effect and no interaction.
4. Change the data so that there is one main effect and an interaction.

C. Collapsing over groups: Use SPSS to conduct a one-way analysis of variance for the antiracist-attitude study in which subjects are divided according to direction of influence (and thus which response-format condition they are in is ignored). Compare the result, including the sums of squares and mean squares, to the main effect for direction of influence in the original example output. Why are they different?

V. Advanced Procedure: Three-Way Analysis of Variance

A. Using the antiracist-attitudes example, add a third independent variable–call it **EXPER** (short for experimenter).

B. Add this variable to the **DATA Editor.**

C. Assume that the first two subjects in each of the six groupings were tested by Experimenter **1** and that the third and fourth subjects in each grouping were tested by Experimenter **2**. Thus, on the data lines, give each subject either a **1** or **2** for this variable.

D. Carry out the ANOVA as described above, but this time add this third independent variable to the Factor box.

217

Chapter 14
Chi-Square Tests

Learning Objectives

To understand, including being able to conduct any necessary computations:

- Categorical or nominal variables.
- Chi-square statistic.
- Expected frequencies in a chi-square test of goodness of fit.
- Chi-square distribution and using a chi-square table.
- Degrees of freedom for the chi-square distribution for the chi-square test of goodness of fit.
- The steps in conducting a chi-square test of goodness of fit.
- Contingency tables.
- Expected frequencies for a contingency table in a chi-square test of independence.
- Degrees of freedom for the chi-square distribution for the chi-square test of independence.
- The steps in conducting a chi-square test of independence.
- Assumptions for chi-square tests.
- Effect size (ϕ and Cramer's ϕ) for a chi-square test of independence.
- Power and needed sample size for a study using a chi-square test of independence.
- Issues regarding minimum sample size for a chi-square test.
- How results of studies using chi-square tests are reported in research articles.

Chapter Outline

I. **Categorical (Nominal) Variables**
II. **Chi-Square Test for Goodness of Fit**
   A. Tests the probability that a distribution of observed frequencies in various categories could have arisen from a population with a hypothesized distribution of frequencies in these categories.
   B. The chi-square statistic reflects the degree of divergence between these observed and expected frequencies.
      1. Discrepancy in a category is observed frequency minus expected (based on the proportion of the total observed sample that would be expected to be in this category given the hypothesized population distribution).
      2. The discrepancy in each category is squared, in part to eliminate the problem of signs.
      3. The squared discrepancy in each category is divided by the expected frequency to keep these discrepancies in proportion to the number of cases that would have been expected.
      4. The chi-square statistic is the sum, over the categories, of each squared discrepancy divided by its expected frequency.
   C. If samples are randomly taken from a population and a chi-square statistic figured on each, these chi-squares follow a mathematically defined distribution (the chi-square distribution).
      1. The distribution is skewed with the long tail to the right.
      2. The distribution's exact shape depends on the degrees of freedom.

3. Table B-4 (in Appendix B of the text) gives the cutoff chi-squares for various significance levels and degrees of freedom.
   D. In a chi-square test for goodness of fit, the degrees of freedom are the number of categories minus 1.
   E. The steps of hypothesis testing are otherwise the same as we have been using all along.

III. Chi-Square Test for Independence
   A. Tests the probability that a sample in which people are measured on two categories could have come from a population in which the distribution of frequencies over categories on one variable is independent of the distribution of frequencies over categories on a second variable.
   B. Data are usually displayed on a contingency table, a two-dimensional breakdown in which the columns represent the categories of one variable, the rows represent the categories of the other variable, and the number in each cell is the frequency for the combination of categories that cell represents.
   C. If the two variables are independent, then the expected frequencies for a given cell is the proportion of its row's observed frequency of the total observed frequency, times the observed frequency for its column. (That is, if the two variables are independent, then the distribution of the frequencies among the cells in any particular column should be in proportion to the distribution of frequencies among the rows overall.)
   D. The chi-square statistic is figured using the observed and expected frequencies in each cell.
   E. The degrees of freedom for a chi-square test for independence are the number of rows minus 1 times the number of columns minus 1. (This is the number of cells whose frequency-data are needed in order to fill in all the other cell's frequency-data, assuming the column and row frequencies are known.)
   F. The steps of hypothesis testing are otherwise the same as we have been using all along.

IV. Assumption for Chi-Square Tests
   A. Chi-square tests are not limited by the kinds of assumptions required for the t test and analysis of variance.
   B. They do require that each observed case be independent of all other cases.

V. Effect Size and Power for Chi-Square Tests for Independence
   A. Estimated effect size for a test of a 2 X 2 contingency table – the phi coefficient (ϕ).
      1. $\phi = \sqrt{\chi^2 / N}$
      2. ϕ has the same range, meaning, and conventions for small, medium, and large effect sizes as the correlation coefficient (r), but is always positive.
   B. Estimated effect size for a test of a contingency table larger than 2 X 2 (Cramer's ϕ).
      1. Cramer's $\phi = \sqrt{\chi^2 / (N)(df_{Smaller})}$
      where $df_{Smaller}$ is the degrees of freedom corresponding to the smaller dimension of the contingency table.

219

2. Cramer's ϕ is interpreted approximately as a correlation coefficient, but the corresponding conventions for small, medium, and large effect sizes depend on the value of $df_{Smaller}$ (see Table 14-8 in the text).

C. Power:
    1. Main determinants of power are effect size, sample size, and degrees of freedom.
    2. Table 14.9 in the text gives approximate power for various sample sizes using the .05 significance level for small, medium, or large effect sizes, over 1 through 4 degrees of freedom.

D. Planning sample size: Table 14.10 in the text gives the approximate number of subjects needed to achieve 80% power for estimated small, medium, and large effect sizes for 1 through 4 degrees of freedom using the .05 significance level.

VI. Controversy: Minimum Expected Frequency

A. Traditionally statisticians recommended a minimum expected frequency of 5 in any cell or category.

B. Recent work suggests that from the point of view of protecting against Type I error, even an expected frequency of 1 in a cell or category is acceptable, so long as the total number of subjects is at least five times the number of cells or categories.

C. However, low expected cell frequencies can substantially reduce power.

VII. Chi-Square Tests as Reported in Research Articles

A. All observed frequencies are usually reported.

B. Chi-square test results follow a standard format--for example, "$\chi^2(2, N=531) = 28.35, p < .001$."

Formulas

I.   Chi-square statistic (X^2)

Formula in words: Sum, over all the categories or cells, of the squared difference between observed and expected frequencies divided by the expected frequency.

Formula in symbols:
$$\chi^2 = \Sigma \; \frac{(O-E)^2}{E}$$

O is the observed frequency for a category or cell.
E is the expected frequency for a category or cell.

II. Expected frequency of a cell in a contingency table (E)

Formula in words: The proportion that a cell's row's observed frequency is of the total observed frequency, times the observed frequency for its column.

Formulas in symbols:
$$E = \left(\frac{R}{N}\right)(C)$$

R is the number of cases observed in this cell's row.
N is the number of cases total.
C is the number of cases observed in this cell's column.

III. Degrees of freedom (*df*) for a chi-square test for independence

Formula in words: The number of columns minus one, times the number of rows minus one.

Formulas in symbols: $df = (N_{Columns} - 1)(N_{Row} - 1)$

$N_{Columns}$ is the number of columns.

N_{rows} is the number of rows.

IV. Estimated effect size for a test of a 2 X 2 contingency table (ɸ).

Formula in words: Square root of result of dividing the figured chi-square statistic by the number of cases in the sample.

Formula in symbols: $\phi = \sqrt{\chi^2 / N}$

V. Estimated effect size for a test of a contingency table larger than 2 X 2 (Cramer's ɸ).

Formula in words: Square root of result of dividing the figured chi-square statistic by the product of the number of cases in the sample times the degrees of freedom in the smaller dimension of the contingency table.

Formula in symbols: Cramer's $\phi = \sqrt{\chi^2 / (N)(df_{Smaller})}$

$df_{Smaller}$ is the degrees of freedom corresponding to the smaller dimension of the contingency table.

How to Conduct a Chi-Square Test for Goodness of Fit

1. **Restate the question into a research hypothesis and a null hypothesis about populations.**
   A. Populations.
      1. Population 1 are people like those in the study.
      2. Population 2 are people who have the hypothesized distribution over categories.
   B. Hypotheses.
      1. Research: Two populations have different distributions of cases over categories.
      2. Null: Two populations have the same distributions of cases over categories.
2. **Determine the characteristics of the comparison distribution.**
   A. The comparison distribution will be a chi-square distribution.
   B. Its degrees of freedom are the number of categories minus 1.
3. **Determine the cutoff sample score on the comparison distribution at which the null hypothesis should be rejected.**
   A. Determine the desired significance level.
   B. Look up the appropriate cutoff on a chi-square table, using the degrees of freedom calculated above.

4. **Determine your sample's score on the comparison distribution. (This will be a chi-square statistic.)**
    A. Determine the actual, observed frequencies in each category.
    B. Determine the expected frequencies in each category (multiply the proportion this category is expected to have times the total number of cases in the sample).
    C. In each category figure observed minus expected and square this difference.
    D. Divide each squared difference by the expected frequency for its category.
    E. Add up the results of Step D over the different categories.
5. **Compare the scores in III and IV to decide whether or not to reject the null hypothesis.**

How to Conduct a Chi-Square Test for Independence

I. **Reframe the question into a research hypothesis and a null hypothesis about populations.**
    A. Populations.
        1. Population 1 are people like those in the study.
        2. Population 2 are people whose distribution of cases over categories on the first variable is independent of the distribution of cases over categories for the second variable.
    B. Hypotheses.
        1. Research: Two populations are different.
        2. Null: Two populations are the same.
II. **Determine the characteristics of the comparison distribution.**
    A. The comparison distribution will be a chi-square distribution.
    B. Its degrees of freedom are the number of rows (the number of categories in one of the variables) minus 1 times the number of columns (the number of categories in the other variable) minus 1.
III. **Determine the cutoff sample score on the comparison distribution at which the null hypothesis should be rejected.**
    A. Determine the desired significance level.
    B. Look up the appropriate cutoff on a chi-square table, using the degrees of freedom calculated above.
IV. **Determine the score of your sample on the comparison distribution. (This will be a chi-square statistic.)**
    A. Set up a two-dimensional contingency table, placing the observed frequencies in each cell.
    B. Determine the expected frequencies in each cell.
        1. Find the marginal totals for each column and row.
        2. Find the overall total.
        3. For each cell multiply the proportion of cases its row represents of the total (the row total divided by the overall total) times the number of cases in its column.
    C. For each cell figure observed minus expected and square this difference.
    D. Divide each squared difference by the expected frequency for its cell.
    E. Add up the results of Step D over all the cells.
V. **Compare the scores in III and IV to decide whether or not to reject the null hypothesis.**

Outline for Writing Essays on the Logic and Computations for Conducting Chi-Square Tests

The reason for your writing essay questions in the practice problems and tests is that this task develops and then demonstrates what matters so very much--your comprehension of the logic behind the computations. (It is also a place where those better at words than numbers can shine, and for those better at numbers to develop their skills at explaining in words.)

Thus, to do well, be sure to do the following in each essay: (a) give the reasoning behind each step; (b) relate each step to the specifics of the content of the particular study you are analyzing; (c) state the various formulas in nontechnical language, because as you define each term you show you understand it (although once you have defined it in nontechnical language, you can use it from then on in the essay); (d) look back and be absolutely certain that you made it clear just *why* that formula or procedure was applied and *why* it is the way it is.

The outlines below are *examples* of ways to structure your essays. There are other completely correct ways to go about it. And this is an *outline* for an answer--you are to write the answer out in paragraph form. Examples of full essays are in the answers to Set I Practice Problems in the back of the text.

These essays are necessarily very long for you to write (and for others to grade). But this is the very best way to be sure you understand everything thoroughly. One shortcut you may see on a test is that you may be asked to write your answer for someone who understands statistics up to the point of the new material you are studying. You can choose to take the same shortcut in these practice problems (maybe writing for someone who understands right up to whatever point you yourself start being just a little unclear). But every time you write for a person who has never had statistics at all, you review the logic behind the entire course. You engrain it in your mind. Over and over. The time is never wasted. It is an excellent way to study.

Essays for Chi-Square Test for Goodness of Fit:

I. Reframe the question into a null and a research hypothesis about populations.

A. Introduce the situation.
   1. State the given (observed) distribution of cases over categories.
   2. State the expected proportional distribution of cases over categories.
   3. Note that there is a discrepancy.

B. State in ordinary language the hypothesis testing issue.
   1. Is this discrepancy so large that we can reject the hypothesis that our observed cases (our sample) represent a world in which the distribution is true generally (that is, in the population).
   2. Thus, you construct a scenario (the null hypothesis) in which the observed distribution is a random sample from a population like that which is expected and see how likely it is under this scenario that just by chance you could have obtained a sample with a discrepancy as large as you actually have.

223

II. Determine the characteristics of the comparison distribution.

A. This step involves figuring out the probabilities of getting different degrees of discrepancy by chance (assuming the null hypothesis is true).

B. The distribution of chance discrepancies (assuming the null hypothesis is true) for a particular way of measuring discrepancy (called chi-square) is called a chi-square distribution.

C. The chi-square distribution is mathematically defined and depends only on the number of categories involved (technically, on the number of categories minus 1).

III. Determine the cutoff sample score on the comparison distribution at which the null hypothesis should be rejected.

A. In this step one figures out how large an actual discrepancy would have to be in order to decide that the probability of getting such a discrepancy under the null hypothesis is so low that this whole scenario of the null hypothesis being true could be confidently rejected.

B. There are standard tables that indicate the size of these discrepancies associated with various low probabilities.

C. Just how unlikely would a discrepancy have to be to decide the whole scenario on which these tables are based (the scenario of no difference) should be rejected? The standard figure used in psychology is less likely than 5% (though 1% is sometimes used to be especially safe). (Say which you are using in your study--if no figure is stated in the problem and no special reason given for using one or the other, the general rule is to use 5%.)

D. Once this decision is made, the cutoff level of discrepancy can be determined from the table. (State the level for your situation.)

IV. Determine the score of your sample on the comparison distribution.

A. Figure the degree of discrepancy for your actual situation.

B. This requires computing a number called a chi-square, which reflects the degree of divergence between observed and expected frequencies over the categories. It is figured in four steps (which you should describe for your example).

1. For each category find the discrepancy between observed and expected in terms of actual scores. (That is, for the expected, multiply the proportion expected times the number of cases in your sample.)

2. Square this discrepancy. (This eliminates the problem of some discrepancies being positive and some negative.)

3. Divide the squared discrepancy in each category by the expected frequency. (This keeps these discrepancies in proportion to the number of cases that would have been expected.)

4. The chi-square statistic is the sum, over the categories, of each squared discrepancy divided by its expected frequency.

V. Compare the scores in Steps III and IV to decide whether or not to reject the null hypothesis.

A. Note whether or not your chi-square exceeds the cutoff and draw the appropriate conclusion. Either:

1. Reject the null hypothesis: The distributions of cases over categories is so discrepant from what you would expect if your sample represents a population with a distribution like that hypothesized that you reject this scenario.

2. Fail to reject the null hypothesis: The result is inconclusive. On the one hand, these results were not extreme enough to persuade you that the discrepancy was due to chance. On the other hand, it is still possible that your sample really does represent a population whose proportional distribution over categories is different from what was expected, but because of the people who happened to be selected to be in your samples from the population, this discrepancy did not show up strongly enough.

B. Be sure to state your conclusion in terms of your particular measures and situation, so it is clear to a lay person just what the real bottom line of the study is.

Essays for Chi-Square Test for Independence:

I. Reframe the question into a research hypothesis and a null hypothesis about populations.

A. Introduce the situation.
1. Make (if it is not given) a contingency table of the observed data and describe it.
2. Explain the notion of independence: That the distribution of cases over categories on one variable is unrelated to the distribution of cases over categories on the other variable.
3. Figure the expected frequencies for the cells in your contingency table under the assumption of independence. (The number in each cell should be the proportion of cases in its column that its row is a proportion of the total.)
4. Note the discrepancy between observed and expected.

B. State in ordinary language the hypothesis testing issue.
1. The hypothesis testing question is whether this discrepancy is so large that we can reject the hypothesis that our observed cases (our sample) represents a world in which the expected distribution of independence is generally true (that is, in the population).
2. Thus, you construct a scenario (the null hypothesis) in which the observed distribution is a random sample from a population in which the distributions of cases over categories are independent and see how likely it is that you could have gotten a discrepancy as large as you actually have under this scenario just by chance.

II. Determine the characteristics of the comparison distribution.

A. This step involves figuring out the probabilities of getting different degrees of discrepancy by chance under the null hypothesis.

B. The distribution of chance discrepancies under the null hypothesis for a particular way of measuring discrepancy (called chi-square) is called a chi-square distribution.

C. The chi-square distribution is mathematically defined and depends only on the number of expected cell frequencies that are free to take on any possible value once the overall numbers in each row and column are set. (This is figured out by multiplying the number of rows minus 1 times the number of columns minus 1.)

III. Determine the cutoff sample score on the comparison distribution at which the null hypothesis should be rejected.

A. In this step one figures out how large an actual discrepancy would have to be in order to decide that the probability of getting such a discrepancy under the null hypothesis is so low that this whole scenario of the null hypothesis being true could be confidently rejected.

B. There are standard tables that indicate the size of these discrepancies associated with various low probabilities.

C. Just how unlikely would a discrepancy have to be to decide the whole scenario on which these tables are based (the scenario of no difference) should be rejected? The standard figure used in psychology is less likely than 5% (though 1% is sometimes used to be especially safe). (Say which you are using in your study—if no figure is stated in the problem and no special reason given for using one or the other, the general rule is to use 5%.)

D. Once this decision is made, the cut-off level of discrepancy can be determined from the table. (State the level for your situation.)

IV. **Determine the score of your sample on the comparison distribution.**

A. Figure the degree of discrepancy for your actual situation.

B. This requires computing a number called a chi-square, which reflects the degree of divergence between observed and expected frequencies over the categories. It is figured in four steps (describe these steps in terms of your example).

1. For each cell find the discrepancy between the number observed and expected.

2. Square this discrepancy (this eliminates the problem of some discrepancies being positive and some negative).

3. Divide the discrepancy in each cell by the expected frequency. (This keeps these discrepancies in proportion to the number of cases that would have been expected.)

4. The chi-square statistic is the sum, over the categories, of each squared discrepancy divided by its expected frequency.

V. **Compare the scores in Steps III and IV to decide whether or not to reject the null hypothesis.**

A. Note whether or not your chi-square exceeds the cutoff and draw the appropriate conclusion. Either:

1. Reject the null hypothesis: The distributions of cases over categories in the two variables is so discrepant from what you would expect if your sample represents a population in which the distributions over the two variables are unrelated to each other that you reject this scenario.

2. Fail to reject the null hypothesis: The result is inconclusive. On the one hand, these results were not extreme enough to persuade you that the discrepancy from the two variables being unrelated was due to chance. On the other hand, it is still possible that your sample really does represent a population in which the variables are related, but because of the people who happened to be selected to be in your samples from the population, this discrepancy did not show up strongly enough.

B. Be sure to state your conclusion in terms of your particular measures and situation, so it is clear to a lay person just what the real bottom line of the study is.

VI. **Figure effect size and evaluate any nonsignificant results in terms of power.**

A. The degree of association between the distributions of cases over categories for the two variables can be indexed by a number that ranges from 0 (no association) to 1 (perfect association).

B. This number is the square root of the result of dividing the figured chi-square by the number of cases (or if greater than a 2 X 2 table, the division is by the number of cases times one less than the number of rows or columns in the smaller side of the table).

C. Give the result for your study and compare it to Cohen's conventions for small, medium and large effect sizes, discussing it as an indication of the degree of association in relation to what is typical in psychology research.

226

D. If you get a nonsignificant result, figure power (using the table).
  1. Explain concept of power as probability of deciding that the population distributions are not independent on the basis of a study with this many subjects, given that there is a true association of a given size in the population.
  2. Figure power twice, once for a small and once for a large effect size in the population and discuss implications for the likelihood of there actually being an effect of a small and large size in the population.

Chapter Self-Tests

Multiple-Choice Questions

1. A variable such as a person's nationality is usually considered to be
   a. rank-order.
   b. quantitative.
   c. nominal.
   d. fractional.

2. The chi-square statistic is the sum, over all categories or cells, of the following calculation made within each category or cell:
   a. the difference between the squared expected frequency and the squared observed frequency.
   b. the product of the expected frequency times the total number of cases observed in all categories or cells.
   c. the squared difference between the observed and expected frequency, divided by the expected frequency.
   d. the difference between observed and expected frequencies, divided by the expected frequency.

3. In a chi-square test for goodness of fit, the research hypothesis is that
   a. the population distribution of means fits the expected distribution of means.
   b. the population distribution of means is different between the two populations.
   c. the distribution of cases over categories differs between Population 1 and Population 2.
   d. the distribution of cases over categories is the same for Population 1 and Population 2.

4. "Independence" in the chi-square test for independence refers to a situation in which
   a. knowing a score's category on one variable gives no information about its category on the other variable.
   b. observed frequencies equal twice the expected frequencies.
   c. the grouping variable is truly causal and not merely predictive.
   d. if any relation exists between the two variables, either could be the cause of the other, but there are no third variables that might explain this relation.

5. A formula for determining the number of cases expected in any one cell of a chi-square contingency table is
   a. $R = (C/N)(E)$.
   b. $E = (R)(C)$.
   c. $R = (E)(R/N)$.
   d. $E = (R/N)(C)$.

6. The number of degrees of freedom in a chi-square test for independence is figured from a formula that requires knowing only

   a. the number of subjects.
   b. the number of subjects and the number of cells.
   c. the number of rows and the number of columns.
   d. the number of rows, columns, and subjects.

7. The one important assumption for the types of chi-square tests you learned in this book is that

   a. the expected frequency of cases must not be larger than the observed frequency.
   b. the population's distributions must be negatively skewed (or at least not positively skewed).
   c. each observed case must be unrelated to all others (that is, no two scores should come from the same subject).
   d. populations of each variable must be distributed normally.

8. The degree of association of a chi-square test of independence for a 2 X 2 contingency table is indicated by

   a. f.
   b. ϕ
   c. Cronbach's τ.
   d. R/N.

9. Power in a chi-square test for independence depends on all of the following EXCEPT

   a. effect size.
   b. whether a one- or two-tailed test is used.
   c. sample size.
   d. degrees of freedom.

10. In a chi-square test of independence, it is now generally thought that it is acceptable to have a low expected frequency (below 5) in a cell provided that

   a. the expected frequencies are all positive.
   b. the total number of subjects is at least five times the number of cells.
   c. there are more subjects than cells.
   d. there are at least 30 subjects.

Fill-In Questions

11. _____ invented the chi-square test.

12. You have taken a random sample of people at your college and asked each which of three fast-food chains he or she prefers. There is a tendency for one chain to be picked more often. To examine whether this preference would be likely to hold in the general population which this sample represents, you would conduct _____.

13. The formula for computing chi-square is $\Sigma[(O\text{-}E)^2/$ _____].

14. In the chi-square test for goodness of fit, the degrees of freedom are _____.

15. If there is no relationship between the variables in a contingency table, they are said to be _____ of each other.

16. In a chi-square test for independence, the expected frequency of a particular cell equals the percent of total observed cases in the cell's _____ times the number of observed cases in the cell's column.

17. Because the chi-square test does not require that the parent populations be _____, it is called a "nonparametric" or "distribution-free" test.

18. Complete the following formula:

    Cramer's ϕ = _____.

19. The power of a study testing hypotheses using the chi-square test of independence is determined by significance level, degrees of freedom, effect size and _____.

20. An organizational psychologist consulting to a hotel chain conducted a survey of people's preference for smoking or nonsmoking rooms and whether the person was on business or nonbusiness travel. The psychologist's report included the following table:

    Observed (and Expected) Frequencies for Room Preference and Travel Type for 80 Surveyed Patrons

    | Travel | Room Preference | | Total | Percent |
	Smoking	Non		
Business	30 (33)	30 (27)	60	75
Nonbusiness	14 (11)	6 (9)	20	25
Total	44	36		80

    $$\chi^2(1, N=80) = 2.42, ns$$

    a. Of business travelers, _____% preferred smoking rooms.
    b. Of the nonbusiness travelers, _____ % preferred smoking rooms.
    c. The phi coefficient for this study was _____.

Problems and Essays

21. Design a five-category study to be analyzed by the chi-square test for goodness of fit. (a) Make up data, (b) analyze it (use the .05 significance level), and (c) describe the underlying logic of the analysis and interpret your "findings" to a person who has never had a course in statistics.

22. An industrial psychologist working for a particular manufacturing company was concerned that one of their four plants might have consistently more worker grievances than the others. Records are kept for a month, during which Plant A had 15 grievances; Plant B, 34; Plant C, 17; and Plant D, 18.

    a. Do these data (which are fictional) suggest that the four plants are different in how many grievances arise? (Use the .05 significance level.)
    b. Explain your analysis to a person who has never had a course in statistics.

23. A survey is conducted of the weight of newborns (recorded as below average, average, and above average) and depression of mothers during pregnancy (rated as severe, mild, or not depressed).

    a. Do the data (which are fictional) in the following table suggest birthweight is related to mother's depression during pregnancy? (Use the .05 significance level.)
    b. Figure the effect size and indicate whether it is large, medium, or small.
    c. Explain your analyses to a person who has never had a course in statistics.

	Level of Mother's Depression During Pregnancy		
Birthweight	Severe	Mild	Not Depressed
below average	8	5	1
average	3	8	12
above average	9	7	7

24. A researcher was interested in gender differences in type of leisure reading selected. The (fictional) data are as follows:

	Type A	Type B	Type C
Women	6	1	6
Men	2	5	4

    a. Do the data (which are fictional) in the following table suggest reading choice varies by gender? (Use the .05 significance level.)
    b. Figure the effect size and indicate whether it is large, medium, or small.
    c. Explain your analyses to a person who has never had a course in statistics.

25. Graduate students in the humanities, social sciences, and natural sciences were surveyed and found to listen to three different types of music when they studied. The relation of field of study to type of music yielded a significant association, $X^2(4, N=60) = 14.32$, $p < .05$.

    a. Figure a measure of association and indicate whether it is a large, medium, or small effect.
    b. Explain the results of the study (including the effect-size result) to a person who has never had a course in statistics.

Using SPSS (11.0 for Windows) with this Chapter

If you are using SPSS for the first time, before proceeding with the material in this section read the Appendix on Getting Started and the Basics of Using SPSS.

You can use SPSS to carry out a chi-square test for independence. You should work through the example, following the procedures step by step.

I. Example

A. Data: A survey was conducted in which 25 people were asked about their religious and political party affiliations. The results for 25 subjects are as follows (with Religion being the first score listed and Political Party being the second score listed):

1, 1
0, 0
0, 1
0, 1
1, 1
1, 1
1, 0
0, 0
1, 1
1, 0
1, 0
1, 0
1, 0
1, 0
1, 0
1, 1
0, 0
0, 0
1, 0
0, 0
0, 1
0, 1
0, 1
1, 0
1, 0

B.   Follow the instructions in the SPSS Appendix for starting up SPSS.

C. Enter the data as follows.

1. Type 1, the score for Religion for the first subject, and press Enter.
2. Type 0, the score for Religion for the second subject, and press Enter.
3. Type the remaining scores for this variable, one per line.
4. In the first space in the second column, type 1, the score for Political Party for the first subject.
5. Type 0, the score for Political Party for the second subject.
6. Type the remaining scores for this variable, one per line.

231

7. To name the two variables, click on the Variable View tab. In the first row of the first column, type RELIGION under the column "Name." Repeat this for the second variable, replacing VAR00002 with POLPAR. Your screen should now appear like Figure SG14-1.

SG14-1

D. Compute the chi-square test as follows:
1. Analyze
    Descriptive Statistics
       Crosstabs
          [Highlight RELIGION and bring it into the Row(s) box. Highlight
           POLPAR and bring it into the Column(s) box.]
             Statistics
               [Check Chi-Square]
                 Continue
                   OK

2. The results should appear as Figure SG14-2.

232

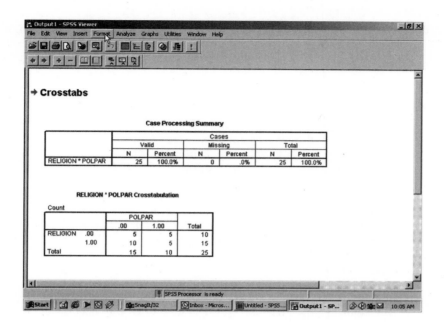

SG14-2

3. Print out this screen of results by going to File and then Print or by clicking on the Print icon.
  a. The bottom part, under the heading of **Chi-Square**, provides several statistics. The only one you need attend to is labeled **Pearson** (this is the ordinary chi-square test). The **Value** of the chi square statistic is **.694** and the **DF** (degrees of freedom) is **1**. The **Significance** refers to the probability of getting a chi-square this extreme. A probability of **.405** is clearly not sufficient enough to reject the null hypothesis of independence at the .05 level.

E. Save your lines of data as follows.
    File
    Save Data
    [Name your data file and designate the drive you would like your data saved in.
        OK

II. Systematic Instructions for Computing a Chi-Square Test of Independence
  A. Start up SPSS.
  B. Enter the data as follows.
    1. Type 0, the score for Religion for the first subject, and press Enter.
    2. Type 1, the score for Religion for the second subject, and press Enter.
    3. Type the remaining scores for this variable, one per line.
    4. In the first space in the second column, type 1, the score for Political Party for the first subject.
    5. Type 1, the score for Political Party for the second subject.
    6. Type the remaining scores for this variable, one per line.

233

7. To name the two variables, To name the two variables, click on the Variable View tab. In the first row of the first column, type RELIGION under the column "Name." Repeat this for the second variable, replacing VAR00002 with POLPAR

C. Compute the chi-square test as follows:

 Analyze

  Descriptive Statistics

   Crosstabs

    [Highlight RELIGION and bring it into the Row(s) box. Highlight POLPAR and bring it into the Column(s) box.]

     Statistics

      [Check Chi-Square]

       Continue

        OK

D. Interpret the results.
 1. The contingency table (check it for accuracy).
 2. The chi-square statistic, its degrees of freedom.

E. Save your lines of data as follows.
 File
  Save Data
  [Name your data and designate the drive you would like your data saved in].
   OK

III. Additional Practice

(For each data set, conduct a chi-square test for independence and compare your results to those in the text.)

A. Text examples.
 1. Use the data in Table 14-4 for comparing morning or night people use different forms of transportation.
 2. Use the data in Table 14-7 whether first generation college students differ from others in first semester dropouts.

B. Practice problems in the text.
 1. Set I: 7, 8.
 2. Set II: 22, 23.

Chapter 15
Strategies When Population Distributions Are Not Normal: Data Transformations, Rank-Order Tests, and Computer-Intensive Methods

Learning Objectives

To understand, including being able to conduct any necessary computations:

- Assumptions for the major parametric statistical tests.
- Implications of violating assumptions.
- Recognizing violations of the normality assumption.
- Rationale of data transformations.
- Procedures of major data transformations.
- Rationale of rank-order tests.
- Applications of rank-order tests.
- Rank-order transformations followed by standard parametric tests.
- Relative advantages and disadvantages of data transformations, rank-order tests, and computer-intensive methods.
- Randomization tests and approximate randomization tests.

Chapter Outline

I. **Assumptions in the Standard Hypothesis-Testing Procedures**
   A. Most require meeting two assumptions.
      1. Populations have normal distributions.
      2. Populations have equal variances.
   B. Violation of assumptions can increase or decrease Type I and Type II error, often in unpredictable ways.
   C. Recognizing violations of assumptions.
      1. Difficult to do with only sample data.
      2. Extreme skewness, kurtosis, or outliers of samples suggest population distribution is not normal.

II. **Data Transformations**
   A. Application of some regular mathematical procedure to each score (such as taking the square root of each).
   B. Done to make scores in the sample follow normal distribution in the hope that they will then represent a population that is normally distributed.
   C. Justified when underlying meaning of intervals between scores are arbitrary.
   D. Major types of transformations:
      1. Square root.
      2. Log.
      3. Inverse.
      4. Arcsine.
   E. Transformations do not change order of scores.
   F. Carried out by trial and error until a transformation creates a distribution in the sample that appears normal.
   G. After the transformation, the ordinary parametric test is applied.

III. Rank-Order Methods

A. Involve converting scores to ranks.

B. Distribution free and nonparametric.

C. Rank-order tests are available that correspond to each major parametric method (see Table 15-6 in the text).

D. Rank-order tests operate based on a known distribution of any set of ranks (rectangular) and involve precise computations of probability of getting a pattern of ranks as extreme as that observed in the study.

E. Some statisticians have recommended applying ordinary parametric tests after making a rank-order transformation.

F. Rank-order tests are particularly appropriate with data measured at the rank-order (ordinal) level.

    1. Rank-order measurement has less information than the standard equal-interval measurement.

    2. Some psychologists argue that our typical measures are not truly equal-interval, so that we should always transform to ranks.

IV. Comparison of Methods

A. Data transformation.

    1. Advantage is that it permits the use of familiar and sophisticated parametric techniques.

    2. Disadvantages.

        a. No transformation may work to make the data meet assumptions.

        b. May distort meaning of scores.

B. Rank-order tests.

    1. Advantages.

        a. Can always be applied.

        b. Particularly suitable for rank-order data.

        c. Underlying logic is very simple and direct.

    2. Disadvantages.

        a. Less commonly understood than standard parametric methods.

        b. In many complex situations no standard rank-order methods have been developed.

        c. May distort meaning of scores.

    3. In the past, ease of computation by hand was an advantage.

V. Controversies and recent developments

A. The use of computers to analyze data has made new procedures available and practical. Two such procedures are randomization tests and bootstrapping.

B. Randomization test.

    1. Figures probability that a particular organization of the data (such as the division of scores into an experimental and control group) represents a difference or association that is very unlikely in light of all possible organizations of the data.

    2. Not practical for situations with sample sizes of the magnitude used in much psychology research.

C. An approximate randomization test is practical. It figures differences or associations for a randomly selected large number (say, 1000) of the possible organizations of the data and bases the probability on these results.

D. Advantages and Disadvantages
    1. Advantages.
       a. Underlying logic is very simple and direct.
       b. Can be applied to almost any situation, even ones for which no standard test has been invented.
    2. Disadvantages.
       a. New, so that the cautions and limitations are not well worked out.
       b. New, so that standard statistical software packages do not include them.

VI. Procedures Used When Populations Appear Nonnormal, as Described in Research Articles

A. Data transformations are typically described at the start of the Results section, with a description of the distribution of the data that were transformed.

B. Rank-order tests are described in the same way as other tests, often giving a Z statistic (for the normal approximation of the distribution of the underlying rank-order statistic).

How to Conduct Hypothesis Tests When Populations Appear Nonnormal

1. Examine data to see if the distributions suggest a nonnormal population distribution, then decide which method to use.

A. If data transformation does not distort the underlying meaning of the data and there is a transformation that makes the data meet the assumptions, this method is appropriate.

B. If the data are rank-order scores or most reasonably considered as ranks, and if a rank-order test is available, this method is particularly appropriate.

C. If the data would be distorted by transformation or putting in rank order, if assumptions can not be met in these ways, or if no existing statistical test applies to the situation, then computer-intensive methods are appropriate.

2. Carry out one of the two methods:

A. Data transformation.
    1. Examine the sample data to estimate the kind and degree of nonnormal shape of the population distribution.
    2. Apply the transformation that seems to offer the best correction.
       a. Square root for a moderately skewed distribution.
       b. Log for a highly skewed distribution.
       c. Inverse for a very highly skewed distribution.
    3. Examine the transformed sample distribution; if it still clearly suggests a nonnormal population distribution, try a different transformation.
    4. Once an appropriate distribution has been created, carry out a standard parametric hypothesis test using the transformed scores.

B. Rank-order test.
    1. Transform all scores to ranks, ignoring which group the subject is in (however, if computing a correlation, rank each variable's scores separately), giving average ranks for ties.
    2. Carry out the hypothesis test in one of these ways.
    3. Use one of the standard nonparametric tests (for which you have not learned the procedures in this text).

Outline for Writing Essays on the Logic and Computations for Conducting Hypothesis Tests When Populations Appear Nonnormal

The reason for your writing essay questions in the practice problems and tests is that this task develops and then demonstrates what matters so very much–your comprehension of the logic behind the computations. (It is also a place where those better at words than numbers can shine, and for those better at numbers to develop their skills at explaining in words.)

Thus, to do well, be sure to do the following in each essay: (a) give the reasoning behind each step; (b) relate each step to the specifics of the content of the particular study you are analyzing; (c) state the various formulas in nontechnical language, because as you define each term you show you understand it (although once you have defined it in nontechnical language, you can use it from then on in the essay); (d) look back and be absolutely certain that you made it clear just *why* that formula or procedure was applied and *why* it is the way it is.

The outlines below are *examples* of ways to structure your essays. There are other completely correct ways to go about it. And this is an *outline* for an answer–you are to write the answer out in paragraph form. Examples of full essays are in the answers to Set I Practice Problems in the back of the text.

These essays are necessarily very long for you to write (and for others to grade). But this is the very best way to be sure you understand everything thoroughly. One shortcut you may see on a test is that you may be asked to write your answer for someone who understands statistics up to the point of the new material you are studying. You can choose to take the same shortcut in these practice problems (maybe writing for someone who understands right up to whatever point you yourself start being just a little unclear). But every time you write for a person who has never had statistics at all, you review the logic behind the entire course. You engrain it in your mind. Over and over. The time is never wasted. It is an excellent way to study.

I. **Explain that ordinarily one could use a standard statistical procedure to resolve the issue (test the hypothesis raised by the essay question).**
   A. Name the procedure that would be appropriate (such as a t test or analysis of variance).
   B. However, explain that these standard procedures require certain conditions be met to use them.
   C. One of these conditions is that the distribution of scores in the larger groups (populations) that your data are supposed to represent must follow a bell-shaped pattern known as a normal curve.
   D. However, in the data at hand, the scores do not seem to come from populations distributed in the shape of a normal curve. (Explain what leads you to this conclusion.)
   E. Thus one of several alternatives have to be used.
II. **If data transformation is selected, explain it.**
   A. The purpose is to make data more likely to be representative of a normally distributed population.

238

B. Data transformation is acceptable when the underlying meaning of the intervals between scores are arbitrary and the transformation does not change the order of the scores.

C. Deciding which transformation to use depends on which will make the sample data most closely follow a normal curve; summarize the trial-and-error process you carried out in working the problem.

D. Once the data are transformed, one can carry out the normal hypothesis test.

E. Describe the logic and computations in the steps of the appropriate hypothesis testing procedure you apply.

III. If a rank-order method is selected, explain it.

A. This method is used in three situations.

1. The data suggest a nonnormal population and transforming to ranks creates a situation with a known distribution. This is acceptable when the underlying meaning of the values of the variable are arbitrary.

2. The meaning of the intervals between values of the variables is inconsistent; converting to ranks, while reducing the amount of information, leaves only that information which one can be confident is accurate.

3. The data are in the form of ranks to begin with and standard methods assume equal interval measurement.

B. Describe transformation into ranks, noting how any ties are handled.

C. Explain that you will then carry out a normal hypothesis test using the ranked data.

D. Describe the logic and computations in the steps of the appropriate hypothesis testing procedure you apply.

E. Note that statisticians have found that although ranks do not have a normal distribution, using the standard statistical procedures (parametric tests) with ranked data gives approximately accurate results.

Chapter Self-Tests

Multiple-Choice Questions

1. When it comes to normality, in practice most researchers assume

a. the population is NOT normally distributed, until normality is verified by special procedures.
b. the population is normally distributed unless the sample's histogram is drastically nonnormal.
c. the sample is normally distributed unless the population's histogram is drastically nonnormal.
d. the sample is NOT normally distributed, until normality is verified by special procedures.

2. A square-root transformation is often used when the data are

a. bimodally skewed.
b. positively skewed.
c. negatively skewed.
d. normally distributed.

3. Data transformations are justified by all of the following arguments, EXCEPT

   a. the transformed data might better represent a population that is normally distributed.
   b. if there is not an inherent meaning in a score's number (as in the case of most psychological scales), transformations give a reflection of reality that is at least as accurate as the original picture.
   c. transformation makes the hypothesis testing procedure more stringent by increasing sample sizes.
   d. after transformations, scores that were higher are still higher (that is the order of the scores is unchanged).

4. "Non-parametric tests" use data which

   a. are transformed using antilogs.
   b. do not require estimating population parameters.
   c. are transformed using logs.
   d. are normally distributed.

5. Which of the following rank-order tests corresponds to a t test for dependent means?
   a. Wilcoxin signed-rank test.
   b. Wilcoxin rank-sum test.
   c. Kruskal-Wallis h test.
   d. Spearman Rho.

6. If you convert scores to ranks and then carry out an ordinary analysis of variance,

   a. the results will be seriously distorted because the distribution of scores is not normal.
   b. the scores must first be converted to logs before the rank transformation.
   c. the results will be quite accurate because ranks are normally distributed.
   d. the results will be a good approximation if the F table is used to determine significance and quite accurate if special tables are used.

7. If a measure is equal-interval, then a difference between the scores of 2 and 3 is about the same as the difference between the scores of

   a. 2.4 and 2.6.
   b. 1 and 1.5.
   c. 4 and 9.
   d. 10 and 11.

8. All of the following are advantages of rank-order tests, EXCEPT

   a. they are particularly useful when the data are not clearly equal-interval.
   b. the logic is simple and direct, requiring no elaborate construction of hypothetical distributions and estimated parameters.
   c. there are many more such tests available than standard parametric tests, so that it is more likely that one of these can be used than a standard parametric test.
   d. they are more familiar to readers of research in psychology than are computer-intensive methods.

Fill-In Questions

9. Data transformations are used when the distribution of the population is thought to be _____.

10. A single score that has a big effect on the mean of a group and therefore likely to distort significance tests comparing that group to other groups is called a(n) _____.

11. A log transformation has a similar but weaker effect than a(n) _____ transformation.

12. Because there is no need to estimate population values, rank-order tests are called _____.

13. The parametric version of the Wilcoxin rank-sum test is the _____.

14. The null hypothesis of a(n) _____ test is that the two populations have the same median.

15. When conducting a rank-order test with a large sample, a Z score is figured which is compared to a(n) _____.

16. If a measure is _____, then the meaning of the difference between scores of 27 and 29 is the same as that of 5 and 7.

17. _____ do not require either normal population distributions or equal variances when testing hypotheses and can be applied even to situations in which no ordinary statistical tests exist.

Problems and Essays

18. Describe the distribution of the following scores:
    a. 60 182 189 193 4654
    b. 4.8 5.4 5.8 5.9 6.3 6.9

19. In a study of the effect of expecting to be liked on attraction, ten participants were randomly assigned to meet a stranger under conditions in which they did or did not expect the stranger to like them. This was followed by a short interaction after which the participants indicated how attracted they were to the person as a friend. Here are the scores:

    Did not expect to be liked: 77, 83, 88, 91, 98
    Did expect to be liked: 46, 57, 58, 66, 99
    a. Conduct a t test for independent means using the raw scores (use the .05 level, two-tailed).
    b. Conduct another t test using square-root transformed scores.
    c. Discuss the reasons for using the transformation and the implications of the difference in results of these two methods.

241

20. Do adults who changed elementary schools over five times in their childhood have a different number of "good friends" than those who only attended one school? A small sample was drawn, and the frequent movers had 3, 1, 9, 13, and 6 good friends, while those who had not moved had 1, 4, 5, 2, and 1 good friend.

    a. Conduct the appropriate standard parametric hypothesis testing procedure, but using ranks. (Use the .05 significance level.)

    b. Explain your analysis to a person who has never had a course in statistics.

21. A researcher wanted to know if caffeine increased tactile sensitivity. She tested 10 participants, 5 in the caffeine condition, and 5 in the caffeine-free condition. Her (fictional) results are as follows:

Caffeine	Caffeine-free
10	5
13	4
12	10
9	8
9	6

    a. Conduct the appropriate standard parametric hypothesis testing procedure, but using ranks. (Use the .05 significance level.)

    b. Explain your analysis to a person who has never had a course in statistics.

22. A memory researcher compared number of symbols forgotten over one week under two different kinds of interference. In the results section the researcher reported "the Gonzales-Scott interference condition produced significantly greater interference than did the Janoff interference condition, based on a Mann-Whitney U test, $Z = 3.21$, $p < .01$."

    a. Explain why the researcher might have used the Mann-Whitney U test instead of an ordinary t test for independent means.

    b. Explain the meaning of the Z (in a general way–you need not describe how it was figured) in the context of the study.

    c. Suggest one other alternative approach the researcher could have used.

Using SPSS (11.0 for Windows) with this Chapter

This chapter assumes you are familiar with the basics of using SPSS and have worked examples from previous chapters.

You can use SPSS to carry out data transformations. (SPSS can also carry out certain rank-order tests. However, like most standard statistics programs, SPSS does not carry out any of the computer-intensive procedures.)

You should work through the example, following the procedures step by step. Then look over the description of the general principles involved and try the procedures on your own for some of the problems listed in the Suggestions for Additional Practice. Finally, you may want to try the suggestions for using the computer to deepen your understanding and explore some of the advanced SPSS procedures, the rank-order tests.

I. Example
  A. Data: Number of books read in the past year by four children who are not, and four children who are, highly sensitive. These are fictional data from a text example. For the children who are not highly sensitive, the numbers of books read are 0,3,10, and 22; for the highly sensitive children, 17, 36, 45, and 75.
  B. Follow the instructions in the SPSS Appendix for starting up SPSS.
  C. Enter the data as follows.
      1. Type one line per subject, using a 1 for not highly sensitive and a 2 for highly sensitive.
      2. Name your variables HIGHSENS and BOOKS. Your screen should now look like Figure SG15-1.

Figure 15-1

243

D. Carry out a square root transformation:
    Transform
        Compute
            [Name your new variable by typing SQRBOOKS in the Target Variable box]
                [Type SQRT(BOOKS) in the Numeric Expression box. Your screen should now
                    look like Figure SG15-2]
                        OK

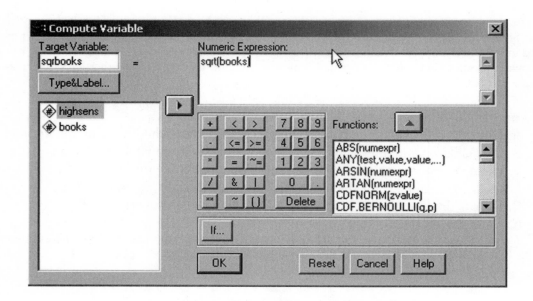

Figure SG15-2

E. Carry out a t test for independent means, using the square-root transformed
    variable:
        Analyze
            Compare Means >
                Independent Samples t test
                    Move SQRBOOKS into Test Variable(s) box and HIGHSENS into
                        Grouping Variable box]
                            Define Groups
                                [Type 1 for Group 1 and 2 for Group 2]
                                    Continue
                                        OK

F. Your results should look like Figure SG15-3.

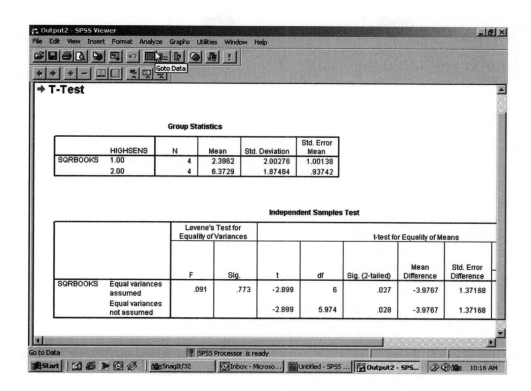

Figure SG15-3

G. Save your lines of data as follows:
    File
      Save Data
       [Name your data and designate the drive you would like your data saved in]
         OK

II Systematic Instructions for carrying out a Data Transformation
  A. Start up SPSS.
  B. Enter the data as follows.
     1. Type one line per subject, using a 1 for not highly sensitive and a 2 for highly sensitive.
     2. Name your variables HIGHSENS and BOOKS.
  C. Carry out a square root transformation:
    Transform
      Compute
       [Name your new variable by typing SQRBOOKS in the Target Variable box]
        [Type SQRT(BOOKS) in the Numeric Expression box.]
         OK

D. Make a histogram to check whether the sample of scores on the transformed variable seems to represent a normal distribution. (If it does not, try another transformation.)

E. Carry out the statistical procedure in the usual way, but using the variable representing the transformed scores.

F. Save your lines of data as follows.

    File
      Save Data
        [Name your data file and designate which drive you would like your file saved in.]
        OK

III. Additional Practice

A. For each data set carry out the appropriate data transformation followed by the appropriate statistical procedure and compare your results to those in the text.

B. Use any of the data sets from Chapters 3 and 8 through 10.

IV. Using the Computer to Deepen Your Knowledge

A. Effects of data transformation.

    1. Use SPSS to compute a t test for independent means using the books-read example, comparing a square root, log, and inverse transformation; and make a histogram for the untransformed scores and for each transformation. Record the t score obtained under the various conditions.

    2. Do the same with the t test example from Chapter 10 (the new-job-program experiment). Record the t score obtained under the various conditions.

    3. Do the same with the example of a t test for dependent means in Chapter 9 (the surgeons'-reaction-time study), being sure to modify both Quiet and Noisy scores in the same way. Record the t scores obtained under the various conditions.

    4. Do the same with the correlation example from Chapter 3 (the manager's-stress example). Change each variable separately, keeping the other in its original form. Then try some combinations. Record the correlations obtained under the various conditions.

    5. Compare the results. What trends are there and what do they mean? (Evaluate these trends in terms of how well the transformations do and do not approximate a normal curve.)

B. Evaluate the effect of transformations in creating normal sample distributions: Using one of the larger data sets from Chapter 1 or 2 of the text, try several data transformations. For each, produce a histogram. (You may also want to compute skew and kurtosis, as described in the advanced procedures section of the SPSS discussion in Chapter 2 of this *Study Guide and Computer Workbook*.)

Chapter 16
Integrating What You Have Learned: The General Linear Model

Learning Objectives

To understand, including being able to conduct any necessary computations:

- The hierarchical relation among the four major parametric methods.
- The general linear model.
- Equivalence of bivariate regression and correlation and multivariate regression/correlation with one grouping variable.
- Equivalence of the t test for independent means and a two-group analysis of variance.
- Equivalence of the t test for independent means and a significance test of a correlation coefficient in which the predictor variable is a two-level numerical variable.
- Graphic interpretation of the above point.
- Equivalence of the analysis of variance for two groups and the significance test of the correlation coefficient in which the predictor variable is a two-level numerical variable.
- Equivalence of the analysis of variance for three or more groups and multiple regression/correlation in which the predictor variables are two-level numerical variables.
- How psychologists choose among mathematically equivalent methods.
- Regularity and generative theories of causality.
- Criteria for judging an observed relationship as causal.

Chapter Outline

I. Multiple Regression/Correlation (Review)
A. Yields a systematic rule for predicting values of a measured variable.
B. In raw score form the rule is stated this way:

$$\hat{Y} = a + (b_1)(X_1) + (b_2)(X_2) + (b_3)(X_3) + \ldots$$

C. The correlation between the set of grouping variables and the measured variable is called a multiple correlation (R).
D. R^2 is the proportionate reduction in squared error gained by using the multiple-regression prediction rule compared to simply predicting the measured variable from its mean.
E. R and R^2 can be tested against the null hypothesis that the population value is 0.

II. The General Linear Model
A. A person's score on a measured variable is conceived as the sum of three influences.
  1. Some fixed influence that will be the same for all individuals.
  2. Influences of variables we have measured, on which people have different scores.
  3. Other influences not measured (error).

B. Stated as a formula, it looks like this:

$$Y = a + (b_1)(X_1) + (b_2)(X_2) + (b_3)(X_3) + [\text{etc.}] + e.$$

C. This formula is like a multiple regression formula.
   1. Influence 1 corresponds to the a in a raw-score multiple regression prediction rule.
   2. Influence 2 corresponds to the bs (b_1, b_2, etc.) and Xs (X_1, X_2, etc.) in a multiple regression equation.
D. But in some ways it is not the same as a multiple regression formula.
   1. The formula is for the actual, not the predicted, score on the measured variable.
   2. The formula includes Influence 3, which is what accounts for the errors in prediction.
E. It is called a linear model because the equation does not include any squared or higher power terms.

III. Bivariate Regression and Correlation in Relation to Multiple Regression: Bivariate regression is the special case of multiple regression/correlation in which there is only one predictor variable.

IV. The t Test for Independent Means as a Special Case of the Analysis of Variance
   A. The t test for independent means is equivalent to the analysis of variance when the analysis is of two groups.
   B. Both t and F can be understood as ratios of signal to noise. (Numerators are based on difference or variation among means of groups; denominators of both are based on variation within groups.)
   C. Below are the details about this equivalency.
      1. The numerators are based on differences or variations among means of groups.
      2. The denominator of t is partly based on pooling the estimates of variances from data within each group; the denominator of F is the pooled estimate of variances from data within each group.
      3. The denominator of t involves dividing by the number of participants in each group; the numerator of F (when using the method for equal sample sizes of Chapter 11) involves multiplying by the number of participants in each group .
      4. For analyses conducted on the same data (comparing means of two groups):
         a. The t score is exactly the square root of the F.
         b. The degrees of freedom for the t are the same as the denominator degrees of freedom for the F.
         c. The cutoff t equals the square root of the cutoff F.

V. The t Test for Independent Means as a Special Case of the Significance Test of the Correlation Coefficient
   A. The following points are true of the significance test of the correlation coefficient.
      1. It tests the null hypothesis that in the population there is a correlation of 0.
      2. The comparison distribution is a t distribution with degrees of freedom equal to the number of participants minus 2.
      3. The score on the comparison distribution is a t score, with

$$t = (r) \left(\sqrt{N-2} \, / \, \sqrt{[1-r^2]} \right)$$

   B. A comparison of means of groups (the focus of a t test for independent means) can be thought of as a nominal variable with two levels.

C. Representing a nominal variable with two levels as a numerical variable, using any two arbitrary numbers to stand for the two levels, permits one to conduct a correlation between that variable and the measured variable.

D. The t test for independent means is equivalent to the significance test of a correlation coefficient in which one of the variables has only two levels. That is, analyses conducted on the same data yield equivalent results.
    1. Both methods give the same t.
    2. Both methods give the same degrees of freedom.
    3. Both methods yield the same cutoff t score and the same conclusions regarding significance.

E. Creating a scatter diagram for the two-group situation further illustrates the relation.
    1. The mean of each group is the same as the predicted score (from the regression equation) for each of the levels of the two-level numerical variable.
    2. The variation between the two means is equivalent to the slope of the regression line–the greater this is, the more likely the t is significant.
    3. The variation within each of the groups is equivalent to the spread around each predicted value in the scatter diagram–the smaller this is, the more likely the t is significant.

VI. **The Analysis of Variance as a Special Case of the Significance Test in Multiple Regression/Correlation**

A. The analysis of variance for two groups is equivalent to the significance test of a bivariate correlation in which the predictor variable has two levels.

B. This link is seen most clearly in comparing the computation of the proportion of variance accounted for (R^2) in analysis of variance using the structural model approach and the proportionate reduction in error (r^2) in bivariate regression.
    1. The within-group sum of squares (SS_{Within}) in analysis of variance is the sum of the squared differences of each score from its group's mean; the sum of squares for error (SS_{Error}) in regression is the sum of the squared differences of each score from the predicted score (which, when there are only two levels of the predictor variable, is the same as the mean on each level of that predictor variable). Thus, $SS_{Within} = SS_{Error}$.
    2. The total sum of squared error (SS_{Total}) in analysis of variance is the sum of the squared differences of each score from the grand mean; the total sum of squared error (SS_{Total}) in regression is the sum of the squared difference of each score from the mean of the measured variable (which is the same number as the grand mean in analysis of variance). Thus, SS_{Total} in analysis of variance is equal to SS_{Total} in regression.
    3. The between-group sum of squares in analysis of variance can be figured as SS_{Total}-SS_{Within} (this is because $SS_{Total}=SS_{Within}+SS_{Between}$); the reduction in squared error in regression is SS_{Total}-SS_{Within}. Thus, $SS_{Between}$ in analysis of variance equals the reduction in squared error in regression.
    4. In analysis of variance, $R^2 = SS_{Between}/SS_{Total}$; in regression, r^2 = reduction in squared error / SS_{Total}. Since $SS_{Between}$ = reduction in squared error, and SS_{Total} is the same in both, R^2 in analysis of variance equals r^2 in regression.
    5. If one put the sums of squares in a regression analysis into an analysis of variance table and figured an F, it would yield the same F as the analysis of variance.

C. The analysis of variance for more than two groups is equivalent to the significance test of a multiple regression/correlation in which the predictor variables each have two-levels and there are one fewer such predictor variables than there are groups.

249

1. A comparison of means of several groups can be thought of as a nominal variable with as many levels as there are groups.
2. Such a many-leveled nominal variable can not be made into a single numerical variable because the numerical levels assigned would imply specific ordered and quantitative relations among the levels.
3. Such a many-leveled nominal variable can be made into a set of two-level numerical variables such that each represents being in or not being in one of the groups. (This is called nominal coding.)
4. It takes one less two-leveled variable than there are groups because the last group is represented by a case not being in any of the preceding groups.

D. The proportion of variance accounted for (R^2) in an analysis of variance for more than two groups is equivalent to the proportionate reduction in error (R^2) of a multiple regression/correlation in which the predictor variables each have two-levels, and there is one fewer of the predictor variables than there are groups.

VII. **Choice of Test when Results Would Be Equivalent**
A. It is based in part on tradition and what people are used to.
B. It is based in part on people confusing a correlational research design with a correlational statistic.

VIII. **Controversy: Causality.**
A. One view of causality is the regularity theory.
1. It is associated with the philosophers Hume and Mill.
2. It considers X to be a cause of Y if three conditions are met.
a. X and Y are regularly associated.
b. X precedes Y.
c. There are no third causes that precede X that might cause both X and Y.
3. In psychology research this idea of regular association is indicated by a significant correlation.
4. In psychology research the requirement of no third causes is handled in one of two ways.
a. Ideally there is random assignment to levels of X.
b. As a makeshift when random assignment is not possible, groups are equated by statistical methods that look for third causes among variables measured as part of the research.
B. Another view of causality is the generative theory.
1. It is associated with the philosophers Aristotle, Aquinas, and Kant.
2. It requires everything required for the regularity view.
3. In addition, it requires that the researcher be able to identify a plausible explanation for the way in which X influences Y.

Outline for Writing Essays on the Equivalence of Various Methods

The essays for this chapter involve explaining the equivalences of two different ways of carrying out computations for the same data. What is important in this case is to lay out and explain, in a step by step manner, each of the linkages involved. Your explanations should explicate the reasoning for why two numbers are equivalent–it is not enough just to point to the equality.

The outlines below are *examples* of ways to structure your essays. There are other completely correct ways to go about it. And this is an *outline* for an answer–you are to write the answer out in paragraph form. Examples of full essays are in the answers to Set I Practice Problems in the back of the text.

t Test as a Special Case of Analysis of Variance

1. **Carry out the computations for the data using the two methods (use the method for equal sample sizes introduced in Chapter 11).**
2. **Make a chart showing equivalencies, similar to the main section of Table 16-2 in the text.**
3. **Explain each parallel.**
    A. The degrees of freedom for the *t* are the same as the denominator degrees of freedom for the *F*–because in both cases the estimate of the population variance based on the variation within the groups is based on this number of degrees of freedom.
    B. The cutoff *t* equals the square root of the cutoff *F* because the procedures are mathematically equivalent, except that the resulting *t* is the square root of the resulting *F*.
    C. Numerators of *t* and *F* are both based on differences among means of groups– because in both cases the statistic should be larger if there is greater differences among the groups (which is what is being tested).
    D. The denominator of *t* is partly based on pooling estimates of variances from data within each group; the denominator of *F* is a pooled estimate of variances from data within each group (note that $S_{Pooled}^2 = S_{Within}^2$)–these are the same because in both cases we want to divide, or reduce the effect of the difference between groups, in proportion to the amount of variation, or noise, within each group.
    E. The denominator of *t* involves dividing by the number of participants in each group; the numerator of *F* involves multiplying by the number of participants in each group–these divisions or multiplications are done in both cases to take into account the fact that we are dealing with means of groups, which do not vary as much as individual cases (explain this in more depth following explanations in Chapters 7, 10, and 11).

t Test for Independent Means as a Special Case of the Significance Test for the Correlation Coefficient

1. **Carry out the computations for the data using the two methods.**
2. **Explain the equivalence of a two-category numerical variable in the correlation to the two-category nominal variable in the *t* test.**
    A. The difference between groups on a measured variable equals the association of the variable that represents what the groups differ on with the measured variable.
    B. Thus, a difference in a *t* test for independent means is the same as an association between its independent and measured variable.

C. If you substitute a two-level numerical variable for a two-level nominal variable (giving each group one number), the correlation with this variable is not affected (except for sign) by the two numbers you pick–this is because in correlation everything is converted to Z scores and with Z scores a variable with only two numbers always comes out to the same two Z scores (if there are equal numbers of cases in the two groups, the Z scores are all +1s and -1s).

D. Thus, the resulting correlation accurately represents the association between the original nominal variable and the measured variable.

3. **Explain each parallel in the significance test.**

A. The null hypothesis for the t test is that there is no difference between populations on the measured variable and for the correlation, that there is a 0 association. These are equivalent because both are hypothesizing no relation between the independent and measured variable.

B. Both are tested using a t distribution (this is because in both cases you are working with populations whose variance is not known).

C. State that the degrees of freedom are the same in both cases (you needn't explain this).

D. The computations lead to the same t score.

   1. This is because they are testing the same thing.

   2. Another way to understand this is that both calculations are based on the same comparison.

      a. A t test for independent means is larger when there is more difference between the group means and less variation within each group.

      b. A correlation is larger (as is the t figured from the correlation coefficient) when there is a maximum difference between the scores at each level of the grouping variable (that is, if there are two groups, and there is maximum difference between the means of the two groups) and minimum variation among the scores at each level of the grouping variable (that is, if each level is a group, there is minimum variation within groups). Illustrate this with a scatter diagram for your data.

Proportion of Variance Accounted for in Analysis of Variance (R^2) for Two Groups as a Special Case of Proportionate Reduction in Error in Regression (r^2)

1. **Carry out the computations for the data using the two methods (for the analysis of variance, be sure to use the structural model approach from Chapter 12).**

2. **Explain the equivalence of a two-category numerical variable in the correlation to the two-category nominal variable in the analysis of variance.**

A. The difference between groups on a measured variable equals the association of the variable that represents what the groups differ on with the measured variable.

B. Thus, a difference in group means in an analysis of variance is the same as an association between its independent and measured variables.

C. If you substitute a two-level numerical variable for a two-level nominal variable (giving each group one number), the correlation with this variable is not affected (except for sign) by the two numbers you pick–this is because in correlation everything is converted to Z scores, and with Z scores a variable with only two numbers always comes out to the same two Z scores (if equal numbers in the groups, +1 and -1).

D. Thus the resulting correlation accurately represents the association between the original nominal variable and the measured variable.

E. Thus the association between the independent and measured variable in analysis of variance, measured by R^2, refers to the same thing as the association in correlation and regression, which can be assessed as r^2.

3. **Explain each parallel in the computations.**

A. $SS_{Within} = SS_{Error}$.

1. The within-group sum of squares (SS_{Within}) in analysis of variance is the sum of the squared differences of each score from its group's mean.
2. The sum of squares for error (SS_{Error}) in regression is the sum of the squared differences of each score from the predicted score (which, when there are only two levels of the predictor variable, is the same as the mean on each level of that predictor variable).
3. This equivalence arises because in both cases the error or noise is the variation within groups or levels of the grouping variable.

B. SS_{Total} is the same in both analyses.

1. The total sum of squared error (SS_{Total}) in analysis of variance is the sum of the squared differences of each score from the grand mean.
2. The total sum of squared error (SS_{Total}) in regression is the sum of the squared difference of each score from the mean of the measured variable (which is the same number as the grand mean in analysis of variance).
3. This equivalence arises because in both cases the baseline error or variance to be reduced or accounted for is the total variation of each score from the overall mean of all the scores.

C. $SS_{Between}$ = reduction in squared error.

1. The between-group sum of squares in analysis of variance can be figured as $SS_{Total} - SS_{Within}$ (this is because, $SS_{Total} = SS_{Within} + SS_{Between}$).
2. The reduction in squared error in regression is $SS_{Total} - SS_{Within}$.
3. This equivalence arises because in both cases the amount of variance accounted for (or error reduced) is the total error less the amount that remains even after dividing participants into groups (or predicting their scores based on their group membership).

D. R^2 in analysis of variance equals r^2 in regression.

1. In analysis of variance, $R^2 = SS_{Between}/SS_{Total}$.
2. In regression, r^2 = reduction in squared error (which is the same as $SS_{Between}$) / SS_{Total}.
3. This equivalence arises because proportion of variance accounted for and proportionate reduction in error are both about how much knowing the value of the grouping variable improves your ability to predict the score on the measured variable.

Proportion of Variance Accounted for in Analysis of Variance (R²) for More than Two Groups as a Special Case of Proportionate Reduction in Error in Multiple Regression (R²)

1. **Do not attempt to carry out the computations–this has not been covered in this course.**
2. **Explain the logic (without computations) of the points above about the equivalence of R^2 in analysis of variance with two groups and r^2 in bivariate regression.**
3. **Add an explanation of the logic of nominal coding to convert an analysis of variance problem to a multiple regression problem.**
   A. A comparison of means of several groups can be thought of as a nominal variable with as many levels as there are groups.
   B. Such a many-leveled nominal variable can not be made into a single numerical variable because the numerical levels assigned would imply specific ordered and quantitative relations among the levels.
   C. Such a many-leveled nominal variable can be made into a set of two-level numerical variables such that each represents being in or not being in one of the groups. (This is called nominal coding.)
   D. It takes one less two-leveled variable than there are groups because the last group is represented by a case not being in any of the preceding groups.
   E. Since the information included in this set of two-leveled numerical variables is the same as the information in the original many-leveled nominal variable, the analysis of variance using the nominal variable yields exactly the same result as the multiple regression using the set of two-leveled numerical variables.

Chapter Self-Tests

Multiple-Choice Questions

1. The analysis of variance is a special case of

   a. chi-square tests for independence.
   b. *t* tests.
   c. multiple regression/correlation.
   d. bivariate correlation and regression.

2. A person's score on a particular measured variable can be conceived of as the sum of all of the following influences, EXCEPT

   a. other measured variables on which people have different scores.
   b. other influences not measured.
   c. some fixed influence that will be the same for all individuals.
   d. other variables which have no correlation with a person's score.

3. If you are comparing the means of two groups to test if they are different, you can use all of the following EXCEPT a(n)

a. t test for independent means.
b. t test for dependent means.
c. bivariate correlation.
d. analysis of variance.

4. $t^2 =$

a. F.
b. ϕ.
c. Z.
d. R^2.

5. The t test for independent means is a special case of the bivariate correlation, in which the predictor variable of the correlation has

a. rank-order values.
b. continuous values.
c. exactly two values.
d. integrated determinants.

6. On a scatter diagram representing a correlation in which one of the variables has only two levels, the pattern which will produce the largest correlation is one on which the difference between the averages of the scores at the two levels is _____ and the variation among the scores at each of the levels is _____.

a. small; moderate.
b. large; moderate.
c. small; large.
d. large; small.

7. When using the bivariate prediction rule, the sum of squared errors figured in a bivariate correlation is the same as _____ in the analysis of variance.

a. $SS_{Between}$.
b. SS_{Total}.
c. SS_{Within}.
d. R^2.

8. Suppose an experiment is conducted in which participants are randomly assigned to read a news story of one of three types–humorous, serious, or disturbing–and are then measured on their interest in the story. If you were to set up the analysis as a multiple regression predicting scores on interest, how many two-level numerical variables would be required?

a. 1.
b. 2.
c. 3.
d. 4.

9. Students identified themselves as predominantly light hearted, studious, unfocused, or pragmatic. This variable was nominally coded, with three variables, so that Variable A was a 1 if the subject was light hearted, but 0 if not. Variable B was 1 if studious, 0 if not. Variable C was 1 if unfocused, 0 if not. If a subject scored 0 on the three variables, how had she identified herself?

    a. light hearted.
    b. pragmatic.
    c. unfocused.
    d. studious.

10. An organizational psychologist measures self-esteem when people begin working for the company (X) and job satisfaction (Y) one year later, finding a strong, significant correlation. Which of the criteria for causality (according to the "regularity" theory) does this study FAIL to meet?

    a. X and Y are regularly associated.
    b. X precedes Y.
    c. there are no other causes that precede X that might cause X and Y.
    d. none of the above are unmet–that is, the study meets all three.

Fill-In Questions

11. Bivariate correlation is a special instance of _____.

12. In the formula, "$Y = a + (b_1)(X_1) + (b_2)(X_2) + (b_3)(X_3) + e$," the symbol(s) representing the fixed influence that applies equally to all individuals is(are) _____.

13. The t score and the F ratio are both fractions in which the numerator is influenced by _____ and the denominator by _____.

14. In a t test for independent means, the number of participants influences the t score mainly by making the denominator smaller, because one divides a key aspect of the denominator (the pooled population variance estimate) by the number of participants in each group. In one method of conducting an analysis of variance, the corresponding adjustment in the computation of the F ratio involves making the _____ larger, because one _____ ("multiplies" or "divides") the population variance estimate (pooled from the estimates within each group) by the number of participants in each group.

15. When there are only two groups, the square root of the F ratio equals _____.

16. The _____ is a special case of the correlation coefficient–the case in which the predictor variable has only two values.

17. _____ is comparable to analysis of variance, except that the former has numerical predictor variables, while analysis of variance has nominal predictor variables.

18. SS_{Total} in the analysis of variance is the same as _____ in regression.

19. Suppose a nominal variable, major, was nominally coded as follows: Humanities (yes=1, no=0), Social Science (yes=1, no=0), Natural Sciences (yes=1, no=0), Arts (yes=1, no=0), and Other (not coded). What would be the scores of a person whose major was Natural Science? _____.

20. According to Diana Baumrind, the two common ways of understanding causality are the "regularity" theory of causality and the "_____" theory of causality.

Problems and Essays

21. For the following data (a) figure a *t* test for independent means, (b) figure an analysis of variance, (c) make a two-column chart of the major computations in which the parallel computations are laid out next to each other, and (d) explain each of the parallels to a person who understands both the *t* test for independent means and the analysis of variance, but is unfamiliar with their relationship.

Group 1	Group 2
30	25
18	12
38	31
16	22
21	15

22. For the following data (a) figure a *t* test for independent means; (b) figure a correlation coefficient; (c) using the formula $t == (r) \left(\sqrt{N-2} / \sqrt{[1-r^2]} \right)$, determine the significance of the correlation coefficient; (d) explain how it is possible to figure a correlation coefficient for data set up as two groups; and (e) make a scatter diagram of the data and use it to discuss the parallels between the *t* test for independent means and the correlation coefficient and its significance test. (Both of your explanations–d and e–should assume the reader is familiar with the *t* test for independent means and the correlation coefficient, but not with their relationship.)

Group 1	Group 2
2	0
3	3
1	1
1	1
3	0

Using SPSS (11.0 for Windows) with this Chapter

The material in this section assumes you are already familiar with using SPSS for correlation, regression, the *t* test for independent means, and the one-way analysis of variance (as described in the Using SPSS sections of Chapters 3, 4, 10, and 11).

You can use SPSS to carry out the various procedures on the same data set, in order to see the relations among them. You should work through the example, following the procedures step by step. Then try the procedures on your own for some of the problems listed in the Suggestions for Additional Practice. Finally, you may want to try the suggestions for using the computer to deepen your understanding.

I. Example

A. Data: Use the data entered in Chapter 10 for the job-program experiment. (To bring up the file, go to

File

Open

[Select the drive and filename you wish to open]

OK

B. Compute the *t* test again (to have the output for reference). The result is shown in Figure SG16-1.

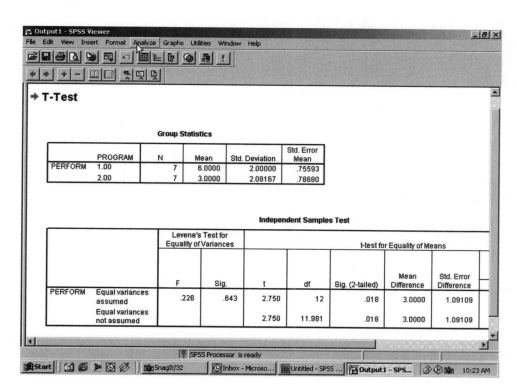

Figure SG16-1

259

C. Compute an analysis of variance for the same data by following the instructions from Chapter 11. Place PERFORM in the Dependent Box and PROGRAM in the Factors box. The result is shown in Figure SG16-2. Compare this result to the results in Table 16-2 and 16-4 in the text.

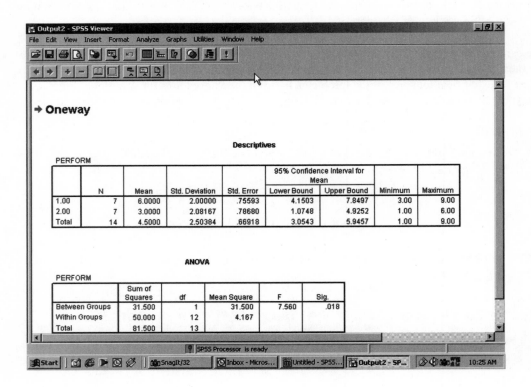

Figure SG16-2

D. Create a scatter diagram and compute a correlation coefficient for these data by following the directions in Chapter 3. The results are shown in Figures SG16-3 and SG16-4. Compare these results to those in the text.

E. Carry out a regression analysis for these data by following the directions in Chapter 4. When SPSS carries out these commands, the results are shown in Figures SG16-5 and SG16-6.

Figure SG16-3

Figure SG16-4

261

Figure SG16-5

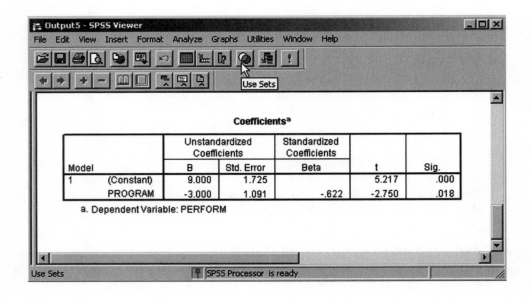

Figure SG16-6

262

II. Additional Practice: Carry out this entire set of analyses for all the *t* test data sets listed in the SPSS section of Chapter 10 of this *Study Guide and Computer Workbook*.

III. Using the Computer to Deepen Your Knowledge: Nominal Coding

A. Enter the data in Table 16-6 of the text as follows.

      1. Label the variables as CRIMORNO (for Criminal record or not), CLEARORNO (for Clean record or not), and GUILT (for participant's rating of defendant's guilt.)

      2. Enter the appropriate codes and scores for the 15 subjects, one line per subject.

B. Carry out a regression analysis as follows.

      1. Analyze

          Regression >

                Linear

                [Highlight Guilt and move into the Dependent box. Highlight CRIMORNO and CLEAORNO and move into the Independent variable box.]

                    OK

      2. Tell SPSS to carry out the analysis and compare these results to those obtained from the analysis of variance on these data in Chapters 11 and 12.

C. Try this procedure again, this time setting up your own nominal coding, for another one-way analysis of variance–use one of the chapter examples or problems using analysis of variance from Chapters 11 or 12.

D. Make a list of all the similarities.

Chapter 17
Making Sense of Advanced Statistical Procedures in Research Articles

Learning Objectives

To understand each of these statistical techniques in a general way, so that you can recognize it in a research article, understand why it was done and what the results reported in an article mean, and make sense of the key terminology:

- Hierarchical and stepwise multiple regression.
- Partial correlation.
- Reliability.
- Factor analysis.
- Causal modeling, including path analysis and latent variable modeling.
- Analysis of covariance.
- Multivariate analysis of variance and covariance.
- Issues in the controversy over whether statistics should be controversial.
- How to read results involving unfamiliar statistical techniques.

Chapter Outline

I. **The Two Main Categories of Advanced Statistical Techniques**
  A. Those that focus on associations among variables (these are variations and extensions of correlation and regression).
    1. Hierarchical and stepwise multiple regression.
    2. Partial correlation.
    3. Reliability.
    4. Factor analysis.
    5. Causal modeling.
  B. Those that focus on differences among groups (these are variations and extensions of analysis of variance).
    1. Analysis of covariance.
    2. Multivariate analysis of variance and covariance.
II. **Brief Review of Multiple Correlation and Regression**
  A. Multiple regression is about predicting scores on a criterion variable from two or more predictor variables.
    1. A multiple-regression prediction rule includes a set of regression coefficients, one to be multiplied by each predictor variable.
    2. The sum of these multiplications is the predicted value on the dependent variable.
    3. When working with Z scores, the regression coefficients are standardized regression coefficients, called beta weights (ßs).
  B. Hypothesis testing: Significance can be figured both for each regression coefficient and the overall prediction rule.

III. Hierarchical and Stepwise Multiple Regression
A. Both methods examine the influence of several predictor variables in a sequential fashion.
B. Hierarchical multiple regression follows a hypothesized order.
   1. Procedure: It figures the correlation of the first predictor variable with the dependent variable, then how much is added to the overall multiple correlation by including the second-most-important predictor variable, and then perhaps how much more is added by including a third predictor variable, and so on.
   2. It requires a specific theoretical basis for the order in which the regression is carried out.
C. Stepwise multiple regression is used in exploratory studies–it determines which predictor variables of many that have been measured usefully contribute to the prediction.
   1. Procedure.
      a. It figures the correlation of each predictor variable with the dependent variable and identifies the one with the highest correlation. (If none of these correlations are significant, the procedure stops.)
      b. It next figures the multiple correlation of each of the other variables in combination with the one just identified as having the highest correlation by itself to see which combination produces the highest multiple correlation. (If none of these multiple correlations add significantly to the predictability over just using the first variable, the procedure stops.)
      c. It next figures the multiple correlation of each of the remaining variables in combination with the highest two to see which combination produces the highest multiple correlation. (If none of these multiple correlations add significantly to the predictability over just the first two, the procedure stops.)
      d. The process continues in this way until all variables are included in the prediction rule or adding the next best variable does not add significantly to the predictability.
   2. Caution: The prediction formula that results is the optimal small set of variables for predicting the dependent variable, *as determined from the sample studied*–when tried with a new sample, somewhat different combinations often result.

IV. Partial Correlation
A. This is the degree of association between two variables, over and above the influence of one or more other variables.
B. A variable over and above the influence of which the partial correlation is figured is said to be *held constant, partialled out*, or *controlled for*. (These terms are interchangeable.)
C. The partial correlation coefficient is interpreted like an ordinary bivariate correlation except one should remember that some third variable is being controlled for.
D. You can think of a partial correlation as the average of the correlations between two variables, each correlation figured among just those Participants at each level of the variable being controlled for.
E. Partial correlation is often used to help sort out alternative explanations in a correlational study.
   1. If the correlation between two variables dramatically drops or is eliminated when a third variable is partialled out, it suggests that the third variable was behind the correlation.
   2. If the correlation between two variables is largely unaffected when a third variable is partialled out, it suggests that the third variable is not behind the correlation.

V. Reliability Coefficients

A. Reliability, the accuracy and consistency of a measure, is the extent to which if you were to give the same measure again to the same person under the same circumstances, you would obtain the same result.

B. Reports of computations of reliability of a measurement are very common in research articles.

C. Test-retest reliability.
   1. This is the correlation between the scores of the same people who take a measure twice.
   2. It is often an impractical or inappropriate approach to reliability, since having taken the test once could influence the second taking.

D. Reliability as internal consistency.
   1. Split-half reliability is the correlation between two halves of the same test.
   2. Cronbach's alpha can be thought of as the correlation between scores on two halves of a test, averaging such computations for all possible divisions of the test into halves.

E. Interrater reliability is the amount of similarity between judges (raters). It is also referred to as interjudge reliability, interrater agreement, or interjudge agreement.

F. In general a test should have a reliability of at least .7, and preferably closer to .9, to be considered useful.

G. If a measure has low reliability, it tends to reduce the correlation between it and any other variable. (This can be adjusted for in bivariate correlation using a correction for attenuation.)

VI. Factor Analysis

A. This is a widely used procedure applied when a researcher has measured people on a large number of variables.

B. It identifies groupings of variables (called *factors*) such that those within each group correlate with each other but not with variables in other groupings.

C. The correlation between a variable and a factor is called the variable's *factor loading* on that factor.

D. A widely used convention is to consider a variable part of a factor on which it has a loading of .3 or greater.

E. Researchers usually give each factor a name based on the variables that load highly on it. (These names can be misleading.)

F. Tables of the results of factor analyses usually give the factor loadings for each factor and also often give the percentage of variance that the factor as a whole accounts for in the entire set of original variables.

VII. Causal Modeling

A. Path analysis: A test of whether the pattern of correlations among the variables fits with a specific theory of regarding which variables cause which.
   1. This procedure focuses on a diagram with arrows connecting the variables, indicating the hypothesized pattern of causal relations among them.

2. It is based on the correlations among the variables; for each arrow the researcher can figure a path coefficient.
   a. A path coefficient indicates the extent to which the variable at the start of the arrow is associated with the variable at the end of the arrow, after controlling for all variables that also point to this variable.
   b. A path coefficient is the same as a beta in multiple correlation/regression, with the variable at the start of the arrow as a predictor variable, the variable at the end of the arrow the dependent variable, and all the other variables in the path diagram which also point to the variable at the end of the arrow as other predictor variables in the regression equation.
3. A path analysis is considered to provide support for the hypothesized causal pattern if the path coefficients for the major arrows are all significant and in the predicted directions

B. Structural equation modeling
   1. It is an extension of path analysis with several advantages.
      a. It produces an overall measure of how well the model fits the data.
         i. One fit index is called RMSEA (root mean square error of approximation).
         ii. The smaller the RMSEA the better the fit.
      b. It includes a significance test–but the null hypothesis is that the model fits.
      c. It permits modeling of latent variables (as assessed by a set of manifest variables).
   2. The path diagram.
      a. Manifest variables are shown in squares.
      b. Latent variables are shown in circles.
      c. The measurement model, the relation of the manifest to the latent variables they assess, usually involves arrows from each latent variable to its associated manifest variables.
      d. The causal model usually involves arrows showing the relations among the latent variables.
   3. Limitations.
      a. A well-fitting model that is not a significantly bad fit is still only one of the possible models that could fit the data.
      b.. It shares limitations of all methods ultimately based on the correlation coefficient.
         i. Association does not demonstrate direction of causality.
         ii. It only takes into account linear relationships.
         iii. Results are distorted by restriction in range.

VIII. Procedures that Compare Groups and Independent and Dependent Variables
A. The focus is on differences between group means.
B. There are two main kinds of variables
   1. Independent variable: The variable considered the cause
      a. In analysis of variance, it divides the groups from each other
      b. Similar to the predictor variable in regression.
   2. Dependent variable: The variable considered as effect
      a. This is the variable that is measured and represents the effect of the experimental procedure.
      b. Similar to the criterion variable in regression.

IX. Analysis of Covariance (ANCOVA)
A. This procedure is the same as an ordinary ANOVA, except that one or more variables are partialed out.
B. A variable partialed out is called a covariate.
C. The rest of the results are interpreted like any other analysis of variance, except that the researcher may report *adjusted means* (the means of each group after the effect of the covariate is partialled out).

D. The analysis of covariance is generally used in one of two situations.
    1. One situation is the analysis of a random-assignment experiment in which some nuisance variable is partialled out.
    2. The other situation is in a study in which it is not possible to employ random assignment, and variables on which groups may differ are partialled out. (This use is more controversial.)
E. ANCOVA assumes that the correlation between the covariate and the dependent variable is the same in all the cells.

X. **Multivariate Analysis of Variance (MANOVA) and Multivariate Analysis of Covariance (MANCOVA)**
A. Multivariate statistical techniques involve more than one dependent variable.
B. The most widely used multivariate techniques are MANOVA and MANCOVA.
C. MANOVA is simply an analysis of variance in which there is more than one dependent variable.
D. MANOVA tests each main and interaction effect of the independent variables on the combination of dependent variables.
E. A significant effect in MANOVA, which could be due to any one of the dependent variables, is usually followed up by a series of ordinary "univariate" analyses of variance on each dependent variable separately.
F. MANCOVA is a MANOVA in which one or more variables are partialled out of the analysis.

XI. **Overview of Statistical Techniques Considered: Most of the techniques covered in this course can be understood as representing the various combinations of the following possibilities.**
A. Association versus difference test.
B. One versus many independent variables.
C. One versus many dependent variables.
D. Whether or not any variables are controlled.

XII.   **How to Read Results Involving Unfamiliar Statistical Techniques**
A. Even well-seasoned researchers periodically encounter unfamiliar statistical methods in research articles.
B. In these cases, you can usually figure out the basic idea.
    1. Usually there will be a p level given and just what pattern of results is being considered significant can be discerned from the context.
    2. Usually there will be some indication of effect size (degree of association or the size of the difference).

Chart of Major Statistical Techniques
(From Table 17-8 in the text)

Association or Difference	Number of Independent Variables	Number of Dependent Variables	Any Variables Controlled?	Name of Technique
Association	1	1	No	Bivariate Correlation & Regression
Association	Any number	1	No	Multiple Regression (Including Hierarchical & Stepwise)
Association	1	1	Yes	Partial Correlation
Association	Many, not differentiated		No	Reliability Coefficient, Factor Analysis
Association	Many, with specified causal patterns			Path Analysis Latent Variable Modeling
Difference	1	1	No	t-Test
Difference	Any number	1	No	Analysis of Variance
Difference	Any number	1	Yes	Analysis of Covariance
Difference	Any number	Any number	No	Multivariate Analysis of Variance
Difference	Any number	Any number	Yes	MultivariateAnalysis of Covariance

Chapter Self-Tests

Multiple-Choice Questions

1. Suppose a researcher wants to know what the correlation between one predictor variable and the dependent variable will be, and then how much is added by adding another predictor variable, and then perhaps even a third predictor variable. The sequence is planned in advance based on theory. What is this called?

   a. Multivariate analysis of variance.
   b. Time-series analysis.
   c. Hierarchical multiple regression.
   d. Canonical correlation analysis.

2-3 Suppose that you want to know the relation between stress and study habits, over and above the fact that people tend to study less on Friday and the weekends.

   2. What is this called?

      a. Stepwise regression.
      b. Partial correlation.
      c. Factor loading.
      d. Factor analysis.

   3. In this particular case, what is being done?

      a. A Cohen's Kappa is being figured ignoring the day of the week.
      b. Study habit is held constant.
      c. Day of the week is being controlled for.
      d. Kendall's Tau is being applied hierarchically (that is, first with and then without including the day of the week in the analysis).

4. Which of the following is the best example of test-retest reliability?

   a. The responses of half the items on a test are correlated with the responses on the other half of the test.
   b. A group of people are given a test, but half are given one test and half are given a different but similar test and their scores on the two tests are correlated.
   c. A group of people are given a test on one occasion and then later the same people are given another very similar test and the two sets of scores are correlated.
   d. A group of people are given the same test on two separate occasions and the scores are correlated.

5. Computing reliability by correlating scores on two halves of a test raises the problem of which way to split the items in half. With Cronbach's alpha, in effect

   a. the halves are split by comparing odd and even numbered items.
   b. the test is simply split in half by top half and bottom half.
   c. it is split randomly.
   d. all possible splits are done and then the results are averaged.

6. Suppose that a researcher wants to look at the relations among a large number of variables measured in a study. She wants to know how the variables clump together and which variables don't seem to correlate. What procedure would be best for her to use?

a. Factor analysis.
b. Hierarchical multiple regression.
c. Stepwise multiple regression.
d. Partial correlation.

7. In a path analysis arrows are drawn between variables. An exogenous variable is

a. a variable that is completely isolated with no arrows going away or toward it.
b. a variable that is at the start of a causal chain, having no arrows to it within the path diagram.
c. a variable that only has arrows going to it within the path diagram.
d. a variable that has arrows going both to it and away from it within the path diagram.

8. Which of the following is NOT an advantage of latent variable modeling over ordinary path analysis?

a. The computer calculates an overall measure of how good the model fits the data.
b. It includes latent variables in the analysis.
c. It rules out the possibility that any other pattern might create a better path diagram.
d. A kind of significance test can be figured.

9. How is an analysis of covariance (ANCOVA) different from an analysis of variance (ANOVA)?

a. ANCOVA allows you to control for the effect of an unwanted variable, whereas an ANOVA does not.
b. ANOVA allows you to control for the effects of an unwanted variable, whereas an ANCOVA does not.
c. ANCOVA allows you to use a factorial design, whereas an ANOVA does not.
d. ANOVA allows you to use a factorial design, whereas an ANCOVA does not.

10. How are MANOVAs and MANCOVAs different from ANOVAs and ANCOVAs?

a. They allow you to use two or more predictor variables, whereas ANOVAs and ANCOVAs do not.
b. They allow you to partial out variables, whereas ANOVAs and ANCOVAs do not.
c. They are more accurate than ANOVAs and ANCOVAs, but you can only use one predictor variable.
d. They allow you to use more than one dependent variable, whereas ANOVAs and ANCOVAs do not.

Fill-In Questions

11. _____ is an exploratory technique in which the researcher is trying to find the best small set of predictor variables for some dependent variable based on results of a study that measured a large number of predictor variables.

12. _____ Kuder-Richardson-10 (KR-20) is like Cronbach's alpha except it is used when the items in the measure are all _____.

13. A _____ is the correlation between a variable and its factor.

14. In an ordinary path analysis, each path coefficient is like a _____ in multiple regression.

15. In one type of causal modeling, some of the variables included in the model are not actually measured, but can be included because they are considered to be the cause of variables that are measured in the study. These variables that are not measured are called _____ variables.

16. The variable held constant in a partial correlation is analogous to a _____ in an analysis of covariance.

17. A researcher is planning a study comparing the effects of three kinds of psychotherapy on depression. Depression will be measured in each subject by both a behavioral and a questionnaire measure. In addition, the researcher wants to control for initial differences in expectations of benefits prior to therapy. The appropriate statistical technique for the entire analysis is a(n) _____.

18. Multiple-regression techniques and causal modeling techniques are examples of methods that focus on association, while analysis of variance and multivariate analysis of variance are examples of techniques that focus on _____.

19. The Neyman-Pearson view of statistics was in opposition to the view held by _____ (who was also the inventor of the analysis of variance).

Essays

20. A study is conducted which examines the influence of various factors on success in graduate school. Explain the (fictional) results, as shown in the following table, to a person who has never had a course in statistics.

Hierarchical Multiple Regression (Dependent Variable = Reported Success in Graduate School)

Predictor Variable	R^2 for All Variables Entered	Increment in R^2
Social Class	.04	.04
Undergraduate Record	.15*	.11*
Social Skills	.18**	.03
Desire to Succeed	.25**	.07*

*$p < .05$ **$p < .01$

21. A study was conducted in which women rated themselves on their practice of seven health behaviors. Explain the (fictional) results, as shown in the following table, to a person who has never had a course in statistics.

Factor Analysis

Variable	Factor 1	Factor Loadings Factor 2
Eats Adequate Fiber	.73	.13
Controls Fat Intake	.68	.21
Controls Sugar Intake	.71	.14
Tooth Flossing	-.03	.53
Daily Exercise	.23	.49
Wears Seat Belts	.06	.38
Breast Self-Exams	.25	.38

22. A (fictional) study is conducted comparing achievement-test scores of high school students of five different ethnic groups. The researchers report their results as follows:

Although previous studies have shown differences among these ethnic groups on this achievement test, the present study, which used parental income and language skills as covariates, did not find any reliable difference; the analysis of covariance was not significant, $F(4,248) = 1.63$. This nonsignificant finding is especially impressive in light of the large sample size employed in our study.

Explain this result (including discussing issues of power regarding a null hypothesis result) to a person who has never had a course in statistics.

23. A study was conducted which examined marital happiness among four groups of married adults–women with no children, mothers of a newborn infant, men with no children, and fathers of a newborn infant. This created a 2 X 2 design (parental status X gender). Marital happiness was measured using three variables: a standard marital happiness questionnaire, number of positive words included in a story written in an experimental setting about the spouse, and ratings of the subject's marital happiness by the subject's closest friend. The (fictional) results of the study were reported as follows:

A multivariate analysis of variance (MANOVA) yielded a main effect for gender, Wilks' Lambda $F(1,418) = 14.31$, $p < .01$, and an interaction effect, Wilks' Lambda $F(1,418) = 9.38$, $p < .01$. The main effect for parental status was not significant, Wilks' Lambda $F(1,418) = 2.13$. Follow-up univariate analyses were significant only for the questionnaire measure. For the gender main effect, women were less satisfied with their marriage than men, $F(1, 361) = 16.33$, $p < .01$. The interaction effect was also significant, $F(1, 361) = 8.14$, $p < .01$. Based on a post-hoc analysis (Neuman-Keuls), the pattern of means associated with this interaction suggest that, for women, being a parent of a newborn is associated with less marital happiness, whereas for men there is little difference in marital happiness between those who are and are not fathers of newborn infants.

Explain this result to a person who has never had a course in statistics.

Using SPSS (11.0 for Windows) with this Chapter

The material in this section assumes you are already familiar with using SPSS from previous chapters.\

Because SPSS is intended for beginning statistics students it includes only a few of the advanced procedures covered in this chapter. One of the advanced procedures considered in Chapter 17 of the text that is included in the student version of SPSS is analysis of covariance. Thus, as an illustration, there is an example for you to try. However, please note that in practice it is important when conducting an analysis of covariance first to check if you have met the special assumption that the correlation of the dependent variable with the covariate should be the same in each cell. The procedure for making this check can be done in SPSS, but making sense of it involves statistical issues well beyond what it is reasonable to cover in a beginning course.

I. Example Data for Analysis of Covariance
    A. The data to be used are an extension of the fictional experiment comparing the effects of information about a previous criminal record on rated guilt of a defendant in a mock trial.
    B. In this example, the idea is to reduce extraneous variance by controlling for scores on a questionnaire given to all Participants prior to the study which measured their general attitude towards defendants in criminal trials–how likely they feel it is that a person in that situation is guilty.
    C. The scores on this additional variable, in the order that Participants' data were entered in Chapter 10, are 8, 5, 2, 7, 6, 7, 3, 5, 7, 4, 5, 5, 8, 4, and 3.

II. Enter the Data Lines for the Analysis
    A. If you completed the SPSS example for Chapter 11, you should have the basic data saved in a file. Call up that file by doing the following:
        File
          Open >
          Data
            [Highlight (name of file).SAV]
          OK
    B. When the file appears make the following changes.
        1. Add the variable **INITATT** in the third column of each subjects data.
        2. For each subject, add the score for this new variable after the other two numbers already entered. (Thus, the first data line should be **1 10 8**; the second data line, **1 7 5**; etc.
        3. Your data window should appear like Figure SG17-1.

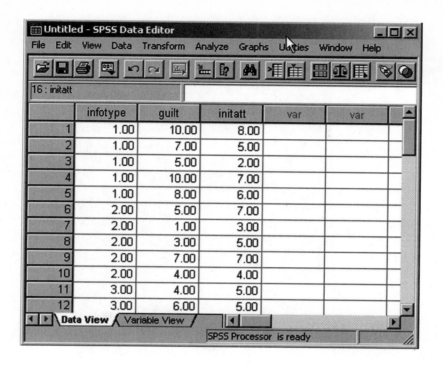

Figure SG17-1

III. Carry Out the Analysis

A. Look over the columns of numbers and note that these numbers are fairly closely correlated with the guilt ratings. But also note that for those in the Criminal-Record group (the first group) the initial attitudes are all a bit lower than their ratings, suggesting that they are seeing this person as guiltier than they usually do. Similarly, for the Clean-Record group, the initial attitudes were generally higher than their guilt ratings, suggesting that for this group they saw the person as less guilty than usual.

    1. Analyze
       General Linear Model >
         Simple Factorial
           [Highlight GUILT and move it into the Dependent box. Highlight
               INFOTYPE and move it into the Fixed Factor(s) box.]
           Define Range
             [Type in 1 for Minimum and 3 for Maximum]
           Continue
             [Highlight INITATT and move into Covariate(s) box. Your
            screen should now look like Figure SG17-2.]
               Options
                  [Check Hierarchical]
                  Continue
                      OK

B. The results should appear as shown in Figure SG17-3.

Figure SG17-2

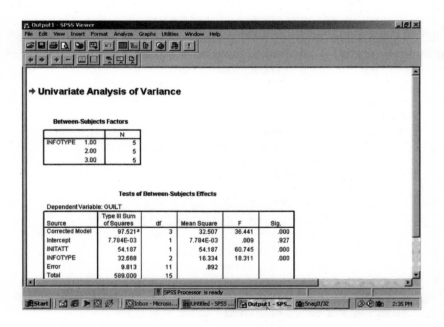

Figure SG17-3

276

C. Inspect and interpret the results.
  1. The F on the **INFOTYPE** line is adjusted for the covariate. That is, it is the result of the analysis of variance comparing the three groups *controlling for* Initial Attitude.
  2. Compare this result to that for the ordinary analysis of variance (as in Chapter 10).
     a. Notice that the F here of **18.311** is considerably higher than the F of 4.07 computed in the analysis without the covariate.
     b. Notice that the within-group population variance estimate (here called the **Error**) of **.892** computed in this analysis of covariance is much lower than the within-group population variance estimate of 5.33 computed in the original analysis without the covariate.

277

Answers to Self-Test Problems

Note. Answers to problems and essays include numerical results only.

Chapter 1

Multiple-Choice: 1-b, 2-d, 3-a, 4-a, 5-c, 6-c, 7-b, 8-c, 9-a, 10-c

Fill-Ins:

11. values, intervals
12. numeric
13. rank-order variables
14. histogram
15. bimodal
16. rectangular
17. positively, skewed to the right
18. ceiling effect
19. normal curve
20. Kurtosis

Problems/Essays

21. A grouped frequency table is preferred over an ordinary frequency table when the scores range over a great many different values. Using an ordinary frequency table in such a situation would fail to give a simple description because there would be so many different values to look at, while the grouped frequency table in this situation gives a more readily grasped summary of the pattern of scores.

22. (a)

Score	Frequency	Percent
4.0	7	23.3
3.9	2	6.7
3.8	3	10.0
3.7	3	10.0
3.6	3	10.0
3.5	7	23.3
3.4	2	6.7
3.3	2	6.7
3.2	1	3.3

The histogram is bimodal.

23.

Score	Frequency	Percent
17	1	2.5
16	1	2.5
15	2	5.0
14	3	7.5
13	4	10.0
12	2	5.0
11	5	12.5
10	6	15
9	3	7.5
8	5	12.5
7	3	7.5
6	3	7.5
5	1	2.5
4	0	0
3	1	2.5

The frequency polygon is multimodal.

24a.

Value	Frequency	Percent
22	3	15
21	2	10
20	2	10
19	1	5
18	3	15
17	0	0
16	4	20
14	1	5
13	0	0
12	1	5
11	1	5
10	1	5
9	1	5

b. Shape is unimodal.

25. a.

Interval	f
40-44	1
35-39	1
30-34	0
25-29	2
20-24	6
15-19	9
10-14	12
5-9	8
0-4	4

c. Shape: Unimodal, skewed to the left

26. A floor effect is when most of the scores are near the bottom of the scale because it is not possible to get a lower score on this measure. For example, if you were to measure the number of words spelled wrong on a second grade spelling test completed by fifth graders, most of the fifth graders would spell none of the words wrong so the scores would pile up at zero.

Chapter 2

Multiple-Choice: 1-b, 2-d, 3-a, 4-b, 5-b, 6-d, 7-a, 8-c, 9-b, 10-d

Fill-Ins:

11. mean
12. central tendency
13. 5
14. mode
15. median
16. outlier
17. $SD^2 = \Sigma(X-M)^2/N; \ SD^2 = SS/N$
18. the mean
19. standard deviation
20. $Z=(X-M)/N$

Problems/Essays

21. $M = \Sigma X/N = 40/8 = 5$
    $SS = (3.1-5)^2 + (3.8-5)^2 + (4-5)^2 + (4.5-5)^2 + (5.4-5)^2 + (6-5)^2 + (8.7-5)^2 = 21.4$
    $SD^2 = SS/N = 21.4/8 = 2.68;\ SD = \sqrt{SD^2} = \sqrt{2.68} = 1.64$

22. $M = 17.4$
    $N = 25$
    $SD^2 = 18.40$
    $SD = 4.29$

23. $M = 9.20$
    $N = 10$
    $SD^2 = 3.96$
    $SD = 1.99$
    If $X = 12,\ Z = 1.41$

24. The person's score was equal to the mean of the group. Half of the scores were above this score, and half were below.

25. Z for sales aptitude: $Z = (X-M)/SD = (50-40)/4 = 10/4 = 2.5$
    Z for education aptitude: $Z = (95-80)/20 = 15/20 = .75$
    Greater aptitude in relation to others: Sales.

26. Raw score for Mary: $X = (Z)(SD) + M = (1.23)(6.5) + 42 = 50$
    Raw score for Susan: $(-.62)(6.5) + 42 = 38$

Chapter 3

Multiple-Choice: 1-d, 2-c, 3-d, 4-b, 5-d, 6-d, 7-c, 8-c, 9-c

Fill-Ins:

10. tiredness
11. a curvilinear correlation
12. a negative correlation
13. positive

014. -1
15. significant
16. 9
17. lower
18. binomial effect size display

Problems/Essays

19a. General pattern: positive linear correlation

b. General pattern: positive linear correlation

c.

Eggs/Day		Cholesterol		
Raw	Z	Raw	Z	$Z_X Z_Y$
2	0	210	.33	0
0	-1.07	100	-1.47	1.57
1	- .53	180	- .16	.09
5	1.6	270	1.31	2.09

$M=2$ $M=9$ $\Sigma=3.75$

$SD=1.87$ $SD=61.24$

$r = Z_X Z_Y/N = 3.75/4 = .94$

d. Proportion of variance accounted for $= r^2 = .94^2 = .88$

e. Example answer: Eating eggs could cause higher cholesterol; people who have high cholesterol may choose to eat more eggs; some third factor, such as upbringing or genetic influences, may have the effects of making people have high cholesterol and also a liking for eggs.

20. a.

ATTENDAN

b. General pattern: positive linear correlation.

c.

Raw	Z	Raw	Z	$Z_X Z_Y$
30	1.88	97	1.36	2.56
20	-0.5	82	-0.09	0.05
22	-0.05	99	1.56	-0.08
15	-1.74	67	-1.54	2.68
18	-1.01	72	-1.05	1.06
24	0.43	80	-0.28	-0.12
21	-0.29	94	1.07	-0.31
25	0.68	86	0.30	0.20
26	0.92	77	-0.57	-0.52
19	-0.77	75	-0.76	0.59

$M = 22.2$ $M = 82.9$ $\Sigma Z_X Z_Y = 6.11$

$SD = 4.15$ $SD = 10.34$

$r = \Sigma Z_X Z_Y / N = 6.11/10 = .611$

d. Proportion reduction in error $= r^2 = .611^2 = .37$

e. Example answer: people who attend class score better on exams; people who score better on exams may be more inclined to attend class; a third variable, such as being conscientious about homework, may cause students to attend class and score better on exams.

e. Example answer: people who attend class score better on exams; people who score better on exams may be more inclined to attend class; a third variable, such as being conscientious about homework, may cause students to attend class and score better on exams.

21. a.

b. Negative linear correlation.
c. Size of gang   Rated Willingness to Help Campaign

Raw	Z		Raw	Z	$Z_X Z_Y$
24	-1.2		10	1.6	-1.92
106	.4		4	- .5	- .20
42	- .9		7	.5	- .45
70	- .3		6	.2	- .06
90	.1		5	- .2	- .02
178	1.9		1	-1.6	-3.04

$\Sigma = -5.69$
$r = -5.69/6 = -.95$

d. $r^2 = -.95^2 = .90$

284

e. Example answer: Being in a bigger gang causes leaders to be less willing to help; leaders who are willing to help attract more members; the kind of gang that attracts leaders who are willing to help also attracts large numbers of members.

Chapter 4

Multiple-Choice: 1-a, 2-d, 3-c, 4-c, 5-c, 6-b, 7-d, 8-a, 9-a, 10-c

Fill-Ins:

11. regression
12. 39
13. Constant, regression constant
14. slope
15. error
16. .25
17. proportion of variance accounted for
18. multicollinearity
19. -.72
20. −13.2

Problems/Essays

21a. Predicted Z for performance equals .87 X Z for hours of exercise per week.

b.	Hours exercise Per Week		Performance in Training Program		Prediction from mean			Prediction from Bivariate Rule		
Person Tested	X	Z_x	Y	Z_y	Z_y	Error	Error^2	Z_y	Error	Error^2
1	3	-.5	45	-.54	0	.54	.2	-.51	.03	.00
2	11	1.76	90	1.47	0	-1.47	2.16	.53	.06	.00
3	6	.29	53	-.18	0	.18	.03	.25	.43	.18
4	1	-1.17	25	-1.43	0	1.43	2.04	-1.02	.41	.17
5	4	-.29	72	.67	0	-.67	.45	-.25	-.92	.85

M=5 M=7 SS^T=4.97 SS^E=1.20
SD=3.41 SD=22.35

Proportionate Reduction in Error = $(SS_T-SS_E)/SS_T$=(4.97-1.20)/4.97 = 3.77/4.97 = .76
Check: r= .87; r^2 = .87^2 = .76; same as figured above.

22 a. Predicted $Z_Y = (.93)(Z_X)$

    b. $\hat{Y} = a + bX = 4.26 + (.88)(X)$
       If X = 2, $\hat{Y}$ = 4.94, if X = 0, $\hat{Y}$ = 4.26, if X = 3, $\hat{Y}$ = 6, if X = 7, $\hat{Y}$ = 8.32
       Proportionate reduction in error = $(SS_T - SS_E)/SS_T = (10 - 1.17)/10 = .88$.
       Check: r = .93, $r^2 = .93^2 = .87$.

    c. 7 days

23. a. $\hat{Y} = a + bX$; a = 4.8, b = .9. $\hat{Y} = 4.8 + (.9)(X)$

    b. Proportionate reduction in error = $(SS_T - SS_E)/SS_T = (42.75 - 14.4)/42.75 = .67$.
       Check: r = .81; , $r^2 = .81^2 = .66$.

    c. 12.9

24. a. $\hat{Y}$ = 78.15
    b. $\hat{Y}$ = 67.9

Chapter 5

Multiple-Choice: 1-b, 2-c, 3-b, 4-d, 5-d, 6-b, 7-c, 8-c, 9-b, 10-a

Fill-Ins:

11. 34
12. -1
13. normal curve table, table
14. subjective
15. probability
16. haphazard
17. parameter
18. statistic
19. μ, mu
20. inferential

Problems/Essays

21a. $Z = (X-M)/SD = (55-50)/5 = 5/5 = 1$. Approximation is that 34% are between mean and Z=1. 50% are above the mean, thus 16% (50% - 34%) are above 55.

 b. $z = (40-50)/5 = -2$. 34% + 14% = 48% are between mean and 2 SD from mean. Thus, 2% (50% - 48%) are below 40.

 c. $z = (45-50)/5 = -1$. 34% are between mean and 1 SD below mean. 50% are above mean. Thus total above 40 is 84% (50% + 34%).

 Note: It is easier to solve such problems if you draw pictures of the normal curve and the areas involved.

22a. From normal curve table, top 5% (45% between mean and Z) begins at 1.64 (or you can use 1.65). Thus, corresponding raw score is $X = (Z)(SD) + M = (1.64)(2.8) + 15.3 = 4.59 + 15.3 = 19.89$.

 b. From normal curve table, bottom 10% (40% between mean and Z) begins at -1.28. Thus, corresponding raw score = $(-1.28)(2.8) + 15.3 = 11.72$.

23 a. $Z = 740 - 500 /100 = 2.4$. From the normal curve table, 1% scored higher, 99% scored lower.

 b. $Z = 380 - 500 /100 = -1.2$. From the normal curve table, 88.49% scored higher, and 11.51% scored lower.

24 a. $p = (8+7)/30 = 15/30 = 1/2$ or .5

 b. $p = (8+4)/30 = 2/5$ or .4

Chapter 6

Multiple-Choice: 1-b, 2-d, 3-c, 4-b, 5-a, 6-c, 7-b, 8-a, 9-c, 10-d

Fill-Ins

11. Hypothesis testing
12. people in general
13. Population 1 is taller than Population 2
14. Population 1 is not taller than Population 2
15. Population 2, people in general
16. null hypothesis
17. .01 and .05, 1% and 5%
18. reject the null hypothesis, the research hypothesis is supported
19. 7.5%
20. do not reject the null hypothesis, the study is inconclusive

Problems/Essays

21. Cutoff (.05 level, one-tailed) = -1.65
    Z score on comparison distribution of time to fall asleep is -1.86
    Reject the null hypothesis that time to fall asleep is unaffected by a glass of warm   milk.

22. Cutoff (.05 level, one-tailed) = -1.65
    Z score on comparison distribution of PLANE times is 2.17
    Reject the null hypothesis that the planes from this company arrive no later than planes of airlines in general.

23. Cutoff (.05 level, two-tailed) = ± 1.96
    Z score on comparison distribution of number of items recalled is -1.5.
    Do not reject the null hypothesis, the study is inconclusive.

24. Cutoff (.05 level, one-tailed) = 1.65
    Z score on comparison distribution is –0.35
    Do not reject the null hypothesis, the study is inconclusive

Chapter 7

Multiple-Choice: 1-c, 2-c, 3-b, 4-d, 5-b, 6-b, 7-a, 8-c, 9-b, 10-c

Fill-Ins

11. distribution of means, distribution of means of all possible samples of a given size from the population, sampling distribution of the mean
12. shape
13. 40.8
14. 2
15. -2
16. 30
17. the standard deviation of the distribution of means, σ_M
18. confidence interval
19. point estimate
20. Z test

Problems/Essays

21. Cutoff (.01 level, one-tailed) = 2.33
    Distribution of means: Population $M = 48$; SD^2_M=Population SD^2/N=144/5=28.8, SD_M=5.37; shape=normal.
    M=63; Z score for test group: Z=(63-48)/5.37 = 15/5.37 = 2.79
    Conclusion: Reject the null hypothesis.
    Confidence intervals are 24.45 and 62.48

22. Cutoff (.05 level, one-tailed) = -1.64.
    Distribution of means: Population $M = 38$; SD^2_M=Population SD^2/N=36/10=3.6, SD_M=1.90; shape=normal.
    Z score for test group: Z = (36-38)/3.6 = -2/1.90 = -1.0
    Conclusion: Do not reject the null hypothesis.
    Confidence intervals are 40.88 and 31.11

23. Cutoff (.05 level, two-tailed) = ±1.96
    Distribution of means: Population M =3.4 ; SD^2_M=Population SD^2/N = .09/30 = .003; SD_M=.06.
    Shape = normal
    Z score for test group: Z = (3.1 – 3.25)/.06 = -2.5.
    Conclusion: Reject the null hypothesis.

Chapter 8

Multiple-Choice: 1-d, 2-d, 3-c, 4-a, 5-b, 6-b, 7-b, 8-a, 9-c, 10-b, 11-b

Fill-Ins:

12. effect size
13. medium
14. meta-analysis
15. alpha, significance level
16. beta, 1-power
17. 84%
18. 98%
19. minimum meaningful effect size
20. standard deviation of the population of individual cases; variance of the distribution of individual cases
21. standard deviation of the distribution of means; variance of the distribution of means

Problems/Essays

22a. $\mu_1 = 3.8\text{-}2.5 = 3.55$; $\mu_2 = 3.8$; $\sigma = 1.5$; $\sigma_M = \sqrt{(1.5^2/25)} = .30$.
   Z score cutoff on the Population 2 distribution of means = -1.65.
   Raw score cutoff on the Population 2 distribution of means =
   $(-1.65)(.30) + 3.80 = 3.30$.
   Corresponding Z score on the Population 1 distribution of means =
   $(3.30\text{-}3.55)/.30 = -.83$.
   Power (using normal curve table to determine area below -.83) =
   50% - 29.67% = 20.33%.

c.   Effect size = $(3.55\text{-}3.80)/1.50 = -.17$; small effect size.

d.   Example answers:
   1. Give a stronger lecture-and thus provide a basis for increasing the expected difference between known and hypothesized means.
   2. Use only children of a particular age-and thus hopefully reduce the population variation.
   3. Use more accurate measurement of consumption of candy (perhaps use records over a two-week period)--and thus hopefully further reduce the population variance.
   4. Use more subjects-and thus reduce the variance of the distributions of means.

23a. $\mu_1 = 74$; $\mu_2 = 68$; $\sigma = 12$; $\sigma_M = \sqrt{(12^2/30)} = 2.19$.
   Z score cutoff on the Population 2 distribution of means = 2.33.
   Raw score cutoff on the Population 2 distribution of means =
   $(2.33)(2.19) + 68 = 73.10$.
   Corresponding Z score on the Population 1 distribution of means =
   $(73.10\text{-}74)/2.19 = -.41$.
   Power (using normal curve table to determine area below -.41) =
   50% + 15.91% = 65.91%.

c.   Effect size = $(74\text{-}68)/12 = .5$; medium effect size.

d.   Example answers:
   1. Use an even sadder movie if possible-and thus provide a basis for increasing the expected difference between known and expected mean.
   2. Use a more accurate memory test if one is available (one that has a lower amount of variation in the general population)-and thus further reduce the population variance.
   3. Use more subjects-and thus reduce the variance of the distributions of means.
   4. Use the .05 significance level-and thus make the cutoff on the Population 2 distribution of means not so extreme.

24.   Conclusion is that the research hypothesis (that ball players like to chew gum more than the general public) is probably false and the null hypothesis (that ball players liking of gum is no different from that of the general public) is probably true.
   Explanation: With high power, it is easy to reject the null hypothesis if it is false. Thus, had it been false, it probably would have been rejected. Since it was not rejected, it probably is not false.

290

25. Conclusion: Result could be due to a very small effect size so that it may not be of practical importance.
Explanation: With very high power, it would have been easy to reject the null hypothesis even if the true effect were very small.

26. Type 1 error, correctly rejecting the null hypothesis when the research hypothesis is true, correctly failing to reject the null hypothesis when the null hypothesis is true, Type II error.

Chapter 9

Multiple-Choice: 1-c, 2-b, 3-a, 4-b, 5-a, 6-a, 7-d, 8-c, 9-c, 10-d

Fill-Ins:

11. degrees of freedom
12. population mean
13. N, sample size, number of cases in the sample
14. robust
15. .8
16. larger
17. control group
18. greater, larger
19. level of significance, alpha level
20. normal distribution, normal curve

Problems/Essays

21. t test for a single sample
    t needed (df=5), p< .05, 1-tailed = -2.015
    M = 17; S^2=4.4; S_M= .85; t= -3.53
    Reject null hypothesis.

22. t test for a single sample
    t needed (df = 5), p < .05, 2-tailed = ±2.571
    M = 6.17, ; S^2 = 6.966, ; S_M =1.08, t = -0.77
    Do NOT reject the null hypothesis.

23. t test for dependent means
    t needed ($df = 4$), $p < .05$, 1-tailed = 2.132
    Difference scores = .07, .18, .14, .18, -.13
    $M=.088$; $S^2 = .017$; $S_M = .003$; $t = 26.08$
    Reject null hypothesis.

24. t test for dependent means
    t needed ($df = 4$), $p < .05$, 1 tailed = -2.132
    Difference scores = -3, 3, 2, -7, -8
    M = -2.6, $S^2 = 25.3$, ; $S_M = 2.25$, $t = -1.156$
    Do NOT reject the null hypothesis

26. t needed ($df=8$), $p < .05$, 1-tailed = -1.86
    Difference scores = -2, -2, -4, -2, -6, -1, +1, +4, 0
    $M = -1.33$; $S^2 = 8.25$; $S_M = .96$; $t = -1.39$
    Do NOT reject null hypothesis.

Chapter 10

Multiple-Choice: 1-b, 2-a, 3-b, 4-c, 5-d, 6-d, 7-d, 8-b, 9-b, 10-c

Fill-Ins:

11. independent means
12. equal
13. distribution of means
14. the distribution of differences between means
15. standard deviation
16. normally distributed
17. variance
18. S_{POOLED} (pooled estimate of the standard deviation of the populations)
19. less
20. t(23)= 3.21, p < .01, one-tailed

21. t-test for independent means; t needed (df, $p < .01$, 2-tailed) = ± 3.3356.
    TRAINING: $N=5$, $df=4$, $M=15.8$, $S^2=2.7$; NO TRAINING: $N=5$, $df=4$, $M=16$, $S^2=6.5$.
    S_{POOLED} = [(4/8)(2.7)]+[(4/8)(6.5)] = 4.6; $S_{M1}^2=4.6/5=.92$; $S_M^2=.92$;
    $S_{DIFFERENCE}=.92=.92=1.84$; $S_{DIFFERENCE}= 1.36$.
    $t=(15.8-16)/1.36= -.15$.
    Do NOT reject the null hypothesis. The results of the study are inconclusive as to whether self-defense training enhances self-confidence.

22. t-test for independent means; t needed (df=5, p<.05, 1-tailed) = 2.015.
  PLACEBO: N=4, df=3, M=90.3, S^2=184.9; CONTROL: N=3, df=2, M=88, S^2=133.
  S_{POOLED}^2=[(3/5)(184.9)]+[(2/5)(133)]=164.15; S_{M1}^2=164.15/4=41; S_{M2}^2=164.15/3=54.7;
  $S_{DIFFERENCE}^2$=41+54.7=95.7; $S_{DIFFERENCE}$=9.78.
  t=(90.3-88)/9.78=.24.
  Do NOT reject the null hypothesis. The results of the study are inconclusive as to whether this placebo procedure can produce an increase in intelligence.

23. t-test for independent means; t needed (df = 8, 2 tailed) = ±2.306.
  Men: N = 5, M = 80.8, df = 4, S^2 = 51.2; Women: N = 5, df = 4, M = 83.2, , S^2 = 46.09.
  S_{POOLED}^2 = [(4)(51.2)/8 + (4)(46.09)/8] = 23.045.
  S_{M1}^2 = 23.045/5 = 4.609; ; S_{M2}^2 = = 23.045/5 = 4.609
  $S_{DIFFERENCE}^2$ = 9.218; $S_{DIFFERENCE}$ = 3.04
  t = 80.8 – 83.2 / 3.04 = -0.79.
  Do NOT reject the null hypothesis.

Chapter 11

Multiple-Choice: 1-a, 2-a, 3-b, 4-d, 5-c, 6-a, 7-b, 8-d, 9-d

Fill-Ins

10. equal (the same)
11. within
12. one
13. the signal
14. S_M^2, variance of the distribution of means
15. distribution of means
16. population
17. less than

Problems/Essays

18. F needed (df=2,12; p<.05) = 3.89
  Small: M=60.6, S^2=33.3; Standard: M=60.2 S^2=89.2; Large: M=54.2, S^2=59.2
  GM= 58.3; S_M^2=12.9; $S_{BETWEEN}^2$=64.3; S_{WITHIN}^2= 60.6; F=1.06.
  Do NOT reject the null hypothesis.

19. F needed (df=3,8; $p < .01$) = 7.59
COLLEGE: M=4.33, S2=2.33; PSYCHOLOGISTS: M=6, S2=1; LAWYERS: M=6, S^2=1; PUBLIC: M=4.33, S^2=.33.
GM=5.17; S_M^2=.93; $S_{BETWEEN}^2$=2.8; S_{WITHIN}^2=3; F=2.39.
Do not reject null hypothesis.

20. F needed (df = 2, 12; $p < .05$) = 3.89
English: M = 6.4, , S^2 = 12.3; Psychology: M = 5.6, S^2 = 3.3; Business: M = 7.4, S^2 = 9.3; GM = 6.47; ; S_M^2= .812; $S_{BETWEEN}^2$= 4.06; S_{WITHIN}^2= 8.3; F = 4.06/8.3 = 0.49.
Do NOT reject the null hypothesis.

21. F needed (df=3, 76; $p<.01$)=4.06 (using figure for df=3,75).
GM=3.87; S_M^2=1.70; $S_{BETWEEN}^2$=34; S_{WITHIN}^2=3; F=11.33
Reject the null hypothesis; the research hypothesis is supported.

Chapter 12

Multiple-Choice: 1-c, 2-d, 3-a, 4-a, 5-a, 6-c, 7-c, 8-a, 9-c, 10-b 11-b

Fill-Ins:

12. SS_B, $(M-GM)^2$, the sum of each scores' group's squared deviations from the grand mean
13. 89 + 105 = 194
14. 14 + 60 = 74
15. 75 + 45 = 120
16.

Source	SS	df	MS	F
Between	40	04	10	5
Within	50	25	2	
Total	90	29		

17. Bonferroni procedure
18. post-hoc comparisons, a posteriori comparisons
19. .06
20. .01
21. No coffee

Problems/Essays

22. F needed ($df = 2, 7; p < .01$) = 9.55
    Analysis of Variance Table

Source	SS	df	MS	F
Between	48.2	2	24.1	22.9
Within	7.4	7	1.1	
Total	55.6	9		

Decision: Reject the null hypothesis.

23. F needed ($df = 2, 8; p < .05$) = 4.46
    Analysis of Variance Table

Source	SS	df	MS	F
Between	5.06	2	2.53	3.09
Within	6.59	8	.82	
Total	11.65	10		

Decision: Do not reject the null hypothesis.

24. F needed ($df = 2, 9; p < .05$) = 4.26

Source	SS	df	MS	F
Between	6.50	2	3.25	0.74
Within	39.5	9	4.39	
Total	46.00	11		

Decision: Do not reject the null hypothesis.

Chapter 13

Multiple-Choice: 1-c, 2-a, 3-c, 4-c, 5-b, 6-c, 7-d, 8-d, 9-c, 10-a

Fill-Ins:

11. interaction
12. 5 X 3, 3 X 5
13. parallel
14. interaction effect
15. between
16. grand mean, overall mean
17. N_{cells}, number of cells

18. R^2, the proportion of variance accounted for, effect size
19. number of levels of the variable with which it is crossed
20. repeated-measures, within-subjects

Problems/Essays

23. b.

Levels of Independent Variable I

		A	B	C	
Levels of Independent}	SHORT	6	6	6	6
Variable II	} LONG	4	6	8	6
		5	6	7	

c. Main effects for independent Variable I and interaction effect.

24. F needed for main effect of ethnicity (df=2, 12; $p < .05$) = 3.89
    F needed for main effect of parent's income (df = 1, 12; $p < .01$) = 9.33
    F needed for interaction effect (df = 2, 12; $p < .01$) = 6.93

Analysis of Variance Table

Source	SS	df	MS	F	reject?	R^2
Between-Groups						
Ethnicity	1.44	2	.72	.93	no	.13
Parent's Income	18.00	1	18.00	23.14	yes	.66
Interaction	66.33	2	33.17	42.64	yes	.88
Within-Group	9.33	12	.78			

25. $R_{Region}^2 = .17$; $R_{Weight}^2 = .03$; $R_{Region \times Weight}^2 = .38$

Chapter 14

Multiple-Choice: 1-c, 2-c, 3-b, 4-a, 5-d, 6-c, 7-c, 8-b 9-b, 10-b

Fill-Ins

11. Karl Pearson
12. chi-square test for goodness of fit
13. E

14. the number of categories minus 1
15. independent
16. row
17. normal; normal distributions; normally distributed
18. $\sqrt{\chi^2/(N)(df_S)}$
19. sample size; number of cases
20. a. 30/60= 50%; b. 14/44=32%; c. $\sqrt{(2.42/80)}$ = .17

Problems/Essays

22. χ^2 needed (df=3, p<.05) = 7.815

	O	E	O-E	$(O-E)^2$	$(O-E)^2/E$
Plant A	15	21	-6	36	1.71
Plant B	34	21	13	169	8.05
Plant C	17	21	-4	16	.76
Plant D	18	21	-3	9	.43
	84	60	0		X^2=10.95

Decision: Reject null hypothesis.

23. χ^2 needed (df=4, p< .05) = 9.488

Birthweight Percent	Level of Mother's Depression During Pregnancy			Total
	Severe	Mild	Not Depressed	
below average 23.3	(4.7) 8	(4.7) 5	(4.7) 1	14
average 38.3	(7.7) 3	(7.7) 8	(7.7) 12	23
above average 38.3	(7.7) 9	(7.7) 7	(7.7) 7	23
TOTAL 99.9	20	20	20	60

χ^2= 10.76

Decision: Reject null hypothesis.

Cramer's $\phi = \sqrt{[10.76/(60)(2)]} = .30$, medium effect size

24. χ^2 needed (df=5, p<.05) = 12.592

Type of Novel

	A	B	C	Total
Women	6 (4.3)	1 (3.25)	6 (5.4)	13
Men	2 (3.6)	5 (2.75)	4 (4.6)	11
Total	8	6	10	24

$\chi^2 = 4.93$

Decision: Do not reject the null hypothesis.

25. Cramer's $\phi = .35$, medium effect

Chapter 15

Multiple-Choice: 1-b, 2-b, 3-c, 4-b, 5-a, 6-d, 7-d, 8-c

Fill-Ins:

9. non-normal; skewed; kurtotic
10. outlier
11. inverse
12. nonparametric tests; distribution-free tests
13. *t*-test for independent means
14. rank-order
15. normal curve, normal distribution
16. equal-interval
17. randomization

Problems/Essays

18. a. skewed right (due too an outlier)
    b. approximately normal

19.a. t needed (df=8, 1-tailed, $p < .05$) = 2.306

	Did not expect	Did expect
M	87.4	65.2
S^2	63.3	407.7
SM^2	47.1	47.1

$S_P{}^2 = 235.5$
$S_{DIF}{}^2 = 94.2$ $S_{DIF} = 9.71$
$t = (87.4-65.2)/9.71 = 2.29$

Did not expect to be liked: 77, 83, 88, 91, 98
Did expect to be liked: 46, 57, 58, 66, 99
Do not reject null hypothesis

b. Square root transformed data

	Did Not Expect	Did Expect
	8.77	6.78
	9.11	7.55
	9.38	7.62
	9.54	8.12
	9.90	9.95
M	9.34	8.00
S^2	.18	1.41
$S_M{}^2$	.16	.16

$S_P{}^2 = .80$
$S_{DIF}{}^2 = .32$ $S_{DIF} = .57$
$t = (9.34-8.0)/.57 = 2.35$
Reject null hypothesis.

20. t needed (df, two-tailed, p < .05) = 2.306

Movers			Non-Movers	
Raw	Rank		Raw	Rank
3	5	1	2	
1	2	4	6	
9	9	5	7	
13	10	2	4	
6	8	1	2	

M	6.8	4.20
S^2	10.7	5.20
$S_M{}^2$	1.59	1.59

$S_P{}^2 = 7.95$
$S_{DIF}{}^2 = 3.18$ $S_{DIF} = 1.78$
$t = (6.8-4.2)/1.78 = 1.46$
Do not reject null hypothesis.

21. t needed (df = 8, one-tailed, p < .05) = 1.860

Caffeine		Caffeine-free	
Raw	Rank	Raw	Rank
10	7	5	2
13	10	4	1
12	9	10	7
9	5	8	4
10	7	6	3

M = 7.6	M = 3.4
$S^2 = 3.8$	$S^2 = 5.3$
$S_M{}^2 = 0.91$	$S_M{}^2 = 0.91$

$S_P{}^2 = 4.55$
$S_{DIF}{}^2 = 1.82$ $S_{DIF} = 1.35$
t = (7.6 – 3.4)/1.35 = 3.11
Do not reject the null hypothesis

22. Mean difference for our distribution: $-.16$
$(20)(.05) = 1$, score must be the most extreme score

Mean differences in order of the layout in the problem are as follows:

-1.6	-3.4	-4.27	-1	-.07
- .93	2.33	-2.73	.53	-.33
1.6	3.4	4.27	1	.07
.93	-2.33	2.73	-.53	.33

Mean differences in order of smallest to largest:
-.427, -3.4, -2.73, -1.6, -1, -.93, -.53, -.33, -.07, .07, .33, .53, .93, 1, 1.6, 2.33, 3.73, 3.4, 4.27

Actual mean is fifth highest.
Therefore, do not reject null hypothesis.

Chapter 16

Multiple-Choice: 1-c, 2-d, 3-b, 4-a, 5-c, 6-d, 7-c, 8-b, 9-b, 10-c

Fill-Ins

11. multiple regression.correlation
12. *a*
13. differentiate between (or variation among)group means; variation within groups
14. numerator; multiplies
15. the *t* score
16. *t*-test for independent means, analysis of variance with two groups
17. multiple regression/correlation
18. SS_{Total}
19. 0,0,1,0; Humanities = 0, Social Sciences = 0, Natural Science = 1, Arts = 0
20. generative

Problems/Essays

21. *t*-test for independent means
$df=8$
needed t $(p<.05)=2.306$
$S_P^2=71.65$
$S_{M1}^2=71.75/5=14.33$; $S_{M2}^2=14.33$
$S_M^2=6.48$
(Denominator divided by n=5)
$S_{DIF}^2=14.33 + 14.33=28.66$;
$S_{DIF}=\sqrt{28.66}=5.35$
$t= 3.6/5.35=.68$
Do not reject the null hypothesis.

Analysis of Variance
$df= 1, 8$
needed $F(p<.05)=5.32$; $\sqrt{5.32}=2.307$
$S_W^2=71.65$
$S_B^2=(6.48)(5)=32.4$

(Numerator multiplied by n=5)

$F=32.4/71.65 = .45$; $\sqrt{.45} = .67$
Do not reject null hypothesis.

22. . *t*-test for independent means
$df=(5-1) + (5-1)=8$
needed t $(p<.05)=2.306$
$S_1^2=1$ $S_2^2 = 1.5$ $S_P^2=1.25$
$S_{M1}^2=1.25/5= .25$; $S_{M2}^2=.25$
$S_{DIF}^2= .25 + .25 = .5$;
$S_{DIF}=.71$
$t= 1.1/.71=1.55$
Do not reject the null hypothesis.

Correlation Coefficient
$df= 10-2=8$
needed t $(p<.05)=2.306$
Code X as 1 or 0; $SD_X=.5$; $M_X=.5$
$M_Y=1.5$; $SD_Y=1.12$
$\Sigma(Z_X Z_Y)=4.47$; $r= 4.47/10 = .45$
$t= (.45)(\sqrt{8})/ \sqrt{(1-.45^2)} = 1.61$

Do not reject null hypothesis.

23. Analysis of Variance

Source	SS	df	MS	F
Between	2664.5	1	2664.5	3.67
Within	4359	6	726.5	
Total	7023.5			

Correlation Coefficient
Code X as 1 or 0; $SD_X=.5$;
$M_X=.5$; $M_Y=1.5$; $SD_Y=1.12$
$\Sigma (Z_X Z_Y)=-4.91$; $r= -4.91/8 = -.61$

$R^2 = 2664.5/7023.5 = .38$

Subject	X	Y	M_Y	$(Y-M_Y)$	$(Y-M_Y)^2$	$(\hat{Y}- \bar{Y})$	$(Y-\hat{Y})$	$(Y-\hat{Y})^2$
1	1	204	173.25	30.75	945.56	191.5	12.5	156.25
2	1	215	173.25	41.75	1743.06	191.5	23.5	552.25
3	1	166	173.25	-7.25	52.56	191.5	-25.5	650.25
4	1	181	173.25	7.75	60.06	191.5	-10.5	110.25
5	2	138	173.25	-35.25	1242.56	155.0	-17.0	289.00
6	2	189	173.25	15.75	248.06	155.0	34.0	1156.00
7	2	121	173.25	-52.25	2730.06	155.0	-.34.0	1156.00
8	2	172	173.25	-1.25	-1.56	155.0	17.0	289.00

Σ 0. 00   7023.48   0.00   4359.00

$r^2 = (7023.48-4359)/7023.48 = 2664.48/7023.48 = .38$

24.

Pigeon	S or Not	G or Not	R or Not	Light Detection Level
		Strain		
1	1	0	0	.014
2	0	1	0	.058
3	1	0	0	.028
4	0	0	1	.101
5	0	0	0	.024
6	0	1	0	.077
7	0	0	1	.088
8	0	0	0	.023
9	1	0	0	.019
10	1	0	0	.010
11	0	0	1	.075
12	0	0	0	.043
13	0	0	0	.028
14	0	0	1	.098
15	0	1	0	.071
16	0	1	0	.083

Chapter 17

Multiple-Choice: 1-c, 2-b, 3-c, 4-d, 5-d, 6-a, 7-b, 8-c, 9-a, 10-d

Fill-Ins

11. Stepwise multiple regression, stepwise regression
12. dichotomous, having two values
13. factor loading
14. beta, standardized regression coefficient
15. latent
16. latent variable causal modeling, structural equation modeling
17. covariate
18. analysis of covariance, ANCOVA
19. differences
20. Fisher

Appendix I

How to Get Started and the Basics of Using SPSS

When working through your first SPSS example in the chapters in this *Study Guide and Computer Workbook*, you will need to have either first learned the basics of using SPSS by studying this appendix or you will need to be turning back and forth to this appendix as you work through that first example. Either way, allow an extra hour or so for your first attempt at SPSS.

SPSS is very easy to use once you have learned a few basics of how the program operates. It is also easy to master these basics—or at least it will seem that way after you are started. But facing starting up on your own, particularly if you are not a computer whiz, can seem daunting. Thus, the easiest way to begin is to have someone who is familiar with the program lead you through it.

If you need to learn on your own, the manual that comes with your SPSS disks provides everything you need. Indeed, if it has any fault it is that it provides more than you need. That is, it teaches you every bell and whistle of the program, when all you really need for your purposes is a very small subset of all these details. Thus, this Appendix is designed to help you get started by covering the very minimum of what you need to start up and use SPSS. Once you are comfortable with these basics, if you choose you can go back to the manual and start getting fancy. But all you will ever need for purposes of this course are the basics we cover here, plus what is covered in the SPSS section of each chapter in this *Study Guide and Computer Workbook*.

In this Appendix we do assume that you are familiar with basic computer terminology such as "file," "saving a file," and "cursor." We also assume you are familiar with the fundamental operations of the computer system you will be using—how to turn it on, type in instructions, move between directories, and how to quit a session at the computer. Finally, we assume you are a little used to working with computers and how finicky they are about your giving instructions exactly.

Before You Start

To use SPSS, the program must be saved onto the hard disk of the computer you will be using (the program is too long to fit on a single soft disk). This is called installing the program. If the program has not been already installed for you onto the computer you will be using, you will have to do so yourself, following the instructions in the manual that came with the disks. Actually, once you get started, instructions on the screen lead you through the process fairly effortlessly. However, the best recommendation is to work through the installation with the help of someone knowledgeable. (But, once again, try to deter that person from doing anything beyond the standard, straight-forward setup.)

Throughout the various chapter sections on using SPSS in this *Study Guide and Computer Workbook*, we will assume that you have set up SPSS on your computer in such a way that you know how to move to the appropriate directory to begin an SPSS session and that once in that directory you can save and recall files.

Beginning an SPSS Session

1. Double click on the SPSS icon. The screen should appear as shown in Figure S-1. Choose "Type in data" and click on OK. The screen should appear as in Figure S-2.

Ending an SPSS Session

1. If you wish to keep any data you have entered into the window, and
   have not already saved it as a file, do so now. (See section below on Saving your Files.)
2. Click on File on the toolbar.
3. Click on Exit.

S-1

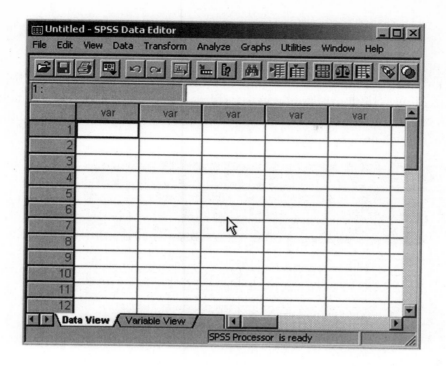

Figure S-2

The Data Lines

The data you use in statistics are usually set up so that each subject studied has a score on one or more variables. For example, in a particular study, each of 10 subjects might have a score on an anxiety test and also a score on an intelligence test. Thus, the data set-up would consist of two variables ("anxiety" and "intelligence"), with scores for each of 10 subjects.

When carrying out a statistical analysis using SPSS, you first name the variable, then type in the lines of data, and finally you tell SPSS what statistical analysis you would like to run by choosing options from the toolbar.

Naming a Variable

Click on the Variable View tab at the bottom of the screen. This will bring up a screen as in Figure S-3 that allows you to define your variables. Under the column "Name" you can define the name for your variable (up to 8 characters). Each row represents each variable that is in your data set.

S-3

Typing in Lines of Data

The cursor should appear in the window above the data grid, and the first box in the grid should be highlighted. Type a number and hit enter. The number should appear in the highlighted box and the second box in that column will now be highlighted. The columns represent all the data for a single variable, while the rows represent all the data for a single subject. SPSS will prompt you to enter each subject's data for a particular variable at the same time before moving on to another variable. However, in some instances it may be easier to enter all the data for a subject at one time before moving on to the next subject's data. In this case, you can use the mouse to click on the box that you would like the data entered into.

Using the Toolbar

In order to run a statistical analysis in SPSS, you must choose options from the toolbar located at the top of the screen. In this *Study Guide and Computer Workbook*, commands on the toolbar will be denoted as such:

Analyze
> Descriptive Statistics>
>> Frequencies
>>> [Highlight VAR00001 and click on the arrow to enter it into the Variable(s) box.]
>>> OK

In this example, you would click on Analyze on the toolbar. A menu will drop down and you will highlight Descriptive Statistics from this menu. A second menu will drop down, and you will highlight Frequencies. Your screen should now look like Figure S-4. Click the mouse button on frequencies. This will bring up a Frequencies screen. In order to tell SPSS which variables you are interested in analyzing, you need to highlight the variable and click on the arrow. This will move the variable over into the Variable(s) box. Now click on OK . The results will appear in the Output Window. You may have to scroll the window up and down in order to see all of the output. If you would like to print out the output, click on File and then Print.

To get back to the data window, click on the SPSS Data View box on the bottom of the screen.

Figure S-4

310

Creating a New Variable

Sometimes you may want to create a new variable based on existing variables. For example, you may want to create a new variable that is the sum of two existing variables. Or perhaps you want to create a variable that is the square root of an existing variable.

1. First enter your data and name your variables (see preceding section).
2. Transform
     Compute
          [Name your new variable in the Target Variable box]
               [Type the computations—using the name of any existing variables along with arithmetic symbols. You can use parentheses to group computations.]
               OK
3. Your new variable will now appear in the Data Window.
4. Example:
   a. To create a variable called SUMXY that is the sum of X and Y, type SUMXY in the Target Variable box. In the Numeric Expression box, type X+Y. You can also highlight the existing variables and use the arrow to move them over into the Numeric Expression box. Your screen should now look like Figure S-5.

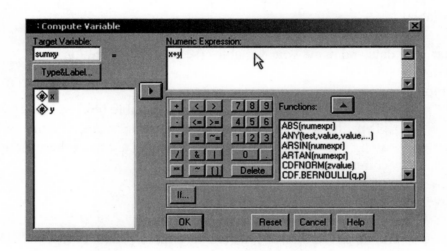

Figure S-5

Saving the Data in a File

Save your lines of data as follows:
  File
    Save Data
       [Name your data (for example Ch1) and designate the drive you would like
       your data saved in.]
          OK

Recalling a Set of Data

    In order to call up an existing data file you would go through the same steps as you would to open an SPSS session, but rather than choose "Type in data" you would choose "Open an existing data source." You would then choose one of the SPSS data sets listed for you (see Figure S-6).

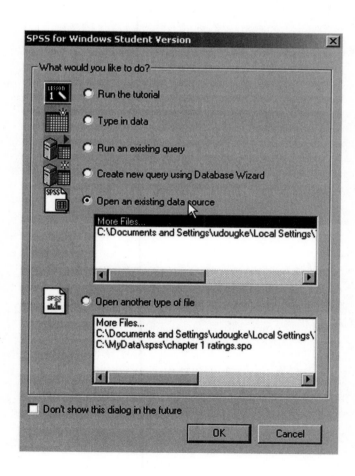

Figure S-6

Flash Cards

(to Cut Out)

Descriptive statistics

Value

1

1

Inferential statistics

Score

1

1

Grouped frequency table

Frequency table

1

1

Variable

Interval

1

1

A possible number or category that a score can have.

Procedures for summarizing or otherwise making more comprehensible a set of scores.

1

1

A particular subject's value on a variable.

Procedures for drawing conclusions based on, but going beyond, the scores actually collected in a research study.

1

1

A frequency table in which the number of subjects is indicated for each interval of values.

A listing of the number of subjects receiving each of the possible values that the scores on the variable being measured can take.

1

1

In a grouped frequency table, each of a specified-sized grouping of values for which frequencies are reported.

A characteristic that can take on different values.

1

1

Rectangular distribution

Frequency distribution

1

1

Interval size

Unimodal distribution

1

1

Histogram

Bimodal distribution

1

1

Frequency polygon

Multimodal distribution

1

1

The pattern of frequencies over the various values; what a frequency table, histogram, or frequency polygon describes.

1

A frequency distribution in which all values have approximately the same frequency.

1

A frequency distribution with one value clearly having a larger frequency than any other.

1

In a grouped frequency table, the difference between the start of one interval and the start of the next.

1

A frequency distribution with two approximately equal frequencies, each clearly larger than any of the others.

1

A bar-like graph of a distribution in which they are along the horizontal axis and the height of each bar corresponds to the frequency of that value.

1

A frequency distribution with two or more approximately equal frequencies, each clearly larger than any of the others.

1

A type of line graph of a distribution in which the values are along the horizontal axis and the height of each point which connects the lines corresponds to the frequency of that value.

1

Symmetrical distribution

Normal curve

1

1,5

Skewness

Kurtosis

1

1

Floor effect

Mean

1

2

Ceiling effect

Central tendency

1

2

A specific, mathematically defined, bell-shaped frequency distribution which is symmetrical and unimodal.

1,5

A distribution in which the pattern of frequencies on the left and right side are mirror images of each other.

1

The extent to which a frequency distribution is too peaked and pinched together or too flat and spread out, in comparison to the normal curve.

1

The extent to which a frequency distribution has the preponderance of cases on one side of the middle.

1

The arithmetic average of a group of scores; the sum of the scores divided by the number of scores.

2

The situation in which many scores pile up at the low end because it is not possible to have any lower score.

1

The typical or most representative value of a group of scores.

2

The situation in which many scores pile up at the high end because it is not possible to have a higher score.

1

Mode

Standard deviation

^{2}

^{2}

Median

Definitional formula

^{2}

^{2}

Raw score

Computational formula

^{2}

^{2}

Variance

Z score

2,5,9,11

^{2}

The square root of the average of the squared deviations from the mean; roughly the average amount scores in a distribution vary from the mean.

2

The value with the greatest frequency in a distribution.

2

The equation directly displaying the meaning of the procedure it symbolizes.

2

If you line up all the scores from highest to lowest, the middle score.

2

An equation mathematically equivalent to the definitional formula that is easier to use for hand computation.

2

An ordinary measurement before it has been made into a Z score

2

The number of standard deviations a score is above (or below, if it is negative) the mean in its distribution.

2

The average of the squared deviations from the mean.

2

Positive linear correlation

3

Negative linear correlation

3

Predictor variable

Linear correlation

3

3,4

3

Scatter diagram

Curvilinear correlation

3

3

A relation between two variables in which high scores on one go with high scores on the other, mediums with mediums, and lows with lows.

3

A relation between two variables in which high scores on one go with low scores on the other, mediums with mediums, and lows with highs.

3

A relation between two variables which shows up on a scatter diagram as the dots roughly following a straight line.

A variable that is used as a basis for estimating scores of individuals on another variable.

3

3,4

A relation between two variables which shows up on a scatter diagram as the dots roughly following a systematic pattern that is not a straight line.

A graphic display of the pattern of relationship between two variables.

3

3

Perfect correlation

Restriction in range

3

3

Correlation coefficient

Correction for attenuation

3,4

3

Statistical significance

Degree of correlation

3,6

3

Proportionate reduction in error

Correlation matrix

3,4

3

The situation in which a correlation is computed when only a limited range of the possible values on one variable are included in the group studied.

3

A relation between two variables which shows up on a scatter diagram as the dots exactly following a straight line; a correlation of r equals 1 or -1.

3

A statistical procedure that computes the correlation between two variables that would be expected if both variables were measured with perfect reliability.

3

The average of the cross-products of Z scores of two variables.

3,4

The extent to which there is a clear pattern of some particular relationship between two variables.

3

The extent to which the results of a study would be unlikely if in fact there were no association or difference in the populations the measured scores represent.

3,6

A table in which the variables are named on the top and along the side, and the correlations among them are all shown.

3

The measure of association between variables that is used when comparing associations obtained in different studies or with different variables; r^2.

3,4

Proportionate reduction in error   **Regression line**

3,4,12,13,16,17   4

Bivariate prediction   **Error (in prediction)**

4   4

Regression coefficient   **Multiple regression**

4   4

Regression constant   **Slope**

4   4

A line on a graph representing the predicted values of the dependent variable for each value of the independent variable.

4

The reduction in squared error using a bivariate or multiple regression prediction rule over the squared error using the mean to predict, expressed as a proportion of the squared error when using the mean to predict.

3,4,12,13,16,17

The actual score minus the predicted score.

4

The prediction of scores on one variable based on scores of one other variable.

4

The prediction of scores on one variable based on scores of two or more other variables.

4

The number multiplied by a person's score on the independent variable as part of a formula for predicting scores on the dependent variable.

4

The steepness of the regression line, or the amount the line moves up for every unit it moves across.

4

In a bivariate or multiple prediction model using raw scores, a particular fixed number added into the prediction.

4

Probability (*p*)

Random selection

5

5

Subjective interpretation of
probability

Haphazard selection

5

5

Population

Parameter

5

5

Sample

Statistic

5

5

A procedure of selecting a sample of individuals to study which uses truly random procedures.

5

The expected relative frequency of a particular outcome.

5

A procedure of selecting a sample of individuals to study by taking whoever is available or happens to be first on a list.

5

Understanding probability as the degree of one's certainty that a particular outcome will occur.

5

A descriptive statistic for a population.

5

The scores of the entire group of subjects to which a researcher intends the results of a study to apply.

5

A descriptive statistic computed from the data about a particular sample of scores.

5

The scores of the particular set of subjects studied that are intended to represent the scores in some larger population.

5

Hypothesis testing   Cutoff sample score

                          6   6

Research hypothesis   Statistical significance

                          6   6

Null hypothesis   Level of significance (α)

                          6   6,7,8

Comparison distribution   Conventional levels of significance

                          6   6

The point on the comparison distribution which, if the sample score reaches or exceeds it, the null hypothesis will be rejected.

6

A systematic procedure for determining whether results of an experiment provide support for a particular theory or practical innovation thought to be applicable to a population.

6

An outcome of hypothesis testing in which the null hypothesis is rejected.

6

A statement about the predicted relation between populations.

6

The probability of obtaining statistical significance if the null hypothesis is actually true.

6,7,8

A statement that there is no difference between the populations.

6

The levels of significance widely used in psychology ($p < .05$ and $p < .01$).

6

The distribution representing the situation if the null hypothesis is true and to which you compare your sample.

6

Directional hypothesis

Distribution of means

6

7

One-tailed test

Variance of a distribution of means

6

7

Nondirectional hypothesis

Confidence Limits

6

7

Two-tailed test

Z **test**

6

7

A distribution of all the possible
means of samples of a given size
from a particular population.

A research hypothesis predicting a
particular direction of difference
between populations.

7

6

The variance of the population
divided by the number of cases in
each sample.

The hypothesis-testing procedure
for a directional hypothesis.

7

6

The upper and lower end of the
confidence interval.

A research hypothesis that does not
predict a particular direction of
difference between populations.

7

6

A hypothesis-testing procedure in
which there is a single sample and
the population variance is known.

The hypothesis-testing procedure
for a nondirectional hypothesis.

7

6

Type I

Beta

Type II

Effect size

Statistical power

Effect-size conventions

Alpha

Meta-analysis

The probability of a Type II error.

Rejecting the null hypothesis when in fact it is true.

8

8

The separation (lack of overlap) between or among populations due to the independent variable.

Failing to reject the null hypothesis when in fact it is false.

8

8

Conventions about what to consider a small, medium, and large effect size.

The probability that the study will yield a significant result if the research hypothesis is true.

8

8

A statistical method for combining the results of independent studies, usually focusing on effect sizes.

The probability of a Type I error; same as significance level.

8

8

t test

Repeated-measures design

9,10

9

Unbiased estimate of the population variance

Within-subject design

9

9

Degrees of freedom

t-test for dependent means

9

9

t distribution

Difference score

9

9

A research strategy in which each subject is tested more than once; same as within-subject design.

9

A hypothesis-testing procedure in which the population variance is unknown.

9,10

A research strategy in which each subject is tested more than once; same as repeated-measures design.

9

An estimate of the population variance, based on sample scores, which is equally likely to over or underestimate the true population variance.

9

A hypothesis-testing procedure in which there are two scores for each subject and the population variance is not known.

9

The number of scores free to vary when estimating a population parameter.

9

The difference between a subject's score on one testing and the same subject's score on another testing.

9

A mathematically defined curve describing the comparison distribution used in a *t* test.

9

Assumption

Weighted average

9

10

Robustness

Pooled estimate of the population variance

9

10

t-test for independent means

Variance of a distribution of differences between means

10

10

Distribution of differences between means

Harmonic mean

10

10

An average in which the scores being averaged do not have equal influence on the total.

10

A condition, such as a population having a normal distribution, required for carrying out a particular hypothesis-testing procedure.

9

An average of the estimates of the population variance from two samples, each estimate weighted by the proportion of its degrees of freedom of the total degrees of freedom.

10

The extent to which a particular hypothesis-testing procedure is reasonably accurate even when its assumptions are violated.

9

It equals the sum of the variances of the distributions of means corresponding to each of two samples.

10

Hypothesis testing procedure in which there are two separate groups of subjects whose scores are independent of each other and in which the population variance is not known.

10

A special kind of average which is more influenced by smaller scores.

10

The distribution of all possible differences between means of two samples; the comparison distribution in a *t* test for independent means.

10

Analysis of variance

F distribution

11

11

Between-group population variance
estimate

Structural model

11

12

Within-group population variance
estimate

Analysis of variance table

11

12

F ratio

Multiple comparisons

11

12

A mathematically defined curve describing the comparison distribution used in an analysis of variance; the distribution of F ratios when the null hypothesis is true.

11

A hypothesis-testing procedure for studies involving two or more groups.

11

A way of understanding analysis of variance as a division of the deviation of each score from the overall mean into parts corresponding to its deviation from its group's mean deviation from the overall mean.

12

In analysis of variance, the estimate of the variance of the population distribution of individual cases based on the variation among the means of the groups studied.

11

A chart showing the major elements in computing an analysis of variance using the structural-model approach.

12

In analysis of variance, the estimate of the variance of the distribution of the population of individual cases based on the variation among the scores within each of the groups studied.

11

Procedures for examining the differences among particular means in the context of an overall analysis of variance.

12

In analysis of variance, the ratio of the between-group population variance estimate to within-group population variance estimate.

11

Planned comparisons

Linear contrast

11

11

Bonferroni procedure

Factorial design

11

12

Post-hoc comparisons

Interaction effect

12

13

Proportion of variance accounted for

Main effect

12

13

A special kind of planned comparison, that is like a correlation, in which, for each subject, one variable is the predicted influence of the group the subject is in and the other variable is the score on what is being measured.   11

Multiple comparisons in which the particular means to be compared were designated in advance.

11

A way of organizing a study in which the influence of two or more variables is studied at once by constructing groupings which include every combination of the levels of the variables.

11

A multiple-comparison procedure in which the total alpha percentage is divided among the set of comparisons so that each is tested at a more stringent significance level.

12

Situations in factorial analysis of variance in which the combination of variables has a special effect which you could not predict from knowing about the effects of each of the two variables separately.

13

Multiple comparisons among particular means which were not designated in advance, but are being conducted as part of an exploratory analysis after the study is completed.

12

Difference between groups on one dimension of a factorial design (sometimes used only for significant differences).

13

An indicator of effect size in analysis of variance; same as the proportionate reduction in error in multiple regression.

12

Cell mean

Least-squares analysis of variance

13

13

Collapsing over factors

One-way analysis of variance

13

13

Dichotomizing

Two-way analysis of variance

13

13

Marginal mean

Repeated-measures analysis of variance

13

13

The recommended approach to factorial analysis of variance when the number of subjects in the cells are not all equal.

13

The mean of a particular combination of levels of the independent variables in a factorial design.

13

Analysis of variance in which there is only one independent variable.

13

A procedure in a factorial analysis of variance in which one of the dimensions (independent variables) is ignored, reducing the overall analysis to one less dimension.

13

Analysis of variance for a two-way factorial design.

13

Dividing a variable into two groups by separating those above and those below the mean.

13

Analysis of variance in which all the levels of the independent variable(s) are measured within the same subjects.

13

In a factorial design, the mean score for all the subjects at a particular level of one of the independent variables; row mean or column meant.

13

Nominal variable

Chi-square statistic (X^2)

14

14

Chi-square test for goodness of fit

Contingency table

14

14

Expected frequency

Independence

14

14

Observed frequency

Chi-square test for independence

14

14

A statistic that reflects the overall lack of fit between the expected and observed frequencies; the sum, over all categories or cells, of the squared difference between observed and expected frequencies divided by the expected frequency.

14

A variable with values that are categories, with no numeric relation; same as a categorical variable.

14

A two-dimensional chart showing frequencies in each combination of categories of two categorical variables.

14

A hypothesis-testing procedure that examines how well an observed frequency distribution of a categorical variable fits some expected pattern of frequencies.

14

The situation of no systematic relationship between two variables.

14

In a chi-square test, the number of cases in a category or cell expected if the null hypothesis were true.

14

A hypothesis-testing procedure that examines whether the distribution of frequencies over the categories of one categorical variable are unrelated to the distribution of frequencies over the categories of another categorical variable.

14

In a chi-square test, the number of cases in a category or cell actually obtained in the study.

14

Categorical variable

Rank-order test

14

15

Phi coefficient (ϕ)

Nonparametric test

14

15

Cramer's phi (Cramer's ϕ)

Distribution-free test

14

15

Data transformation

Parametric test

15

15

A hypothesis-testing procedure which makes use of rank-ordered data.

15

A variable with values that are categories, with no numeric relation; same as a nominal variable.

14

A hypothesis-testing procedure making no assumptions about population parameters; approximately the same as a distribution-free test.

15

A measure of association between two dichotomous categorical variables.

14

A hypothesis-testing procedure making no assumptions about population distributions; approximately the same as a nonparametric test.

15

A measure of association between two categorical variables that is applicable regardless of the number of levels of the two variables.

14

An ordinary hypothesis-testing procedure which makes assumptions about the shape and other parameters of the populations.

15

The application of one of several mathematical procedures (e.g., taking the square root, log, inverse) to each score in a sample in order to make the sample distribution closer to normal.

15

Inverse transformation

Randomization test

15

15

Equal-interval measurement

Approximate randomization tests

15

15

Ordinal measurement

General linear model

15

16

Least-squares model

Nominal coding

16

16

A hypothesis-testing procedure that considers every possible reorganization of the data in the sample in order to determine if the organization of the actual sample data was unlikely to occur by chance.

15

A transformation in which you take the inverse of each score.

15

Approximation to a randomization test in which a computer creates a randomly-determined large number of the possible reorganizations of the data.

15

Measurement in which the difference between any two scores represents an equal amount of difference in the underlying thing being measured.

15

A general formula that is the basis of most of the statistical methods covered in this text.

16

Measurement in which the scores are ranks.

15

Converting a nominal predictor variable in an analysis of variance into several two-level numeric variables.

16

The usual method of determining the optimal values of regression coefficients as those that produce the least squared error between predicted and actual values.

16

Hierarchical multiple regression

Controlling for

17

17

Stepwise multiple regression

Reliability

17

17

Partial correlation coefficient

Test-retest reliability

17

17

Partialing out

Split-half reliability

17

17

Removing the influence of a variable from the association among the other variables; same as partialing out.

17

A procedure in which predictor variables are added in a planned sequential fashion to examine the contribution of each over and above those already included.

17

The degree of consistency of a measure.

17

An exploratory procedure which identifies the best subset of potential predictor variables.

17

The correlation between scores obtained on a measure at two different testings of the same people.

17

The correlation between two variables, over and above the influence of one or more other variables.

17

Correlation of the scores from items representing two halves of a test.

17

Removing the influence of a variable from the association among the other variables; same as controlling for.

17

Cronbach's alpha   Path coefficient

17   17

Factor analysis   Causal analysis

17   17

Factor loading

17   17

Path analysis

17   17

The degree of relation associated with an arrow in a path analysis (including latent variable models).

17

A widely used index of a measure's reliability in terms of the correlations among the items.

17

A procedure, such as path analysis or latent variable modeling, that analyzes correlations among a group of variables in terms of a predicted pattern of causal relations among them.

17

An exploratory statistical procedure that identifies groupings of variables (factors) correlating maximally with each other and minimally with other variables.

17

The correlation of a variable with a factor.

17

A method of analyzing the correlations among a group of variables in terms of a predicted pattern of causal relations.

17

Latent variable modeling

Analysis of covariance

17

17

Structural equation modeling

Covariate

17

17

Measurement model

Multivariate analysis of variance

17

17

Causal model

Multivariate analysis of covariance

17

17

An analysis of variance which is
conducted after first adjusting the
variables to control for the effect of
one or more unwanted additional
variables.

17

A sophisticated type of path
analysis involving latent
(unmeasured) variables, permits a
kind of significance test, and
provides measures of the overall fit
of the data to the hypothesized
causal pattern.

17

A variable controlled for in an
analysis of covariance.

17

Same as latent variable modeling.

17

An analysis of variance in which
there is more than one dependent
variable.

17

In latent variable modeling, the set
of causal paths between latent and
measured variables.

17

An analysis of covariance in which
there is more than one dependent
variable.

17

In latent variable modeling, the set
of causal paths between latent
variables.

17